THE INVERTED MOUNTAINS

CONTENTS

v

ILLUSTRATIONS

ACKNOWLEDGMENT: Photographs number 1, 3, 7, 9, 16, 22 and 23 are printed by courtesy of the National Park Service; numbers 2, 4, 5, 6, 12, 13, 18, 21, 25 and 27, courtesy of Weldon F. Heald; numbers 8, 10, 14, 17, 19, 20, 24, 26, courtesy of E. D. McKee; number 28, courtesy of Orlo Childs; numbers 29, 30, 31, 32 and 33, courtesy of the American Museum of Natural History, New York; number 11, courtesy of Union Pacific Railroad; number 15, courtesy of the Santa Fe System Lines.

INTRODUCTION

There are, of course, no words adequate to describe the titanic splendor of the great canyons of our West, nor are there words delicate enough to describe the grandeur of the light effects at one moment and their delicate translucency at the next. How can a Lilliputian do justice to Gulliver's personality? Perhaps the poet Adelaide Crapsey has done best by the Grand Canyon in a four-line poem. It starts, "By Zeus, shout word of this!" Obviously one must use superlatives. And yet shouts are lost in the immensity of space and chasm of the canyons and the whole of the Canyon Country. Here is an occasion for trumpets, for the beating of great drums, and, if for dancing, a dance in which one leaps into the air. There is nothing like the Canyon Country in all the world.

Charles L. Lummis, the early poetic minister of the out-of-doors Southwest, said of the Grand Canyon just that:

> the greatest thing on earth . . .
> not only the largest, but the most varied and instructive
> example of one of the chief factors of earth building—erosion.

3

Perhaps our best-known American traveler is John L. Stoddard. In a grandiose style appropriate to the Grand Canyon, he wrote of "Nature wounded unto death and lying stiff and ghastly. . . ." Indeed, some people are impressed unfavorably by the rawness of the West. And yet I do not believe Stoddard meant to be derogatory. His description of dawn in the Canyon is fine reading.

The early explorers wrote mostly in stately and somewhat academic form. More expressive was a later generation. Read Harriet Monroe's article in the *Atlantic Monthly* of December, 1899. Or the work of another poet, Joaquin Miller, in the *Overland Monthly* of March, 1901. Almost every important literary figure in America in the late nineteenth century made an attempt at describing the Grand Canyon. Bryce and Zion were then unvisited, and much of the back Canyon Country is still little known. The trouble with describing the canyons today is that the earlier writers have used all the appropriate superlatives.

This volume is something different from the many previous books about the Canyon Country. This is not a book of mere impressions—the first view of misty dawn in the depths, some splendid sunset, some moment of translucent light. This volume is a symposium of experts who have lived intimately with Canyon Country, have learned to read the secrets in the rocks, and are masters of the technique of canyon travel. They know well the famous trails but also have knowledge of remote places. Their long experience and their scientific training prepare them to explain the heroic forces that have created this wonderland. Each expert has spent long time in the Canyon Country, and parts of the book are intensely personal. Each has a store of experiences. They have, each of them, a love of the canyon land which transcends the ecstatic impressions of the casual traveler. They have been deeply stirred by their experience with titanic earth events. They see the canyons not as separate entities but as a part of the whole area. There are portions of mesa land in the region, seldom visited, which are as awe-inspiring as the chasms themselves. Zion National Monument, seldom visited, is said to be more spectacular than Zion Canyon. This volume, then, is something new, something more complete, more interpretive than any book previously offered.

The chasms are inverted mountains. If the entire basin of the Colorado River were filled with plaster, and the resulting cast turned over, we should see a strange but imposing system of mountains. They would look like no mountains known to man on earth, and there would be land forms such as no natural process could evolve, but they would rise more majestically above their bases than any ranges in the United States save perhaps parts of the High Sierra and the Cascades. The vast branchwork of the canyons, with the incomparable Grand Canyon at its heart, is in effect an imposing system of mountains in reverse, a gigantic intaglio of what would be one of the outstanding alpine regions of the world.

But this is not a land of inverted mountains only; the great canyons are graven into a block of rock the remaining higher portions of which stand out as actual mountains in their own right. These mountains are of that distinctive tabular type known as plateaus, and together with the canyons they give character to what is probably the greatest plateau-and-canyon province in the world.

5

The main part of this book is by two men whose contributions, by their vitality, make it very much alive. Their work is scholarly, but each ends with purely personal chapters that show their enthusiastic love of the traits of the inverted mountains. WELDON F. HEALD is an extraordinarily talented person. He likes to be called an alpinist, and in this capacity he has written for the volume *The Sierra Nevada: The Range of Light*. He is by profession an architect, yet he has found time to write successful plays in collaboration with his wife. At eight years of age he was instilled with a love of mountains in Switzerland. Since then he has climbed mountains on three continents and not a few islands. He has boated down the Canyon. How intimately he knows the Canyon Country, and how adventuresome he has been, his journal will tell better than can I.

EDWIN D. MCKEE is a collaborator for the National Park Service and headed there a department of research and education from 1929 to 1941. The lecture and guide service as well as the two museums you will have at your service at the Grand Canyon were instituted by him. He is an Associate Professor of Geology at the University of Arizona and the Assistant Director of the Museum of Northern Arizona. He has written a number of papers and monographs on his field. During the course of his work he has traveled every trail by horse and on foot and has camped in every accessible part of the Canyon.

Of equal distinction in the Canyon Country is HAROLD S. COLTON, who is Director of the Museum of Northern Arizona, the unusual institution outside Flagstaff. He has been with the Museum since its founding twenty years ago, carrying on work in archaeology, direction on archaeological survey, and a study of prehistoric ceramics.

6

INTRODUCTION

So once again in the American Mountain Series I offer you a group of writers with a special enthusiasm for a drama of whose broad vistas and hidden secrets they must tell the citizens of the country.

RODERICK PEATTIE

CHAPTER ONE

CANYON PREVIEW

By *Weldon F. Heald*

WHAT'S IN A NAME?

The very names of some places and regions stir our imagination. They are magic symbols which conjure up mental pictures of romance, beauty, mystery, or grandeur. Zanzibar, Pongo Pongo, The Riviera stimulate in most of us a consuming desire to go and see for ourselves what exceptional qualities set these places apart.

Such a magic name is The Great Southwest. For over a hundred years it has been one of the most powerful, compelling, magnetic word symbols in North America. Into it is compressed a unique pattern in time, space, and color which makes the region one of enchantment and fascination.

The Great Southwest! Aladdin-like the name brings before us a gigantic geological earth drama still being enacted by water, wind, and sand in naked canyons and over barren buttes and plateaus. It suggests a mystery story of prehistoric peoples who came, lived, and left their dwellings, to disappear no one knows where. In the name is a parade of history four hundred years long: Spanish conquistadores resplendent in shining armor;

11

black- and brown-robed priests with crosses and breviaries; stalwart American trappers in buckskin; prospectors leading their burros; Mormon settlers slowly driving wagons west to escape religious persecution. Then there are blue-uniformed army officers, government explorers, Indian fighters, cowboys, cutthroats, rustlers, and bandits. The name stands, too, for the home of present-day red men living in their own ancestral communities with a culture little changed through the centuries. And pervading the word "Southwest" is the dry sharpness of a desert climate and the uncompromising, sun-splashed color of a land sweeping to far horizons under an indigo sky.

One might well ask—what's in a name?

But new images are constantly arising to displace the old. The American Southwest is one of the major geographical and economic regions of the United States. Perhaps an eighth of the area of the country could claim to be Southwestern. Within these wide boundaries in recent years have grown modern cities, industries, and the identical pattern of machine-made civilization which stretches from Bangor to San Diego. The flavor of the old Southwest is still strong and tangy, but it is becoming increasingly diluted with modern sauce.

Fortunately, one sizable section of the Southwest has so far escaped the restless urge of the white man to improve and rearrange the surface of the earth to suit himself. In the carved plateau and canyon wilderness of northern Arizona and southern Utah, nature has cunningly combined such a ruggedly upside-down topography with an adverse climate that hundreds of square miles remain much as they were in the days of the Spaniards. The region today is a pure distillation of all the unique characteristics inherent in the word "Southwest." And it is the

12

color, mystery, and grandeur of this land of Inverted Mountains which our book endeavors to present.

UPSIDE-DOWN COUNTRY

Few regions on the face of the earth are so packed with natural wonders. No other can match its intricate, twisted gorges, symmetrical natural bridges, soaring, varicolored monoliths, and fantastically shaped rock formations. The Arizona-Utah Canyon Country is celebrated throughout the world as the supreme example of wind and water actively altering and shaping a unique landscape. It is a giant experimental laboratory, subsidized by nature, where nothing is too large, difficult, or complicated to be tried out at least once.

The eccentric master workman is the Colorado River. An absolute dictator, it directs the labors of thousands of helper tributaries, big and small. For millions of years this great river and its assistants have been inexorably cutting down, down, through the rock layers of the earth's crust. Century after century melting snows from the Rockies and a billion desert cloudbursts have been sluiced through ever deepening canyons to the Gulf of California. Plateaus have been lowered by the toiling streams, mesas reduced to buttes, buttes to needles, while the Colorado has entrenched itself deep down in an almost continuous gorge 590 miles long.

But this master river is a bit of a genius, too. It has fashioned a land like no other in the world. Most normal landscapes start from a base and build up to hills and mountains. Not so the Colorado River country—here the whole plan is in reverse. The maze of canyons is deeply incised into the earth's surface;

13

each plateau terminates in steep drop-offs downward; roads, railways, towns, and settlements are on top, while beneath them are complicated ranges of countersunk "mountains" hollowed out below the surfaces of the plateaus. From a speeding airliner the country appears like a gigantic upside-down matrix or mold from which has been taken a normal landscape.

Truth-loving scientists will frown at such fanciful conceptions, which play fast and loose with the facts of geology. But to us capricious laymen, who see a statue of Queen Victoria in the eroded rocks of Bryce Canyon and troops of pink elephants carved by nature in the sandstones near Rainbow Bridge, the Arizona-Utah Canyon Country is truly a land of Inverted Mountains.

There are no sharply defined boundaries to this great wonderland of erosion. Broadly speaking, it is a region about the size of the state of Maine contained in an equilateral triangle, 350 miles to the side. The triangle's southern base stretches entirely across northern Arizona from New Mexico to Nevada and roughly follows the line of the Santa Fe Railroad and U. S. Highway 66. The apex thrusts far north into central Utah to the vicinity of the town of Greenriver on the Denver and Rio Grande Railway and U. S. Highway 50.

Let us enter the magic triangle to see if we can discover through mere words why it has acted as a magnet to explorers, scientists, writers, painters, and all classes of adventurous men, women, and children since Don López de Cárdenas crossed the plateaus and suddenly looked down into the Grand Canyon four hundred and eight years ago.

14

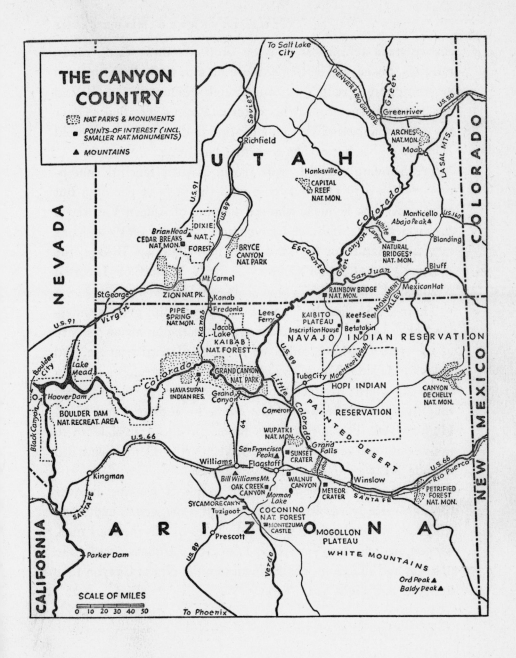

THE CANYON
COUNTRY

- NAT. PARKS & MONUMENTS
- POINTS-OF-INTEREST (INCL. SMALLER NAT. MONUMENTS)
▲ MOUNTAINS

To Salt Lake City

UTAH

NEVADA

COLORADO

Greenriver
ARCHES NAT. MON.
Moab
LA SAL MTS.
U.S. 50

Richfield

Hanksville
CAPITAL REEF NAT. MON.

Monticello
Abajo Peak ▲
Blanding
U.S. 160

Brian Head ▲
CEDAR BREAKS NAT. MON.
DIXIE NAT. FOREST
BRYCE CANYON NAT. PARK

Escalante
Glen Canyon
Colorado
White Canyon
NATURAL BRIDGES NAT. MON.
Bluff
San Juan

Mt. Carmel
St. George
ZION NAT. PK.
Kanab
RAINBOW BRIDGE NAT. MON.
Mexican Hat
MONUMENT VALLEY

PIPE SPRING NAT. MON.
Fredonia
Lees Ferry
KAIBITO PLATEAU
Inscription House
KeetSeel
Betatakin

Virgin
Jacob Lake
KAIBAB NAT. FOREST
NAVAJO INDIAN RESERVATION

U.S. 91
Kanab

Boulder City
Lake Mead
Colorado
GRAND CANYON NAT. PARK
Little Colorado
Tuba City
Moenkopi Wash
HOPI INDIAN
CANYON DE CHELLY NAT. MON.

Hoover Dam
Black Canyon
HAVASUPAI INDIAN RES.
Grand Canyon
RESERVATION

BOULDER DAM NAT. RECREAT. AREA
Cameron
PAINTED DESERT

U.S. 66
64
WUPATKI NAT. MON.

Kingman
San Francisco Peaks ▲
SUNSET CRATER
Grand Falls

Williams
Flagstaff
Canyon Diablo
U.S. 66
Rio Puerco

Bill Williams Mt. ▲
OAK CREEK CANYON
WALNUT CANYON
METEOR CRATER
Winslow
SANTA FE

SYCAMORE CAN'N
Morman Lake
PETRIFIED FOREST NAT. MON.

SANTA FE
Tuzigoot
COCONINO NAT. FOREST
MONTEZUMA CASTLE

ARIZONA

Parker Dam
Prescott
MOGOLLON PLATEAU

U.S. 89
Verde
WHITE MOUNTAINS

CALIFORNIA

NEW MEXICO

Ord Peak ▲
Baldy Peak ▲

SCALE OF MILES
0 10 20 30 40 50
To Phoenix

STONE TREES AND PAINTED SANDS

Most westbound travelers today enter the triangle through its southeast apex. Busy Highway 66, paralleling the Santa Fe tracks, leads gently down from the Continental Divide in New Mexico and follows the broad, dun-colored valley of Rio Puerco into Arizona. By this route the Painted Desert is a dramatically sudden and unexpected curtain raiser to the land of Inverted Mountains.

A five-mile loop road leaves the highway, climbs a slope to the north, and comes out upon the rim. Below and stretching to the distant horizon north is a vast, empty desert. For thousands of years this parched land has looked up at the sun and stars, silent and lifeless except for winds whispering among naked rocks and the occasional sharp hissing of raindrops from vagrant showers. But splashed across the complete desolation are bands of brilliant color—yellow, chocolate, ochre, vermilion —ending in distant cliffs that glow with the vivid pink of a prairie fire. The effect is startling—a dead landscape brought to vigorous, pulsating life by color alone.

Standing on the rim of the Painted Desert, the only sound a breeze soughing through the branches of a gnarled juniper overhead, you first feel the sense of mystery and wonder which grows deeper the longer you know the Canyon Country. There the human spirit seems to expand beyond the confines of our three-dimensional sphere. We touch and become aware of the infinite world of time and space just beyond our everyday vision. That is perhaps as near reality as we can ever come in this busy, human existence.

The southern part of the Painted Desert is included in Petrified Forest National Monument. A paved road leads south for twenty-two miles through this ninety-one-thousand-acre government reservation established by President Theodore Roosevelt in 1906 to preserve the largest and most colorful natural collection of petrified wood in the world.

Somewhere near by in Triassic times, 170,000,000 years ago, grew a forest of subtropical, pinelike trees. Floods came and carried thousands of trunks down into shallow lakes and marshes, which then existed on the present site. Slowly they became buried in mud and sand. Under pressure the wood cells were replaced by silica and such highly-colored mineral solutions as jasper, carnelian, agate, opal, and onyx. These solidified into hard rock with the exact structure and shape of the original wood. Now the stone trees of the Reptile Age have again been uncovered by recent erosion and lie scattered in groups among the desert hills. There are some monster logs among them, measuring up to 150 feet long and 8 to 10 feet through. Within the Monument, too, are the ruins of more than two hundred and forty dwellings of prehistoric Indians who lived and apparently thrived on this inhospitable soil more than a thousand years ago.

West from the Petrified Forest, Highway 66 continues down Rio Puerco Valley to the Little Colorado River, which it crosses at Winslow. Far to the south, rimming the horizon, are the swelling blue outlines of the White Mountains. Round the upper slopes of Baldy Peak and Ord Peak is a high mountain vacation country of pine and spruce forests, meadows, and aspen groves. The best trout fishing in Arizona is found in the cluster of little lakes and clear, cold streams of the White Mountains.

16

Baldy's 11,590-foot summit is one of the highest vertebrae in the elevated backbone which stretches four hundred miles in an unbroken series of heavily forested mountains and plateaus from New Mexico's Mogollon Mountains to the Grand Canyon. At Winslow we begin the long, even climb to the Coconino Plateau, seven thousand feet up on this lofty backbone.

Twenty miles west of Winslow a dirt road leads a short distance south to Meteor Crater. This mile-wide, six-hundred-foot-deep hole in the desert tells the story of a giant meteorite which struck the earth fifty thousand years ago. The crater has long been a subject for scientific speculation. Savants with adding machines have come up with some amazing figures: the meteorite, they say, weighing about 12,000,000 tons, struck with a speed of 144,000 miles an hour and displaced 300,000,000 tons of rock and gravel when it exploded. Drillings show that the huge celestial mass, consisting of iron, nickel, platinum, and even diamonds, buried itself fifteen hundred feet below the floor of its crater. Here, indeed, is an inverted mountain born in violence.

Continuing west we cross Canyon Diablo. It is a jagged gash in the sloping plain, crossed by a bridge 225 feet high. Ahead, the symmetrical volcanic bulk of the San Francisco Peaks looms ever larger, summit snowfields gleaming in the western sky like permanent silver clouds. Before we reach the mountain's flanks we leave the desert, pass through a belt of stunted piñons and junipers, and enter the cool ponderosa pine forests of the plateau. There, at the southwest base of the San Francisco Peaks, is Flagstaff, capital of the Canyon Country.

PINES, RUINS, AND LAVA

Flagstaff is a lumber town. Its hungry, whining sawmills are fed from the hundreds of square miles of pine roundabout. But far-sighted Flagstaff cuts on a selective logging, permanent yield basis so that timber resources today are as great as they were fifty years ago. The prosperous little city of five thousand inhabitants is also the metropolis of the high plateaus, and on its streets mingle lumberjacks, tourists, Mexicans, Indians, cowboys, and ranchers in an easygoing Western cosmopolitanism.

In every direction out of Flagstaff there are things to see. Southward a road leads to Mormon Lake. Although it is normally Arizona's largest natural body of water, four miles long, Mormon Lake's eccentricities are unpredictable. It came into being in 1895, went dry in 1904 and again in 1947 due to prolonged drought. From the "lake" you can continue south through the clean, open, sunny pine woods of Coconino National Forest to the Mogollon Rim. There, at an elevation of seventy-five hundred feet, the Plateau suddenly breaks into downward-plunging cliffs, giving sweeping views out over miles of twisted mountains and ridges to the shimmering deserts of central Arizona. Round Mogollon Rim is famous hunting country—the home of deer, bears, mountain lions, and wild turkeys. Each fall lines of cars drive down off the plateau, their bumpers proudly decorated with limp and lifeless bucks.

Probably one of the most widely known scenic drives in Arizona is through Oak Creek Canyon, fourteen miles south of Flagstaff on Alternate Route 89. From the Plateau's edge the road descends in wide curves two thousand feet to the Can-

18

yon's floor, then follows brawling Oak Creek for fifteen miles through green archways of maple, alder, cottonwood, and oak. Above rise precipitous walls, soaring into cliffs and pinnacles of red and white sandstone. At the Canyon's mouth is a vast amphitheater surrounded by fancifully carved monoliths of fiery red sandstone. A fascinating Forest Service road penetrates this maze of glowing rocks and winds up Schnebley Hill to Mormon Lake and back to Flagstaff.

Sycamore Canyon, a few miles west of Oak Creek, is a similar deep cleft cut into the Plateau's southern rim. It is now included in a forty-seven-thousand-acre National Forest Wild Area. No roads or buildings are permitted, and the few trails traverse a rugged wilderness abounding in game.

Probably no section of the country belongs more completely to you as a citizen of the United States than the canyon triangle of Arizona and Utah. Fully 80 per cent of the area is government owned. Within its borders are three National Parks, eighteen National Monuments, parts of seven National Forests, a National Recreation Area, as well as five Indian Reservations.

National Parks, of course, are set aside by Congress to preserve areas of outstanding quality or containing some extraordinary natural feature. Although maintained for the use and enjoyment of all the people, they are not recreational developments in the usual sense. No private commercial exploitation is permitted within National Parks, and they are preserved essentially in their natural, primeval condition.

National Monuments are usually created from already existing government land by presidential proclamation. Their purpose is to protect areas and objects of historic, prehistoric, and scientific interest. Both parks and monuments are administered

19

by the National Park Service under the Department of the Interior.

National Forests, on the other hand, are managed by the Department of Agriculture on a basis of controlled develop-ment of forest resources. The Forest Service has devised a multiple use plan by which each resource is wisely developed and made available as a permanent national asset. The varied program of the National Forests includes lumbering, reforesta-tion, fire prevention, watershed protection, livestock grazing, and recreational developments such as roads, campgrounds, and homesites leased for the summer. Wild or Primitive Areas, such as the one in Sycamore Canyon, are sections of National Forests set aside as unspoiled pieces of our original wilderness for the enjoyment and inspiration of campers, hikers, and horseback riders.

But archaeology is a rival to natural scenery in this part of Arizona. For thousands of years before the coming of white men the vicinity of Flagstaff was a center of Indian culture. Hundreds of ruined cliff dwellings line canyon walls, and crumbling pueblos still stand atop lonely mesas. The red-skinned Southwesterners attained a high standard of Stone Age culture with agriculture, basketry, pottery, and masonry. But they mysteriously disappeared some six hundred years ago, leaving little inheritance to the modern Indians who replaced them.

For thirty-two years Dr. Harold S. Colton, director of the Museum of Northern Arizona at Flagstaff, has studied the evi-dences of prehistoric Indian occupation in the surrounding area. Using the ingenious tree ring method, Dr. Colton has accurately dated some hundreds of ruins. He learned that between 1060 and 1200 A.D. there occurred a veritable land boom in the region.

20

Thousands of Indians poured in from all directions and clustered gregariously in ever growing towns and villages.

During the boom period which began almost a thousand years ago, beautiful Walnut Canyon, ten miles east of Flagstaff, was a busy, thriving community of cliff dwellings, almost twenty miles long. Wupatki, on a black lava-covered mesa northeast of the San Francisco Peaks, became a great trading center and melting pot for many different tribes. But the boom mysteriously collapsed by 1200 A.D., and the teeming dwellings were abandoned to drought and desert winds. Another village, Tuzigoot, below Oak Creek Canyon in the fertile Verde River Valley, was a bustling place with fifteen hundred people during prehistoric boom days, and near-by Montezuma Castle, the most perfect of all cliff dwellings, shows five periods of building and was occupied continuously from the eleventh to the fifteenth centuries.

These four Indian ruins are now National Monuments. The dwellings have been excavated and repaired somewhat; museums are maintained to display artifacts and to illustrate the daily lives of these early Arizona citizens; and rangers conduct visitors to points of interest. But there are many other remains of prehistoric Indian life near Flagstaff. Turkey Hill Ruins and Elden Pueblo, both near town, are well worth visits.

What caused the sudden influx of peoples into the Flagstaff area nine hundred years ago? The answer is one of the most remarkable pieces of research in American archaeology. In 1930 charred beams were found in a ruined dwelling which indicated that the last eruption of Sunset Crater occurred about 1066 A.D. When the volcano subsided, a blanket of black cinders covered the country for miles around. It gave to the soil such amazing

21

fertility that there was a veritable "land rush" of Indians into the region.

The positive dating of Sunset Crater's eruption also has geological significance, for it was probably the final, dying gasp of one of the world's great volcanic areas. During the last ten to twelve million years, north-central Arizona passed through three periods of violent vulcanism. Earthquakes and explosions shook the land, hundreds of square miles were buried under volcanic ash, smoke and gases filled the air. It was earth building on a grand scale.

Today, spread over an area of two million acres, are great volcanoes, scores of smaller craters, ash deposits, and lava flows. These reminders of an age of fire form a special region designated by geologists as the San Franciscan Volcanic Field. The name comes from the crowning monument to the dead forces of vulcanism—the San Francisco Peaks.

But nothing is certain in this world—even geology—so perhaps we had better not say "dead," but "dormant."

Sunset Crater itself, now a National Monument, is easily reached by Route 89 north from Flagstaff. It is a typical, symmetrical, round-topped cinder cone rising a thousand feet above the surrounding country. Indenting the broad summit is a cup-shaped crater four hundred feet deep. The outer rim of the cone glows with red and yellow ash as if the rays of a setting sun were always upon it.

Other interesting phenomena due to past volcanic action can be seen in the vicinity of Flagstaff. Government Cave, twenty miles northwest, is a wide, arched subterranean passage in a lava flow and may be explored with lanterns for a mile or so. At the west base of Sunset Crater is another lava cave in which

22

ice remains throughout the year. Grand Falls, forty miles north-east, was caused when a stream of molten lava poured into the channel of the Little Colorado River, forcing the stream around the end of the tongue for sixty miles. At the point where the river returns to its channel is a drop of 185 feet. Over the cliff in times of flood the muddy, churning waters pour in a raging, coffee-colored Niagara.

But, wherever you go in the Flagstaff area, the sweeping outlines of the San Francisco Peaks dominate every view. Rising abruptly in grand isolation more than a mile above the plateau, the worn rim of this dead volcano looks down on everything else in Arizona. The barren, arctic top of the highest peak, Humphreys, rises above green, forested slopes to an altitude of 12,611 feet above sea level.

Flagstaff, which has winter temperatures close to those of Hartford, Connecticut, but nearly twice the snowfall, has developed the big, west-facing basin below Humphreys Peak as a winter sports center. With the coming of snow it blossoms into the "Arizona Ski Bowl." There, fifteen miles north of town, are shelters, two ski tows, and six downhill trails, while the deeply snow-covered San Francisco Peaks above make ideal terrain for cross-country skiing.

INDIANS AND IMMENSITY

West from Flagstaff, Route 66 continues over the high Coconino Plateau through pine woods, meadows, and sage flats to Williams, another lumber town nestled at the foot of Bill Williams Mountain. Three miles east a road takes off for the South Rim of the Grand Canyon, fifty-nine miles due north. The

23

Santa Fe also has a spur track to the Canyon, over which Pullmans are routed between Chicago and Los Angeles.

The Canyon road traverses gently rolling plateau, with sagebrush and scattered juniper giving way to pine forest again near the rim. It is calm, unexciting, open country grazed by hundreds of white-faced Herefords. There is nowhere the slightest indication that you are approaching one of nature's supreme triumphs of showmanship. Not until you stand on the very brink does the Grand Canyon burst upon you with the stunning impact of a physical blow.

This all-or-nothing quality of the Grand Canyon contributes enormously to its impressiveness. Were it situated in a mountainous region where its greatness was apparent from afar one would be prepared. But the Grand Canyon does not permit a single glimpse of any of its wonders until it hurls them at you all at once. Perhaps such sudden, abrupt revelation is the dominating characteristic of the upside-down country, but the dramatic, emotional effect is greatest at the Grand Canyon, for it is the main range—the Mount Everest of the Inverted Mountains.

The Grand Canyon is not the deepest gorge in North America. But it is so big and so long that all others would be lost in its vast depths. You may admire the colored delicacy of Bryce Canyon more. You might consider Zion or Rainbow Bridge to be superior masterpieces of erosion. Many do. But it is not so easy to shoulder the Grand Canyon out of first place. For smashing bigness, for overpowering, breathtaking grandeur on an almost unbelievable scale, the Grand Canyon is unique in this world.

But ranking equally with its size is the impression the Can-

Casa Blanca in Canyon de Chelly.

Formation on the upper end of Lake Mead.

The Inner Gorge with Twin Point forming the distant wall, Lake Mead Recreational Area.

yon gives of infinite, unutterable age. A wilderness of peaks, multicolored cliffs, alcoves, and bays carved out of bare rock layers descend one below the other into the depths of the earth beneath you. One glance encompasses eon piled upon millennium back to the beginning of time.

Edwin D. McKee, who knows the canyon as well as any man, wrote of this time sense in his *Ancient Landscapes of the Grand Canyon Region.* "From the rim . . ." he says, "one looks not only down a few hundred feet, a half mile, or even a mile in distance, but one looks back in history through vast periods, measurable not in centuries but in millions and even hundreds of millions of years."

East and west from Grand Canyon Village, with its hotel, lodge, and camps, paved roads closely follow the indented outline of the South Rim. Short spurs lead out to many viewpoints, each giving a new and different frame to the Canyon's immensity. From Hermits Rest, Yavapai, Grandview, Moran, or Lipan points the visitor can watch the ever changing lights in the canyon, the slow procession of sun and shadow under high-piled, white clouds, the drenching brilliance of sunset colors, or the silvered mystery of moonlight.

Beyond Desert View, twenty-three miles from the village, the East Rim road turns away from the Canyon, drops down from the wooded plateau, and heads for the fiery-hued northern section of the Painted Desert. Near Cameron, this road joins Route 89 by which it is fifty-two miles direct south to Flagstaff. Near the road junction is a viewpoint above the Canyon of the Little Colorado River. There the big tributary has cut a sheer, narrow gorge fifteen hundred feet deep on its way to join the great Colorado in the depths of the Grand Canyon.

25

Cameron is the gateway to the Indian Country. North and east across Arizona and into Utah and New Mexico stretches the huge Navajo Reservation. Amid the utter loneliness of vast red and gray plateaus cut by canyons and broken with buttes, is the homeland of fifty thousand seminomadic, sheep-raising Navajos. And completely surrounded by the Navajo is the Hopi Reservation, a country of peace-loving, agricultural Indians who have lived for centuries in their mesa-top, pueblo villages.

White men are forever strangers in the Indian Country. They are descendants of alien conquerors suffered in unemotional silence as necessary evils. The few permanent white residents are mostly government-licensed traders who exchange the Indians' handmade pottery, blankets, baskets, and silver jewelry for white men's manufactured products. Their scattered trading posts generally provide the only contact the average visitor has with the redskinned inhabitants of the reservations.

But part of the fascination of visiting the Indian Country is that you see a section of our land which the white man has never made his own. The Indian belongs, but the feeling grows that the white man never will. The impassive, expressionless faces you meet in the Indian Country seem to say more clearly than words that the red man is waiting, waiting—a thousand years, maybe two—for the white flood to pass. Then the land and the people will continue on and on into eternity as they were before the temporary interruption.

Even the white man's paved boulevards stop at the borders of the Indian Country. If you would enter you must be prepared to drive in mere wheel tracks, across rocky ledges, over shifting sand, and through boulder-strewn washes. If you travel the side roads you should carry water, extra food, chains, and full

26

equipment for getting your car out of rough spots. In wet weather you might as well decide to stay where you are.

The main road through the Indian Country leaves Route 89 a few miles north of the Cameron trading post. It leads east up broad Moenkopi Wash to Tuba City with its Indian school and hospital. There the road to the Hopi towns branches to the southeast. The first of the eleven villages is Moenkopi, within sight of Tuba City, but the other pueblos are scattered over three long mesas, fifty to seventy miles further on.

Living in venerable pueblos which date back five hundred to six hundred years, the Hopis cling tenaciously to their ancient ancestral customs and religion. Nearly every month of the year one of the villages holds colorful ceremonies and dances. Perhaps the most interesting are the *kachina* and the famous snake dances. The latter, held in August, consist of magic incantations of a symbolical character to produce rain. They are open to the public and draw hundreds of visitors each year.

Beyond Hopiland the road leads on into Navajo country to Canyon de Chelly National Monument, an eighty-three-thousand-acre preserve which also includes Canyon del Muerto and Monument Canyon. The three are long, sheer-walled gorges, three hundred to one thousand feet deep, cut into brilliant red sandstone. Prehistoric cliff ruins cling to niches in the massive walls, while present-day Navajos tend sheep and plant their crops below them on the canyons' floors. It is difficult to decide which is more spectacular: looking down into the canyons from the rim road or up to the smooth, red cliffs and towers from below. Like everything else in the Land of Inverted Mountains, Canyon de Chelly casts its own particular brand of spell over you. You are never likely to forget it.

27

MONUMENTS AND ARCHES

Back to Tuba City again, the main road leads on northeastward to Monument Valley and Utah. The way to Rainbow Natural Bridge turns off a few miles beyond Red Lake trading post and leads north over Kaibito Plateau to Rainbow Lodge, seven thousand feet up on the shoulder of spruce-topped Navajo Mountain. There a hundred-mile slice of Arizona serves as a front yard.

The fourteen-mile pack trail from the lodge to the Bridge has few rivals in the world for sheer beauty and grandeur. And the great stone rainbow at the end of the trail is a perfectly cut gem in a wilderness setting of bare, salmon-colored rock. Yet only about six thousand people have made the trip in to Rainbow Bridge National Monument—fewer than visit some of our great National Parks in one day. Nevertheless, may it be many a year before a road is hacked, blasted, and scraped over the incredibly rough country into the inner sanctuary of the Indians' sacred *Nageelid Nonnezoshi,* the-hole-in-the-rock-shaped-like-a-rainbow.

North of the main road, in canyons which bite deeply into Kaibito Plateau, are three of the largest and finest cliff ruins in America—Inscription House, Betatakin, and Keet Seel. Although widely separated, they are combined into Navajo National Monument with headquarters at Betatakin. Any one of them is well worth a side trip.

Wherever you go in the Navajo Reservation you will pass Indians in rickety wagons. The men are usually dressed in blue jeans and shirts, with wide-brimmed, black hats; the women in

28

gaudy blouses and wide-flaring layers of many-hued skirts, and ornamented with heavy silver jewelry. Occasional clusters of circular, one-room, log houses, called hogans, are seen, often swarming happily with children, dogs, and goats. In the distance a lone rider may pass across the plateau against a background of glowing buttes and deep blue sky.

Perhaps you will see the rider with soaring columns of red sandstone rising above him, for Navajo descendants of proud Chief Hoskannini still live, weave their blankets, and watch their flocks amid the unbelievable towers and pinnacles of Monument Valley. Over the Indians' flimsy brush lean-tos on the wide, sweeping floor of the desert valley rise incredible isolated needles, massive perpendicular blocks, and giant, sky-piercing stone fingers a thousand feet high.

Monument Valley is not beautiful. It is too vast, too silent, too empty to touch any human response in us save that of awe. Its effect is as if the aspiring obelisks, giant tombs, and wasting towers were the ruins of some gargantuan forgotten city of which even the memory of its inhabitants has been lost in the mists of time.

The road passes down through the valley into Utah, threading the heart of this realm of unreality. The fantastic shapes of the surrounding monuments have given to them such names as Brigham's Tomb, The Totem Pole, Mitten Buttes, Bear, Rabbit, and Stagecoach. At the top of Monument Pass the great, red rocks cease, and before you stretches the broad valley of the San Juan River, backed by the distant, snow-flecked summits of the Abajo Mountains. In the bottom of the valley, beside the rushing San Juan, lies the little settlement of Mexican Hat. There you can embark upon an adventurous, two-hundred-mile

29

boat trip down the river on fast water through a magnificent, un-inhabited wilderness to Lees Ferry on the Colorado. Several parties make these regularly scheduled, seven-day expeditions each year during the high water of May and June.

Beyond Bluff, twenty-seven miles further up the San Juan, the road leaves the Navajo Reservation and heads due north to Blanding, the first real town since leaving Williams, three hundred and twenty miles back. At Blanding a fair side road leads over the southern flanks of the Abajo Mountains to Natural Bridges National Monument. There are three massive sandstone bridges in the area, their arches carved by stream erosion to heights ranging from 108 to 225 feet. In addition to the bridges, there are two caves and numerous cliff dwellings.

The Monument is on the east edge of the great canyon wilderness of the Colorado. Recently a rough desert road was opened down White Canyon to the river, forty-three miles from Natural Bridges. A ferry connects on the west bank with a barely passable track to Hanksville on Utah State Route 24. This is the only crossing of the Colorado in a distance of almost two hundred miles, and it makes accessible a large new region for lovers of the Canyon Country to explore and enjoy.

Back to Blanding, the main road runs north to Monticello, where it ends. From there on you roll smoothly on paved Route 160, past the lofty La Sal Mountains on the east to the tree-shaded Mormon town of Moab. Just beyond, the highway crosses the Colorado River. Boats and guides can be hired in Moab for trips down the river and up the Green, from its junction with the Colorado to the town of Greenriver. These scenic water journeys through the red rock canyons of the upper Colorado can be made in comparative comfort and safety.

30

The headquarters of Arches National Monument is three miles beyond the bridge. This preserve of fifty-four square miles is literally crammed with the most varied and amazing rock formations in the entire canyon region. The five separate areas within the monument would take months to explore thoroughly. Among the wonders to be seen are eighty-three natural bridges, one of which has a greater span than any other known —291 feet. There are scores of windows cut by countless ages of wind and water through gigantic salmon-pink rock fins and narrow sandstone reefs. In the area are mazes of twisting canyons and broad avenues between weird steeples and spires glowing with brilliant hues ranging from white to deep red. But access roads are few, and trails long, so that the superb collections of unique features in Arches National Monument remain little known.

Twenty-six miles beyond the headquarters, Route 160 joins U. S. Highway 50 east of Greenriver. Here you reach the apex of the Canyon Country triangle. Let us now go back to explore the central section, then complete our survey with a visit to the southwestern corner.

FORESTS IN THE SKY

U. S. Highway 89, which we left at Cameron to take the road through the Indian Country, continues north and crosses the Colorado over Navajo Bridge, 467 feet above the sullen, muddy waters of the river. It then doubles back, south and west, under the long, almost perpendicular escarpment of the Vermillion Cliffs to House Rock Valley. There a herd of bison may oc-

31

casionally be seen grazing peacefully among the cattle on the wide, grassy floor.

The road gracefully loops up out of House Rock Valley and ascends to the vast, dome-shaped expanse of Kaibab Plateau. Within a few miles you experience a sudden and dramatic change of scene. In climbing a mile vertically, the road passes through all the climates, from Sonoran desert to humid Canadian, stacked one above the other like layers in a pousse café. You may cross the Colorado at Navajo Bridge with a blinding sun sending the thermometer soaring above 100 degrees; an hour and a half later on the Kaibab you are traversing northern-looking spruce forests, perhaps in a drenching rain with the temperature in the chilly 60's. The effect is as surprising as if you had caught a rocket plane and jumped from Mexico to Canada in ninety minutes—for the nine-thousand-foot top of the Kaibab has a cooler summer and winter climate than Halifax, Nova Scotia.

The Kaibab Forest covers the entire top of the plateau above an altitude of seven thousand feet. It is a two-hundred-square-mile, moist, green island completely surrounded by a dry sea of barren deserts. This magnificent stand of pine, spruce, and fir contains a billion and a half board feet of timber, and it has long been famous as a hunter's paradise.

A paved road turns south from Jacob Lake following the Kaibab's elongated dome through the heart of the forest to the North Rim of the Grand Canyon. As you drive through open stands of cinnamon-boled ponderosa pines, you may catch a flash from the plumy white tail of the rare Kaibab squirrel as it whisks away over the pine needles. Later, as you climb higher, meadows alternate with somber spruce forests. Here,

32

particularly at sunset, scores of mule deer come to feed and drink at the many little ponds which dot the meadows. But the Kaibab puts on its greatest show in the fall, when the aspens change their leaves from bright green to shimmering masses of yellow and orange. Then you can travel for miles through golden, translucent tunnels under the trees, made more vivid by the contrasting dark green of spruce and fir. Many a traveler stanchly declares that the Kaibab dressed in autumn colors was the climax of his Western trip.

The forests end abruptly at the brink of the Grand Canyon, six thousand feet above the winding ribbon of the Colorado. The viewpoints on the Kaibab Plateau are a thousand feet higher than those of the South Rim, so that Canyon panoramas include a sweeping background of country to the San Francisco Peaks, more than sixty miles southeast. But the air on the higher rim has a stimulating, resilient quality so sparklingly clear that the snows of the sleeping volcano appear to be just across the way.

Back to Jacob Lake, Route 89 follows the Plateau's gentle northern slopes down into Kanab Valley. Below the last pines there opens up before you one of the farthest-reaching and most comprehensive views in the entire Canyon Country. And nowhere is there a panorama more splashed, streaked, and drenched with color than this. To the southwest, barren, brown, and gray Kanab Valley extends to the forested mountains and plateaus above the lower Grand Canyon. Far to the west rise the turreted, polychrome temples of Zion Canyon. Then, toward the north, rise terrace upon terrace separated by steplike red and ivory cliffs. And, topping the last rise, the pink and white slopes of Bryce Canyon lean against the blue sky.

At the foot of the Kaibab grade is Fredonia, the last town

33

in Arizona. Although it is but seven miles from Kanab, Utah, its nearest Arizona neighbor, Littlefield, is 137 miles to the west. Fredonia is the starting point for exploring the sparsely inhabited, little visited plateaus north of the lower Grand Canyon. A road, not much better than wheel tracks in the desert, turns south beyond neighboring Pipe Springs and wanders across Kanab Plateau fifty miles to Toroweap Point. This spectacular perch on the rim of the Colorado's inner gorge is in Grand Canyon National Monument, a reserve of 305 square miles adjoining the National Park on the west, but as yet completely undeveloped for tourist travel.

Over the state line north of Fredonia is Kanab. Its setting of blood-red cliffs and buttes is often used by motion-picture studios for Wild West locations. Doubtless you have witnessed grim stagecoach robberies and heard the exciting thunder of horses' hoofs as good men chased bad, or vice versa, amid the technicolor rocks of Kanab. Beyond the town the road follows up Kanab Creek through a canyon which shows the ravages of sudden summer cloudbursts, then over a divide to Mount Carmel on the headwaters of the Sevier River. At Mount Carmel Junction, the road to Zion National Park branches to the east.

WHITE CLIFFS AND PINK CANYONS

The Zion-Mount Carmel Highway is an outstanding piece of road engineering. For twenty-five miles it traverses a rugged region of water-carved rock which was almost inaccessible before the highway was built. Just after crossing the National Park boundary the road tunnels a mountainside for more than a mile through solid rock. Six great windows pierce the side of the tun-

34

nel, giving the first near views of the towering stone temples of the Virgin rising three to four thousand feet above the floor of Zion Canyon. The road descends from the tunnel in sweeping lariat loops to Park Headquarters in the canyon beside the sparkling Virgin River.

This mild, innocent-looking Virgin has done prodigious work in its day. It alone is responsible for tearing away and gouging out one of the most impressive canyons in America. But for all its power the river is also a consummate artist. It has left a gorge lined on both sides with sheer, smooth-faced cliffs scalloped into alcoves and amphitheaters and topped with domes and towers.

The architecture of Zion is predominantly religious. The individual formations resemble temples, cathedrals, and altars. Some rise in pure white limestone, others in blended pastel shades of red, pink, yellow, lavender, and blue. A road follows the broad, wooded canyon floor under a succession of these superb natural monuments until it is stopped by a sudden narrowing of the gorge to a mere fifty feet.

Such attenuated, V-shaped gorges are a unique feature of the park and the almost inaccessible Zion National Monument adjoining it to the west. There, many of the canyons are impenetrable, sunless slits in smooth, unbroken rock hundreds of feet deep. Away from the ribbon of Zion Canyon, with its road, lodge, campgrounds, and tourists, the combined Park and Monument is a fascinating wilderness of 225 square miles. Few trails exist, and explorers find some of the roughest going in North America. But they also find the stimulation of penetrating an upside-down country so astonishing it is difficult to believe.

Utah's other National Park, Bryce Canyon, is sixty-two miles north of Mount Carmel Junction, where we turned off Route

35

89 to take the highway to Zion. Bryce can be called a canyon only by courtesy. It is actually the edge of a high plateau bitten by erosion into a series of roughly semicircular, intersecting basins. From the rim these basins slope steeply downward for a thousand feet. In Zion you are at the bottom looking up; at Bryce on the top looking down. Perhaps the Piute Indians had the most descriptive name for Bryce that could be devised—"Red-rocks-standing-like-men-in-a-bowl-shaped-canyon."

There are three special features which put Bryce Canyon well up among our top-ranking National Parks. First comes color—of an intensity and variety unique even in a land of color, and superior to any other canyon. It is said that one artist counted sixty different tints, but he was undoubtedly a conservative. Second are the countless shapes of the thousands of rock figures which stand out from the sloping canyon walls in close-packed groups. For pure whimsy and flights of the unfettered imagination the delicate rock sculpture of Bryce is unduplicated anywhere else. Third, the views from the lofty, pine-clad plateau out over hundreds of square miles of the contorted, riven, empty domain of the Colorado River are among the most impressive in the world.

A seventeen-mile road follows the rim from headquarters, near the Park entrance, to Rainbow Point. There, at 9,105 feet, among wind-twisted pines and firs, you are on the tiptop of Paunsaugunt Plateau. On the way up short spur roads and trails lead out to the finest canyon viewpoints. No two are alike—each has its own particular design and composition to bring out the dazzling beauty of Bryce Canyon.

Perhaps the view from Bryce Point is the grandest of all. From a narrow, jutting peninsula of rock you look down over a

36

semicircular, bowl-shaped basin three miles across. From the rim to the floor a thousand feet below, the steep sides bristle with myriads of standing rock figures clustered together in mass formations. There are fluted columns, pilasters, heroic statues, monuments, hoodoos, and skyscrapers by the thousand etched in a complicated pattern of sunshine and shadow. And the whole basin is suffused and glowing with brilliant color. Bright salmon-pink shades imperceptibly into orange; yellow to ivory and pure white. Blues and violets blend into browns and reds. All the colors run, diffuse, and mingle with each other as if stirred in a giant mixing bowl. There are no streaks or harsh dividing lines anywhere.

And above the canyon from Bryce Point you look northward over the parklike pine woods of Paunsaugunt Plateau to the huge, flat-topped promontory of Boulder Mountain. Fascinating back-country roads lead into this little known region, and hunting and fishing trips with guide and pack train can be taken to the hundreds of little lakes which dot the spruce-forested top of Aquarius Plateau and Boulder Mountain. Beyond is Capitol Reef National Monument in the heart of vast Wayne Wonderland. It is an area of almost impassable canyons and unscalable cliffs, but a good road has been built as far as Capitol Reef from the town of Richfield on Route 89. The chief feature of the National Monument is a buttressed cliff of highly-colored rock capped with capitol-like domes of white sandstone.

Thirty miles in an air-line west from Bryce Canyon is Cedar Breaks National Monument, high on the 10,000-foot summit of Markagunt Plateau. Cedar Breaks is a natural amphitheater two thousand feet deep eroded into the sandstone and limestones of the plateau. Similar in formation to Bryce Canyon, it rivals

37

it in color but lacks the innumerable delicately carved spires and pinnacles. Cedar Breaks is in high mountain country. The plateau behind the rim is dotted with clusters of spruce and fir alternating with wildflower meadows. There are several forest-bordered lakes, too, in the adjoining Dixie National Forest. A fair road leads to the top of Brian Head, 11,315 feet, where a wide-sweeping panorama includes the mountains, valleys, and plateaus of southern Utah as well as parts of Arizona and Nevada.

MIRACLE IN THE DESERT

Our sketchy exploration of the Canyon Country triangle leaves us now with only the southwestern corner unvisited. And so we have left until last the most unusual community in America and the greatest man-made lake in the world.

The exceptional community is the home of the Havasupai Indians in the depths of a side gorge of the Grand Canyon.

Fifty miles west of Grand Canyon Village, Havasu Creek burrows into the Plateau, plunging deeper and deeper into the earth in a series of rapids and waterfalls until it meets the Colorado River in a sheer-walled gorge thirty-two hundred feet deep. Halfway down, Havasu Canyon widens into a fertile, green oasis enclosed between towering red walls. For three miles along the creek there are fresh green fields, blossoming orchards, and the tree-shaded houses of two hundred Havasupai. Neither legends nor historians can tell us when these Indians first found this hidden garden spot three quarters of a mile below the barren rim of the Plateau, but no people on earth ever picked a more peaceful place in which to live.

These Indians still keep their native customs, religion, and culture little diluted by white civilization, and, until recent years few visitors rode down the two rough mountain trails from the Rim. But times are changing. The Havasupai—the People of the Blue Water—are being "discovered." Recently even a Quonset hut to serve as an Episcopal missionary chapel was flown by helicopter, amid the fanfare of newspaper publicity, into this unspoiled bit of original America.

The greatest man-made body of water in the world is Lake Mead.

At the extreme western edge of the Land of Inverted Mountains, the towering, 727-foot concrete bulk of Hoover Dam spans Black Canyon between Arizona and Nevada. Behind the dam the waters of the Colorado River have backed up into a sparkling, blue lake. Over a hundred miles long, it winds through a rugged desert region of colorful buttes, mesas, and sandstone temples to its head, buried in the stupendous chasm of the Grand Canyon.

Daily motor launch service is available up this magic water highway. It takes a little time to accustom yourself to cruising on the desert. Islands and reefs flash by the boat, fantastic rock formations rise above the water and dance crazily in their own reflections, and the launch startles echoes from barren cliffs of lonely canyons.

But the Grand Canyon section is the climax of Lake Mead. It is one of the most spectacular waterways in the world, rivaling the fiords of Norway or the inlets of Alaska. The introduction to the Canyon is dramatically sudden. As the launch passes between mile-high portals, you are instantly plunged into mid-

39

afternoon twilight. Above rise rock castles, towers, square bastions, and pointed spires bathed in brilliant sunshine. Deep blue shadows slant across vast amphitheaters and throw fantastic outlines on the canyon walls. The intense contrast between light and shade is startling—as if night and day were struggling for possession for each cliff and slope. You have been transported to a world of titanic forces in which time and man mean nothing.

Mile after mile the launch speeds deeper into the Canyon—by grim ravines curving back to an unknown wilderness, under lacy curtains of travertine rock, and past caves of prehistoric men appearing like swallows' nests in the canyon walls—until muddy water and floating debris warn that the raging giant Colorado is just ahead. You turn back with reluctance, for the explorer's fever has got into your blood. There is a compelling urge to know what mystery is concealed around the next bend.

And that reaction is perhaps the secret of the powerful fascination the entire Canyon Country exerts on almost all who visit it. For no matter how thoroughly you may explore the magic triangle, you never become satiated. The lure of its wide horizons under the blue Southwestern skies grows stronger; you always feel that a new wonder, some unique feature like nothing you have seen before, lies waiting—just behind the next Inverted Mountain.

CHAPTER TWO

FEATURES OF THE CANYON COUNTRY

By Edwin D. McKee

Man is an impatient creature. His usual tendency is to explain great features of nature as the results of sudden catastrophic action. He readily visualizes volcanoes exploding and earthquakes shaking the earth. But he is slow to comprehend the more subtle processes by which the earth's surface is being sculptured. The validity of this idea becomes apparent to one who has spent an hour or more on the rim of Grand Canyon among a newly arrived group of tourists. Attempted explanations of the great chasm involve crustal upheavals, cracks opening up, or volcanic explosions.

For an understanding of the processes involved in forming canyons—both big and small—one need only watch the forming of a gully by a wayside stream. Wherever there is sufficient slope for the stream to attain speed, it picks up and moves along the mud or silt, sand or gravel on its bed. These materials serve as tools. Transported by water, they form an abrasive, like sandpaper, which is responsible for the cutting of canyons. There are many variations in the nature of the tools, in the force that

43

moves them, and in the materials to be cut. For this reason there are many types and varieties of canyons.

My attention was focused for the first time on the effective cutting power of gravel when, as a beginning student of geology, I stood with my professor on the bank of an arroyo or dry stream bed, looking over a mass of rounded gravels covering the bottom. After allowing time for thought, my teacher quietly stated, "The power is gone, but there are the tools," and I realized then that there was a definite relationship between the roundness of these rock fragments and the presence of the embryo canyon before me. The intrepid explorer, Major John Wesley Powell, must have recognized such a relationship, for it is said that in deciding to explore the Colorado River by boat, in 1869, he dismissed the idea of danger from waterfalls on the grounds that such a muddy stream would long ago have removed any such barriers from its course. Thus, he staked his life on his confidence in the erosive power of these tools.

Most canyons of the Colorado Plateau have in common the fact that they are being carved in layers of rock that are in an essentially flat-lying or horizontal position. Where a single layer of resistant rock is involved, as at Zion, Canyon de Chelly, or Segi Canyon, the walls tend to be sheer. On the other hand, where erosion involves relatively weak rocks, as at Bryce Canyon, sides become sloping and in places much dissected. If strata are excessively weak, as in the Painted Desert, regular badlands are developed. In the case of Grand Canyon, not one, but many layers of differing hardness are involved, each reacting to erosion according to its own peculiar characteristics. Here the so-called "triple S"—scarp, shelf, slope—is developed because resistant sandstone and limestone layers form scarps or cliffs

44

whereas weak shales between them form alternating shelves and slopes. This control is one of the major factors in giving Grand Canyon its well-known beauty of symmetry and form.

The arid or semiarid climate of the Colorado Plateau constitutes a second important factor in controlling development of its canyons. General lack of humidity and small annual precipitation are unfavorable to conspicuous rock decomposition and decay. They are, however, responsible for a sparse vegetation, so that when the snows of winter begin to melt, or the summer cloudbursts arrive, there is little plant cover to anchor or hold the rock debris. A single torrential storm may then create as much destruction as an entire season's rainfall in a region of gentle, well-vegetated slopes. Cliffs are undermined; the outer portions of rock walls break off into blocks; gravity aids in pulling the resulting fragments down steep canyon slopes. The result is that erosion under such climatic conditions maintains a characteristic sharp profile which contrasts with the rounded land forms of a more humid region.

Under the relentless attack of various agents of erosion, especially running water, frost action, plant growth, chemical decay, and wind activity, canyon walls constantly are retreating. It is to be expected, therefore, that canyons are widest at their brinks and narrowest on their floors. That the Grand Canyon is ten miles across from rim to rim, but only a few hundred feet wide where the Colorado flows at its bottom, is easily understandable. As the river filed its way downward, the walls have been wearing back to form this great valley. Mostly the process is too gradual to be detected, but from time to time one is privileged to see a striking illustration. In the spring, when warm sunny days cause thawing and rapid melting of snows,

45

the faces of large cliffs have been observed to fall forward and come thundering down the steep slopes below, raising a cloud of dust and breaking up into blocks of many sizes. The roar in many cases is audible from miles away. Equally spectacular are examples of erosion during the time of summer cloudbursts, when waterfalls red with silt pour over normally dry cliffs, and streams carrying rock waste spring up in every ravine and gully.

Erosion is largely responsible for the brilliant coloring so characteristic of most parts of the Colorado Plateau, as well as for architectural forms sculptured in canyon walls. Because of the semiarid or arid climate, oxidation of minerals, especially iron, in the rocks is a normal process. The red, yellow, even much of the green in the rocks is due to relatively minute quantities of iron in various forms of oxidation.

ROCKS THAT DISSOLVE AWAY

An airplane was flying along the southern margin of the great Plateau in Arizona. It was well south of the regular transcontinental route at Winslow when the pilot observed a cluster of large bowl-shaped holes in the earth's surface. They reminded him of the famous Meteor Crater located about sixty miles to the northwest, so, excitedly, he reported that possibly he had discovered the record of a whole swarm of meteorites.

Soon an expedition was sent out to the locality ten miles north and west of the little town of Snowflake. As might have been expected, the holes were not a new "discovery," for they had long been known to the people of that area; nor were they related to meteorites. Nevertheless, they proved to be of great

46

interest. Formed in a massive limestone known as the Kaibab formation, they are the result of solution by accumulated rain waters. In the language of the geologist, they are "sinkholes" or "sinks," and, though similar features are not rare in limestone regions the world over, they are, nevertheless, especially interesting and spectacular where the bare rock walls are exposed to view as in this case. The thirty or forty sinks in this area vary greatly in size, their diameters ranging from a few to several hundred feet. In some examples, a partial collapse due to undermining has caused the rock layers in the walls to be bent or broken in a peculiar manner.

Scattered here and there over the Canyon Country, where limestone surfaces are exposed to the work of solution by rain and snow waters, are other notable examples of sinkholes. One of the most intriguing is Montezuma Well, located in the Verde Valley. The path of approach is up a hill at the top of which is the rim of a circular hole, four hundred feet wide, with steep walls descending to the margins of a lake eighty feet below. Large trees grow along the shore of the lake, and reeds occur out in the water. For years, stories have been prevalent in the area to the effect that the "well" is bottomless; however, soundings recently made from a canoe have disclosed the rather unromantic facts that the lake is only about fifty feet deep and has a flat bottom. The remains of cliff dwellings on the north wall show that Indians once lived on the side of this sinkhole. An interesting though small cavern which serves as an outlet for the water is on the south side.

On the border of the Painted Desert north of Flagstaff is a rather spectacular sinkhole located near a Pueblo Indian ruin known as the Citadel. The setting in which this depression is

47

located is both colorful and picturesque. On the south side of the small, evenly shaped bowl, is the black edge of a thick lava flow that rises as a sheer wall above the limestone. On other sides a platform of bright red shale covers the limestone surface, and other red strata rise as a prominent hill just to the north. Citadel ruins rise above the summit of the hill, and the remains of another pueblo known as Nalakihu are on the platform at its base. Unfortunately for the photographer, even from the hill, this, like most other sinks, cannot be done justice with a camera. It is virtually impossible to get far enough away to show the real shape.

The results of solution work on a large scale are found on the summit of the high Kaibab Plateau north of Grand Canyon. Here, due to the high altitude, precipitation is such that sinks have been developed in many places so that all water immediately passes underground and there are no surface streams. Some of these sinks, such as Jacob Lake and Greenland Lake, located near main roads, are seen by many people and are easy to recognize because of their bowl shapes. However, their rock structure is largely concealed by vegetation. Some in which the bottoms have become silted up contain permanent or intermittent bodies of water; others allow all water to pass through. The most impressive scenic result of this solution process, however, is found in the series of beautiful mountain meadows or "Parks" that extend from north to south, parting the forest cover along the crest of the plateau.

In some areas, waters dissolving limestone operate along cracks or joints instead of developing the type of circular hole just described. One well-known example is the "Bottomless Pits" a few miles southeast of Flagstaff. Here a crack extends

48

downward perhaps a hundred or more feet, probably to the bottom of the limestone formation, but the pit is far from bottomless. It has been widened out sufficiently through solution so that men have been able to go down on ropes to considerable depths. In recent years, however, the owners have kept the top blocked off, considering further exploration to be dangerous. Similar rock cracks are found on and in the vicinity of Wupatki National Monument, where they have acted as death traps for unwary animals traveling across the country. The bones of both modern and prehistoric mammals have been recovered from the bottoms of some of these.

Where solution of limestone has operated actively beneath the surface, caverns are the normal result. Nothing comparable to Carlsbad or Mammoth is known to exist in the Canyon Country, but in northern Arizona numerous small caverns are found in a rather pure limestone formation known as the Redwall. Examples that have been explored and much visited in times past are at Hyde Park near Seligman, Crystal Cave south of Ashfork, and one near the Grandview trail in Grand Canyon. Some stalactites and stalagmites, formed by dripping water depositing calcium carbonate, have been deposited in all of these caverns.

BRIDGES MADE BY NATURE

A Navajo Indian named Ushini Bi-nai-etin (one-eyed man of the Salt Clan) is credited with having been the first to call the attention of white man to what is perhaps the world's most spectacular natural bridge. The story goes that this Navajo had been sent by John Wetherill, noted pioneer and Indian trader, to guide a party of tourists to the bridges of White Canyon,

49

Utah. This was in 1907. Upon his return home to northeastern Arizona, he asked Wetherill why people wanted to ride so far just to see rocks, especially when there was an even larger natural bridge near at hand.

The bridge "near at hand" was Rainbow Bridge, located in a deep, narrow canyon at the base of Navajo Mountain, near the Arizona-Utah border. When Wetherill heard about this large stone arch, his curiosity was greatly aroused, and he made plans to visit it. Temporarily he was balked because of the death of Ushini, the Navajo, who would have served as guide across the wild and desolate sand rock country and through the maze of canyons. Few others knew the route, but in 1909 a Paiute named Nasja-begay (son of owl) agreed to lead the way. Accordingly a party that included John Wetherill, Dr. Byron Cummings, then archaeologist of the University of Utah, and W. B. Douglass of the General Land Office made the trip.

Rainbow Bridge is one of the most remarkable of natural bridges in the world. It is outstanding because of its symmetry, graceful proportions, great size, and brilliant red color. The Navajos call it Nonnezoshi, which means the Great Stone Arch; to the Paiutes it is Barohoini, the Rainbow. In the midst of the great sea of bare, red sandstone forming Rainbow Plateau, this bridge appears tiny and insignificant, dwarfed by the immensity of its surroundings. Yet it has a height of 309 feet, measured from its crown to the creek bed beneath. Its span is 278 feet, and the arch at its summit is 42 feet thick. Thus, from near at hand, the bridge is very impressive.

Rainbow Bridge appears as a huge hoop bent across the inner gorge of Bridge Canyon. One limb is buttressed against the canyon wall; the other curves down to its base on a broad rock platform bordering the present stream canyon. An examination of its relation to the surrounding rock makes the origin of Rainbow Bridge at once apparent. Clearly the bridge itself is carved from a promontory that once projected out into the canyon. At some former time the ancestral stream, flowing at the level of the present bench, formed a large curve around the promontory, cutting away its sides from two directions. Erosion of the even-grained, porous red sandstone gradually narrowed and undermined the ridge until eventually the stream was able to take a shorter, steeper course—its present channel through the promontory. The old curving stream bed was abandoned and left stranded on the rock bench, while the invigorated stream quickly cut downward eighty additional feet to its present level.

Rainbow Bridge is but one of many spectacular natural bridges formed in massive sandstones of the Canyon Country. Its chief rivals from the standpoint of size and beauty are three large gray bridges located in White Canyon and its tributary, Armstrong Gulch, in southeastern Utah. These bridges are also the result of erosion by running water, which, though only seasonal here, has nevertheless been very effective in tunneling through rock walls. Streams, fed by violent summer cloudbursts and melting snows of winter, flood narrow, steep-walled canyons, abrading and undermining cliffs wherever sharp bends or major curves are encountered. The results are clearly illustrated by the abandoned stream curves located adjacent to the stone bridges. These natural bridges vary greatly in size and shape, as is shown in the accompanying table, but all are spectacular. Like Rainbow Bridge, they form the central attraction of a National Monument.

Name	Width	Thickness	Length	Height
Owachomo	35 ft.	10 ft.	200 ft.	108 ft.
Kachina	49	107	186	205
Sipapu	40	65	261	225

Windows, arches, and rock shelters are all common features of the region, less spectacular than, but related to, the famous natural bridges. All of them are developed best in one type of rock, a porous homogeneous sandstone of uniform composition. Such sandstone normally consists of many series of curving layers that slope in various directions—surfaces of the ancient sand dunes from which the rock was formed. These structures, when etched out on the present surface, give a striking and peculiar appearance to the rock; in addition they control the manner in which it breaks, allowing cliff walls to be undermined and developing the arch as a dominating architectural form. Dr. Herbert Gregory, long a student of the erosional forms in this region, states that a regular series of rock types develops, starting with niches, then rock shelters, blind windows, open windows, and finally arches of natural bridges.

Near the town of Payson, Arizona, at the southern edge of the Colorado Plateau, is a large natural bridge that is very different in every respect from the sandstone bridges further north. This one is composed of limestone in the form of travertine and has been developed through the deposition of calcium carbonate by springs that issue forth along the side of a narrow canyon in that area. The deposits of travertine are said to have gradually crept across the valley until their overhanging front bridged Pine Creek. They form a bridge with a span of 400 feet, a width of 600, and a height of 180 feet. This bridge was discovered, and the area homesteaded, by David Gowen, a Scotch prospector, many years ago and has long been noted as a resort. Fruit trees have been planted on the flat top of the bridge, and a trail developed down under it. Intersecting caves occur within the travertine. Altogether it is a delightful and scenic spot.

VULCAN ALTERS THE LANDSCAPE

Volcanoes come, volcanoes go! Throughout the history of the earth new ones are constantly being built up by the accumulation of rock matter thrown out of the ground or by masses of liquid lava pouring out like glue from a tube. Just as constantly they are being destroyed and worn away through the relentless processes of erosion. Those volcanoes that are in the process of erupting are classed as "active"; those that have been active and probably will be active again, though momentarily quiet, are referred to as "dormant"; those that appear to be permanently quiet are said to be "dead."

On the earth's surface today there are approximately six hundred active volcanoes. Dormant volcanoes number a few thousand, though these are extremely difficult to count because the status of many is uncertain. They are great pretenders, constantly "playing possum." Just when one is conceded to be definitely through, off it goes again. Nevertheless, the number of volcanoes that are dead beyond question is very great and includes craters in every stage of destruction. Many have been worn away completely, so that an estimate of the number is impossible to obtain.

In the southern part of the Canyon Country is a giant volcano known as San Francisco Mountain. Although dead for at least several hundred thousand years, and much battered and

53

worn by the elements since volcanic activity ended, it still dominates the landscape of Northern Arizona and rises high above many sister volcanoes in the region. The top of this mountain was originally about three thousand feet above the present rim, and an estimated three cubic miles of volcanic material has been washed down from the vulnerable peak. This, however, is only about 8 per cent of the original total volume of the mountain. The sides appear to be much the same as when they were formed, enabling the layman as well as the geologist to appreciate the true character of this great volcano.

A trip to the mountain's rim is both exciting and instructive. Either by the now much washed-out Weatherford Road on the south side or by trails from the Ski Bowl on the west, the summit may be approached on foot with relative ease. Standing on any of the higher peaks—Humphreys (12,611 feet), Agassiz (12,-340 feet), Fremont (11,940 feet)—or in a saddle between, it is easy to recognize the volcanic nature of the mountain. The rim appears as a great horseshoe opening toward Deadman's Flat on the northeast. Within is a steep-walled valley called Inner Basin, and projecting far into it from the west is a prominent ridge dividing this part of the valley into two parts. The center ridge represents the core or cores developed where successive flows of lava escaped upward through vents. All about this ridge, on the walls of Inner Basin, layers of lava are seen to slope away in every direction, showing clearly the structure of the original crater.

San Francisco Mountain is neither the youngest nor the oldest of the volcanic features of the area but must have been active intermittently a very long time, for five distinct stages are recognized in it. Starting on a platform of black basaltic lava

54

of much greater antiquity, it grew to a height of eighty-eight hundred feet above the surrounding surface as one type of lava after another was poured forth. Its base covered over one hundred square miles, and its volume totaled nearly forty cubic miles. Imagine the spectacle when this mountain was three thousand feet higher than now!

Then came erosion. Rain and temporary streams gullied its sides and washed down its high points. The northeast wall was breached, and an outlet was developed for the large inner valley. Glaciers followed. They filled the valley and moved down it, not only once but three times, leaving a record of well-developed moraines and outwash plains. After this, rain, frost, and other agents continued the work of sculpturing and wearing down the mountain, but still erosion is far from its goal of totally destroying the great giant of the Arizona volcanoes.

VOLCANOES THAT FAILED TO ERUPT

Dominating the skyline of the northern Navajo Country, and visible for many miles in every direction, is a great dome known as Navajo Mountain. It appears as a symmetrical mound rising four thousand feet above the nearly flat platform of Rainbow Plateau. It is a forest-covered island standing in a sea of brilliant red sandstone. From the rim of Grand Canyon, one hundred miles to the southwest, from Bryce Canyon far to the northwest, and from many other points, it is an outstanding landmark.

Navajo Mountain, like many other high peaks isolated in a desert region, is a center of storms. Rain clouds drifting across the surrounding hot, sandy wastes to the southwest commonly congregate about its summit during certain seasons, and at such times violent storms are common. Thus it is that the Navajo Indian, chief inhabitant of the surrounding Canyon Country, associates this mountain with the home of spirits. To him, it is a sacred place, and for this reason he is reluctant to climb it.

Geologic studies indicate that Navajo Mountain was formed when a mass of hot, viscous, volcanic material rose from deep down in the earth and, reaching a certain level, spread out, arching up the once horizontal layers of sandstone and other rock above it. This formed a dome which the geologist calls a laccolith. The molten mass within it failed to reach or to break forth on the surface, so in this respect it differs from a volcano.

Proof of the true nature of a laccolith is not to be found in Navajo Mountain. The great core of volcanic material that supposedly fills its center has never been seen, and the presence of this type of rock can only be postulated, but still geologists feel confident that it is there. Farther north in Utah are the Henry Mountains, long famous because in their various peaks are found illustrations of laccoliths in all stages of dissection by the processes of erosion. Some illustrate the inner cores with covering rocks worn away, others show layers of upwarped sedimentary rocks rising above volcanic cores, while still others appear nearly unscathed like Navajo Mountain. This is the classic area where Dr. G. K. Gilbert, famous geologist-explorer of the Wheeler Surveys, first drew the attention of the scientific world to the true nature of laccoliths.

In the Canyon Country many other excellent illustrations of laccoliths are to be found. These include the La Sal and Abajo Mountains in southeastern Utah and the Carrizo Mountains in northeastern Arizona. All are large mountains dissected enough

56

Trail to Rainbow Bridge, Utah.

Rainbow Bridge.

Looking up at Rainbow Bridge.

Dimensions: 309 feet high; 278 feet inside span; 42 feet thickness at top.

so that the volcanic cores are now exposed to view. A similar but very much smaller example is found in Marble Mountain on the northwest side of San Francisco Mountain near Flagstaff, Arizona. Here the scale is small enough so that the entire structure can be seen and comprehended with ease.

Two prominent hills in the Flagstaff region are of exceptional interest, geologically speaking, because they are hybrids between volcanoes and laccoliths. They are neither one nor the other but appear to be combinations of both, and in this respect they are nearly unique. One of these hills, known as Elden Mountain, is skirted by the transcontinental highway immediately east of Flagstaff and is seen by hundreds of thousands of people annually, though it is doubtful whether more than a handful know of its history or appreciate its character. The other hill, Slate Mountain, is far to the northwest, where it is more isolated, though easily accessible by a Forest Service road that zigzags up to the lookout station at its top. In both of these hills, steeply upturned strata that were pushed up by volcanic pressure are to be seen on the eastern flank, while lavas that reached and covered the earth's surface on the western side plainly show the direction of their movement by congealed lines of flow.

AN ERUPTION AND MAN

A rosy-tinted rim crowns a crater of black cinders. When the sinking sun of late afternoon throws low-angled rays upon it, this hill, due east of San Francisco Mountain, shows striking beauty. The appropriate name of Sunset Crater was given it over half a century ago by the eminent geologist, Major John Wesley Powell. Although but one among four hundred volcanic

57

cinder cones in the Flagstaff region, it is unique in several respects.

Hopi Indians, living on their high mesas to the north beyond the Painted Desert, know and revere this cone. To them it is Polotsmo, the Red Hill, and is believed to be the home of certain *kachinas* or spirits that occasionally visit the Hopi pueblos at the times of dances. The row of pine trees silhouetted on the rim of the crater resembles a line of *kachinas* standing as in a dance, so there is little wonder that this cinder cone is prominent in Hopi folklore.

But neither its red crown nor the Hopi mythology concerning it is the real reason for Sunset Crater's fame. The most striking feature is the recency of its origin. A glance at the two rough, deep black lava streams that have poured out from its base, or at the fresh cinders on its sides, is sufficient to convince even a casual visitor that very recent volcanic activity took place here. Moreover, in 1930 discovery was made of the first of twenty-five pit houses now known to have been buried under a fall of Sunset Crater ash, making possible an almost exact dating of the eruption and allowing a key advance in reconstruction of the Crater's history.

Prior to about the middle of the eleventh century A.D., a few inhabitants, relatives of the modern Pueblo Indians of the region, lived in small pit earth-lodges scattered about the east base of San Francisco Mountain. There they farmed on the alluvial fans, using primitive methods of agriculture. Sometime between the years 1046 and 1071, as determined by a study of tree rings in the beams of the pit houses, Sunset Crater erupted violently. Doubtless many earthquakes preceded the first actual explosion, and it is probable that the families living near the site of eruption all moved to a distance, not without fear and awe, in advance of the main volcanic activity.

First, perhaps, a little "smoke" issued from a crack in the ground. Then quantities of fine dust and coarser cinders probably spewed forth in great clouds. Small stones known as lapilli and large ones referred to as bombs also were thrown high in the air, and, as these materials settled around the vent, a conical mountain grew up. Meanwhile the finer materials were spread far and wide about the growing mountain, forming a dark blanket that covered everything for miles and created a scene of great desolation. Probably for many months, possibly for several years, such activity continued. Much of the time steam and dust remained in the form of great clouds above the cone; frequently rocks heated to the point of incandescence gave a brilliant glow to the sky, especially at night, and at times hot rivers of molten lava gushed forth from the base, hissing and sputtering as they flowed along. One stream became ponded where it was trapped in a valley to the northwest and is now known as the Bonito flow. The other, called Kana-a, had freedom of movement and traveled for many miles down toward the Little Colorado Valley. After further eruption of cinders and ash, all was quiet— the volcano apparently was dead.

Cessation of Sunset Crater's eruption brought unprecedented activity on the part of human inhabitants in this and adjoining areas. Apparently a tremendous "land rush" developed in succeeding years, for it was soon discovered that the black mantle of ash formed an excellent mulch, catching and holding moisture and so providing fine farming land. The archaeological record shows that at this time many families moved in, and a

59

thriving civilization developed. Thus, the products of volcanism that at one moment had frightened and driven out man had aided and brought about his prosperity at another.

Leaving the pageant of "the eruption and man," a drama of some centuries ago, we come to the scene of today. Sunset Crater, the center of the scene, and the spectacular lavas on its sides, are not the only features of interest. Close by the base of the hill is a line of miniature craters, like doll houses beside a mansion. These are known as spatter cones or fumaroles, and their crowns of yellow and other brilliant colors clearly indicate that various gases once found passage through their throats. Near by also is a small cave, formed by a draining away of the lava while cooling. In it ice remains much of the year. The dense cover of black lava effectively absorbs the rays of the sun even in hot summer, while, in the cave below, cold air settles to the bottom. Likewise of interest are "squeeze-ups," formed along fissures in hardened flows where semiplastic lavas were squeezed upward to form thin sheets as much as ten feet high and locally arched over by their own weight. These and many other features of interest well reward the adventurous person who explores about over the volcanic field.

A PANORAMA OF VOLCANISM

Vulcan, god of fire and master of forging and smelting, has left the manifestations of his trade in many parts of this planet's surface, but in few places are they more spectacular than on the Uinkaret Plateau on the north side of Grand Canyon. Compared with famous volcanic fields of many lands, this display is small, yet the variety and striking character of the exhibit, seen with

a single glance of the eye, are such that it commands great wonder. It is a strange spectacle of havoc and wreck. It is a weird
scene of rough black lavas that have flowed across the plateau
surface partly concealing the underlying red and buff rock
layers, and of cone-shaped cinder piles rising like giant anthills
over the terrain.

Mount Trumbull, dominant mountain of the area, reaches
an elevation of seventy-five hundred feet above sea level. From
its summit a multitude of silent symmetrical craters—some
fresh and black, some red from the oxidation of iron—rise in
all directions to heights of several hundred feet. Nearly 170
distant cones, many perfect in form, are seen in a forty-mile
distance stretching northward from the brink of Grand Canyon.
In places they occur in rows of three to eight, elsewhere they
are scattered at random, as in the vicinity of the Canyon rim,
or are clustered into little groups. Each has around its base a
flow or two of once liquid lava that appears to have poured forth
through some subterranean channel.

Southward from the mountain is a particularly weird spot
known as the Witches Water Pocket. It is a broad, desolate
area where the lava is so rough and jagged and so black that it
appears to have flowed forth just yesterday. This is the type of
lava referred to as "malpais," meaning badlands, by the natives
of the southwest. The appropriateness of the term is at once apparent to one who attempts to climb over its surface even for a
short distance. The stoutest shoes are cut to pieces rapidly when
used on its sharp, needle-like surface, and one's footing is precarious, to say the least, because of the irregularities. Little
imagination is needed to visualize how this lava, in the not-
distant past, was frothing and sputtering and creating a great

61

commotion as it slowly but relentlessly advanced across the plateau surface.

The really remarkable feature of the Uinkaret volcanic field, however, is not to be found in any unique character of the lava itself. Rather it is in the intimate interrelationship of lavas and cinder cones, on the one hand, and the Grand Canyon, on the other. Even before the brink of the main chasm is reached, as one approaches from the north down Toroweap Valley, one sees a notable display of large lava streams that have poured from vents, flooded the mesa land above, and cascaded over the valley walls. The black lavas stand out in marked contrast with the light-colored underlying strata of sedimentary origin that show between the various flows like windows beneath drapes. The rock streams have descended fully fifteen hundred feet to the valley floor. There they spread into wide fields and then extend southward to the very brink of Grand Canyon, forming the greatest display of all.

Pouring over the rim of the Canyon, fiery cascades once shot downward three thousand feet toward the Colorado River below, leaving a trail of lava that tells the story almost as clearly as though it were happening before our eyes. In the colorful words of John Wesley Powell: "What a conflict of water and fire there must have been here! Just imagine a river of molten rock, running down into a river of melted snow. What a seething and boiling of waters; what clouds of steam rolled into the heavens!" But this was not all. The lava stream, having reached the bottom of the chasm, appears to have flowed down its channel for many miles, perhaps a hundred, to the lower end of Grand Canyon. Many patches of the lava still remain here and there along the river, giving mute testimony of the former

62

course and extent of this great lava flow, now all but worn away by the mighty Colorado.

Perched on the very brink of the main Canyon, near where the lavas cascaded, are other spectacular displays of the volcanic activity of geologically recent times. On the north side stands a well-formed basaltic cone of cinders, symmetrical and at least six hundred feet high, yet dwarfed in its setting of Canyon cliffs and colossal scenery. Very appropriately it has been named Vulcan's Throne. Across the Canyon, on the South Rim, is an even more intriguing exhibit. It is a ruined cone below which the Canyon walls have receded and exposed to view the black dike that once fed this volcano. In brief, it shows the internal anatomy of a cinder cone as clearly as a textbook illustration.

Early in the volcanic history of the region thick flows of lava, moving southward, largely filled a deep, narrow gorge that once dissected the floor of Toroweap Valley. Approaching Grand Canyon to the south, these lavas piled up at the junction to a height of six hundred feet, thus forming a great dam across the Colorado River and, no doubt, a great lake behind it. Small patches of these lavas still remain, clinging high on the Canyon walls on both sides as though left for proof of nature's great engineering feat. The dam itself has long since been cut away by the ever working force of the Colorado River. Since its destruction still another, though much smaller, dam appears to have been formed and worn away at a place some miles downstream. These events are but fleeting moments in the geologic history of the region, yet from any human standpoint they are immense and impressive.

NECKS OF ANCIENT FIRE MOUNTAINS

Quite in contrast to the well-known scenery of the geologically youthful volcanic fields of Arizona and New Mexico is that formed from the remnants of more ancient volcanism in the land of the Hopi and Navajo Indians. In these areas erosion has so far dissected the region that cones have been entirely removed, and sheets of lava that once covered thousands of square miles are all but gone. In their stead, the old volcanic conduits, once entirely beneath the ground, now rise as giant towers, revealing their inner structure with great clarity. Elsewhere, the dismembered lava flows appear as tiny volcanic patches capping the mesas.

In approaching the villages of the Hopi Indians by the usual routes from the south, one traverses the most extensive of the several areas of volcanic necks in this region. At least thirty individual towers, some castle-shaped, others like chimneys, rise above the plain. Their dark, somber colors make them all the more conspicuous among the delicately tinted sediments of the surrounding badlands. Most of them are in clusters; a few are isolated. In cross section they are round or oval, and their sides show peculiar vertical structures like thin columns, the result of lava shrinkage during the cooling process. At one time in history, the spaces now occupied by these necks were the conduits out of which ash and lava poured, covering the former surface to a thickness of perhaps a thousand feet. All that is gone now, as well as the rock layers that surrounded the necks, but to the geologist the story is clear.

Best known of the volcanic necks in the region is Shiprock,

64

which rises fourteen hundred feet out of the desert and, as its name implies, looks like a great ship at sea. Located near "four-corners," where Arizona, New Mexico, Colorado, and Utah meet, this huge, towering monolith greets all visitors traveling the road from Gallup to Mesa Verde. Unlike necks of the Hopi Butte field, this one and others near it are composed of volcanic fragments cemented together by hot solutions to form a resist-ant, compact mass. The vent which the rock fragments filled doubtless was drilled through the ground by steam explosions, and many of the fragments that form the neck are those that fell back into the conduit. Another feature of Shiprock is a group of thin, vertical dikes or sheets of lava that radiate out from it in all directions, giving the appearance of black walls rising out of the ground. One to the south extends for more than two miles.

Other spectacular volcanic necks occur near Monument Valley in northeastern Arizona. Most famous of these are Agathla, which rises to a height of more than one thousand feet above a conical pedestal of red shale, and Church Rock near Kayenta. Particularly striking is the contrast between the blackness of these and the red color of the near-by sandstone monuments in the valley. In general character and in origin, these rocks are much like Shiprock, formed by repeated explosions that carried fragments upward toward the surface. At one time they, too, were doubtless surrounded by layers of other rock and possessed craters near their present summits.

CHAPTER THREE

FOSSIL LIFE OF THE CANYON COUNTRY

By Edwin D. McKee

ICE-AGE ANIMALS

A group of Navajo Indians had just arrived in Flagstaff for the Fourth of July powwow and celebration. I chanced upon them in the exhibit hall of the Museum of Northern Arizona. There they stood, in a semicircle, intently but silently scrutinizing the skeleton of what must once have been a massive clumsy animal the size of a bear. Finally an old Indian spoke—in Navajo. Then a younger man, and another, and another had his say, each pointing toward some feature of the skeleton and talking with what appeared to be great earnestness.

My curiosity aroused, I finally asked my friend, Jim Kewanwytewa, a Hopi Indian who spoke Navajo, to tell me what kept these men talking so seriously for so long. Jim listened and then gave me the story. These Navajos, he said, knew intimately the wild life of the region and were sure that no animal such as they saw before them existed. In their experience only a porcupine remotely resembled this creature, yet the porcupine was many times smaller. What could it be and where did it come from? Doubtless for years after they pondered these questions.

69

Little wonder was it that the Navajos were baffled. What they saw in Flagstaff were the bones of a western ground sloth, ancient relative of the South American tree sloth and member of the highly specialized and peculiar group of mammals that includes the anteater and the armadillo. What the Navajos could not have known was that not long ago, geologically speaking, these great, slow-moving creatures were common throughout the Canyon Country and the Southwest in general. Doubtless wandering about in small herds, they fed on plants. Long, incurved claws indicate that they walked on only the outside toes of the front feet and put most of their weight on the huge hind feet.

Although the specimen at Flagstaff was excavated from gravel deposits near Springerville, Arizona, evidence of many another sloth of a slightly smaller variety has been found in limestone caverns of the region. At Gypsum Cave, near Las Vegas, Nevada, sloth dung and sloth bones have been found in association with objects of human manufacture, showing definitely that in this region early man was contemporaneous with the sloth. In isolated portions of lower Grand Canyon, more recent explorations have revealed two caves, Rampart and Muav, the floor levels of which have been built up a number of feet with layers of sloth manure or sloth "balls," as the dung is called. Study of plant fragments from within these "balls" indicates that the animals fed on yuccas, century plants, Mormon tea, and other desert plants still growing in the area. This indicates clearly that the sloth inhabited the region not only as recently as the time of latest glaciation, which was about thirty-five thousand years ago, but probably much later. Indeed, after seeing the freshness of the remains, one cannot help harboring the

70

secret though vain hope that a few of these strange creatures might have succeeded in hiding out in some remote corner of Grand Canyon!

Other Ice Age mammals have left their traces in parts of the Canyon region. Around spring deposits, in deep limestone cracks, among stream gravels, and in caves, their bones have been preserved. The arid climate—and luck—have saved the records of many. Some were creatures similar to modern wild animals of the region; others were very different and seem strange and out of place as we contemplate them today. In the latter category is the mammoth, an extinct type of elephant, one of which had its teeth and tusks preserved in the deposits of Charley Day Spring near Tuba. Other mammoth specimens have been found also in Tsegi Canyon, among the gravels at Springerville, and north of Kingman. In fact, it seems probable that these great pachyderms once roamed in considerable numbers between the red cliffs of the Little Colorado Valley, browsing on the stream-course vegetation that doubtless was far more lush then than it is under the desert environment of today.

With the elephants of the Canyon region were camels and horses, animals whose diminutive, ancient ancestors appear to have developed in America many millions of years before. During late stages of the Ice Age or shortly after, these animals appear to have been common in the region, only to become entirely extinct here and throughout America prior to its "discovery" by white man. The horse, of course, was reintroduced by Spaniards in historic times, and somewhat later the camel, too, was brought back, though not to stay. A few years before the Civil War, camels were imported by the War Department for transport service in the desert areas. Lieutenant Beale used

71

them in Arizona but had poor success, and ultimately many of the animals were released near Yuma to wander at will through the region. The record of these is not to be confused with that of the prehistoric camel, which was a different type. Bones of the latter have been found in deep cracks that penetrate the surface of the limestone plateau south of Grand Canyon and that apparently served as death traps.

TREES OF STONE

Shinar' av, the great Wolf God of Paiute mythology, is said by these Indians to have used the trunks of stone trees for combat. Broken and shattered remains of his weapons lie strewn in great profusion over the ground, in various parts of the Canyon Country, marking the sites of fierce battles. Notable examples are found in many parts of Arizona, Utah, and Nevada, but the most spectacular of the warrior god's battlegrounds are at Petrified Forest National Monument, in Beautiful Valley, and near Round Rock in Arizona.

The Navajos have a different explanation for logs of fossil wood. According to Dr. H. E. Gregory of the United States Geological Survey, these Indians consider the petrified trunks to be *yeitsobitsin*, or the bones of Yeitso, who was a monster destroyed by the sun god. The congealed blood of this monster is said to be the black lava flows common in the region.

Petrified "forests" occur in many parts of the world and are of many varieties. Those at Gilboa in New York State are famed as being some of the oldest known; those in Yellowstone National Park are notable because the trees are still standing and one forest is on top of another. But for sheer beauty and

72

brilliant coloring of the stone, and for spectacular size and quantity of logs, the petrified "forests" of the Canyon Country are unrivaled.

Fossil trees of the Petrified Forest represent a number of different types, the most common of which is a conifer related to the modern weird araucarias of South America and Australia. Some of the logs have lengths of one hundred or more feet and widths of several feet. Especially notable, moreover, is the fact that with few exceptions the trees are not standing. They appear battered and worn; their twigs and cones are absent; and the great trunks lie scattered at random through clay or gravel deposits as though they had drifted into their place of burial.

The types of ancient landscape in which these remarkable "forests" developed can be visualized to some extent when the associated forms of life and the character of the sediments that entombed them are considered. In the same deposits are found the teeth and bones and even the entire skulls of ancient crocodile-like animals known as phytosaurs, whose snouts projected far forward and whose eyes were located almost on the tops of their heads. Also common are the bony head plates that served as armor for sluggish, sprawling amphibians, the shells of clams, and the traces of a large variety of ferns, horsetail rushes, and other streamside plants, represented by their imprints and by black carbon residues.

The sediments that contain the petrified wood are the rocks that form the equally famous Painted Desert. They are of two principal types. First, there are resistant layers of cemented gravel and coarse sand that form small cliff walls and the caps of many mesas; second, there are vast accumulations of soft limy mud or marl exhibiting delicate hues of white, gray, brown,

73

yellow, blue, violet, red, purple, and black, mostly in the form of bands. These marls disintegrate readily into a strange "badland" type of topography consisting of low rounded hillocks and mounds with intricately dissected slopes and dendritic stream patterns on their sides. The clays have the property of swelling to several times their normal volume when wet, and they readily turn into sticky mud that flows and finally dries with a network of cracks on the surface.

Both the gravels and the muds of the Painted Desert were formed originally on a vast river floodplain that extended from New Mexico to Nevada and from central Arizona to central Utah. The gravel layers were developed by active streams, flowing probably from high mountains to the south. Logs of trees, later to be petrified, were drifted in at the same time and concentrated in log jams as we find them today. The clays, on the other hand, indicate times of quiet water accumulation. They contain great quantities of volcanic ash which show that somewhere in the region volcanoes were active, pouring forth material that is in large measure responsible for the peculiar character of the Painted Desert clays.

Petrified wood of the Canyon Country is not in reality wood. Aside from a few local deposits preserved as charcoal, it is in the form of stone. The change from wood to stone took place long ago, through the activity of underground waters that carried certain minerals in solution. As the waters passed through tiny pore spaces or interstices in the rock, they dissolved away the original wood, particle by particle, leaving in its place a silica reproduction. In some logs, even the interspaces of the cells were filled with minute quantities of silica. Thus, the shape and

74

character of the wood have been retained, and even the minute details of cellular structure show in certain specimens.

Brilliant coloring, which is an outstanding feature of much of the petrified wood in the Canyon Country, is accountable to the occurrence with the silica of small quantities of iron and manganese oxides. The former are responsible for a great variety of reds, browns, and yellows, whereas the latter normally causes a deep black. In any case the resulting rock is known as chalcedony or, if banded, as agate. Special varieties, depending on color and opaqueness, are referred to as carnelian, chrysoprase, and jasper. Where the iron or manganese oxides have diffused unevenly into the silica, giving mottled or treelike designs, moss agates are formed. In some places, however, instead of replacing wood structure, the silica has been deposited in open cracks or cavities, where, because there was no interference to growth, small but perfect six-sided crystals of quartz have been formed.

COAL SWAMPS AND SEA MONSTERS

Some years ago, while on the quest for certain geologic data, I had occasion to make a trip by pack train down the remote but scenic canyon of the Escalante River in Utah. As the party sat around a campfire one night, discussing experiences and places in the region, our packer, a native sheepherder, pointed southwestward toward the Kaiparowits Plateau and told the story of a burning mountain. For many years, he said, smoke had been issuing from a crack in the rocks. Of those few persons who had chanced to witness the phenomenon, he knew of none who could explain it.

75

Later investigation of Utah's "burning mountain" brought to light the fact that it was indeed the work of fire; that a coal seam under the ground had been slowly burning for an unknown length of time. The coal was but a patch of the vast deposits of this material that occur throughout the Canyon Country wherever rocks of the Cretaceous or chalk age are to be found. This coal is neither so old nor of such high rank as the bituminous and anthracite varieties of eastern America and Europe which constitute such an important source of fuel. Yet the Cretaceous coal of the West occurs in vast quantities over a wide region, and in some future day it may claim much attention.

From a geological standpoint, the term "coal" is closely associated with "swamp." At Gallup, New Mexico, where soft coal is mined commercially on a large scale, or along the Mogollon Rim in Arizona and among the High Plateaus of Utah, where it is dug out for local consumption, and on the Hopi Indian Reservation, where it has been used since prehistoric times, the black beds indicate plant accumulations in ancient swampy areas. Seldom are the plant structures clearly preserved in the coal itself, but, in shales and sandstones that surround the coal, many leaves, stems, and other vegetable remains show excellent detail. Among the varieties of plants represented, one of the commonest is the sequoia, a relative of the modern redwood and the big tree of California. Other common types are willows, poplars, and tulip trees, all hardwoods which are believed to have appeared on earth for the first time during the Cretaceous period.

Cretaceous coal swamps must have bordered a great inland sea that occupied much of the present Rocky Mountain area. As the margins of this sea slowly advanced and retreated across the then flat surface of the region, beach sands and shallow water muds alternately covered and were covered by deposits of the land. Lagoons and estuaries with swampy forest growth at the sides, beaches, and bars, all came and went, many leaving their records in the deposits. Striking as are the plant remains of the land, no less interesting are the evidences of marine animals that were entombed in the black muds of the sea. Oyster shells are common, and the broken fragments of these form entire beds or layers in various parts of the region. Delicately sculptured, coiled shells of ammonites, animals related to the modern squid and octopus, are locally found by the thousands. Most exciting of all, however, are the bones of giant sea reptiles which come to light here and there in the Cretaceous rocks, for they were of the "Age of Reptiles." One interesting case was the discovery in Black Mesa, Arizona, of the flipper of a large plesiosaur—a long-necked, slow-swimming type that had a length of about thirty feet.

TRACKS THAT GO UPHILL

The Hermit Trail, about a mile from its start on Grand Canyon's rim, descends a great three-hundred-foot cliff of Coconino sandstone in a winding course appropriately named the White Zigzags. Here, early in the present century, a discovery was made that aroused tremendous interest on the part of scientist and layman alike. Well-preserved, five-toed animal tracks, evenly spaced and clearly impressed, were found on the smooth, even surfaces of white sandstone layers. Clear as though formed just yesterday in the dust of the trail, these footprints, showing claw, toe, and heel marks, could be traced for many

77

feet across sloping slabs, and in numerous places passed from view only where the containing layer of sandstone was covered by other layers in the Canyon wall.

Early rumors were followed by official reports; official reports were followed by scientific expeditions—three of them under the leadership of Dr. Charles Gilmore of the National Museum. Extensive quarrying operations and careful searching for several seasons brought to light many hundreds of trackways representing a truly impressive array of animal types. Dr. Gilmore believed them to have been made by reptiles. Some of the tracks were those of animals not larger than small lizards, others of creatures having large feet and a stride nearly a yard in length. Some indicated short-limbed, heavy, wide-bodied animals, while still others suggested those having long, slender limbs and narrow bodies. Strangely enough, no bones or skeletal remains were found or have since been found either in this area or elsewhere in the sandstone containing the tracks.

Of all the many interesting features of the footprints in the Coconino sandstone of Grand Canyon none appeared more odd or caused more speculation than the fact that virtually all of the toemarks pointed up the sloping surfaces of the rock layers. Only three exceptions were noted in many hundreds of cases. Subsequent studies showed that the sloping rock surfaces were formed on the steep lee-sides of ancient sand dunes, probably in a vast desert region, but why did the reptiles go up, and not down, these dunes?

Fifteen years passed after this question was first raised. Suggestions had been offered, but no serious attempt to solve the riddle had yet been made. Why did the tracks all go uphill? Discussing the problem before a class of three hundred geology

78

students at the University of Arizona, I suggested that they consider the problem for a week, after which I promised to ask for ideas in a test. The results were remarkable. Reports from many sources described campus activities relating to the "lizard problem." At odd times and odd places little groups of students argued out their theories or made crude experiments with sand piles to prove their cases. Finally the exam came, and with it the question.

An amazing variety of ideas was the result. Some were sound and logical, others weird and fantastic. Probably the commonest was some variation of the theory that the reptiles were fleeing from a catastrophe such as a flood or volcanic eruption, or that they were migrating in a given direction in search of food or water. Other suggestions were that the reptiles had wings, and that after climbing the dunes they would glide down; or that because of the steepness of the slopes the animals would go backward down the hills. A more plausible hypothesis was that the uphill tracks were made under good preserving conditions, that is, when the sand was damp, whereas the downhill tracks were formed in dry sand and not preserved. Still another suggestion of merit was that the reptiles walked up the lee sides of the dunes but went down the less steep windward sides, and on these their tracks were destroyed.

Finally came a time when it was decided to conduct a series of experiments to determine, if possible, the true cause of the lack of downhill tracks in the Coconino sandstone. At the Museum of Northern Arizona in Flagstaff, preparations were made. Dune sands from the Painted Desert, with grain size and sorting similar to those of the Coconino, were collected. A large

79

chuckwalla lizard and several smaller reptiles were obtained. In a long box or trough miniature dunes were constructed, and a lizard was placed at the base of one. The observers waited excitedly to see the results, but nothing happened. Either the chuckwalla refused to move or, if prodded, would swish its tail and run, thus destroying all of its tracks.

But persistence won out. It was discovered that when the end of the trough containing the lizard was darkened and the opposite end was placed in sunlight, the reptile would travel toward the sun, crossing the dunes en route. Once this problem was solved, it was an easy matter to find the answer to the bigger problem of why the tracks went uphill. It was seen that on the steep slopes of the lee side the animal pressed its feet firmly into the sand, making clear tracks, but whenever it attempted to go downhill on the same slope it would hold back to keep from sliding, with the result that the sand would avalanche and destroy the footprints. Thus, another mystery was unraveled.

SEASHELLS ON MOUNTAINTOPS

One day, as I was examining a well-preserved petrified seashell embedded in the rim rock at Grand Canyon, an elderly man and his wife were attracted to where I was kneeling. Idle curiosity, no doubt, brought them there, and I suspect that they were wondering to themselves whether I was on the trail of some gold nuggets or was just queer. But when the man, who proved to be a farmer from the Dust Bowl, saw what I was examining, he began to show a serious interest. He recognized the fossil as an animal of the sea, yet he was aware of the fact that this fossil was a mile and a half above the ocean and in a region that was very dry. He thought a while, then, turning to his wife, observed, "The sea must have been here once."

The Dust Bowl farmer had made a discovery for himself. He realized for the first time in his life that the seas had not always been where we find them today. He must have recognized, furthermore, that the rocks of Grand Canyon and the fossils in them had been raised out of the ocean, for surely the sea could never have stood seven thousand feet above its present level. Had he investigated further he would have found that the region has been down under the sea not once, but perhaps seven times. Strata in the walls of Grand Canyon testify to this fact. At numerous different levels are found marine limestones containing fossil sea animals like those on the top, whereas between these layers are others presenting equally clear evidence that they were formed above sea level. So the story has been one of constant change—up and down.

Marine fossils on the rim of Grand Canyon tell far more than that the region was once under the sea. Identical lamp shells or brachiopods, which are the animals most abundantly represented, are found also in areas including central Utah, southern Arizona, New Mexico, and western Texas, showing within broad limits the distribution of the ancient seaway. Horn corals and sea lilies, both of which are common, suggest that the sea was warm, clear, and shallow, for it is in such an environment that the modern relatives of these animals live. The spines of sea urchins, the teeth of sharks, and the skeletons of siliceous sponges throw further light upon the character of the sea floor and its life as represented by this particular limestone deposit.

From place to place along modern sea coasts, the life varies according to type of bottom, depth, temperature, and a host of

81

other environmental factors. Apparently similar conditions were prevalent in the seas of two hundred million years ago. Tracing the limestone formation of the Grand Canyon rim eastward and southward, the character both of the rock and of the fossils in it is found to change with approach to the ancient strand. At Bottomless Pits near Walnut Canyon is one of the most famous fossil quarries of this near-shore environment. Every rock in this locality is filled with the molds and casts of sea animals. It is sport to collect here, for the abundance and variety of types seem unlimited. Mollusks of both the snail and the clam groups are most numerous, but there are heads and tails of crablike creatures known as trilobites, occasional coiled shells of animals related to the octopus and squid, and the long, straight, tubelike shells of scaphopods, often called elephant-tusk shells. Apparently the brackish waters of this area teemed with life, and its record is such as to excite the enthusiasm of anyone interested in the history of the past.

CHAPTER FOUR

THREE HUNDRED YEARS OF SPAIN

By Weldon F. Heald

The West is so raw and new," complained a lady with a Back Bay accent on the California-bound Santa Fe *Chief*. "I feel lost in a country without background or history."

Outside the car window an interminable, dun-colored desert slipped by, bounded on the horizon by barren, tawny peaks. Except for the ribbon of paved road paralleling the tracks, and an occasional ugly new filling station, the landscape was empty. The road and railway did look raw and new, as if they were tenuous threads of civilization through a country history had touched lightly, if at all.

But the Boston lady was wrong. If you don't insist that the only history worth considering is that in which your own ancestors figured prominently, you find that the Southwest has had the most colorful and romantic past of any section of the United States, and a longer human history than New England and the middle Atlantic Coast.

Man has lived in the Southwest for perhaps five thousand years. Human remains have been found in caves with the bones of the extinct ground sloth. There are innumerable ruins of past redskin cultures, some dating back a thousand years. The oldest continuously inhabited village in the country is in Arizona. The second European colony within the present boundaries of the United States was established on the banks of the Rio Grande in 1598, antedating Jamestown by nine years. And Spanish explorers peered down into the Grand Canyon in 1540 —eighty years before the Pilgrims landed on Plymouth Rock.

How did it come about that Santa Fe was founded before Boston, and Europeans were crisscrossing the arid, inhospitable Southwest before the colonists on the East Coast had pushed back into their fertile hinterland? The reason is that the American Southwest formed a frontier of one of the greatest colonial empires ever known, fully two hundred years before a restless United States began to expand westward.

In the early sixteenth century, Spain was in her vigorous prime. Her tough, young, resilient sons were tacking across the Atlantic and Pacific oceans in all directions, adding new and fabulous lands to the growing empire in the name of God and the Spanish monarch. The world was first circumnavigated under the flag of Spain, Pizarro subdued the Incas of Peru, and Hernando Cortés conquered Aztec Mexico.

In 1522, Cortés was proclaimed by his sovereign, Charles V, Governor, Captain-General, and Chief Justice of the territories of New Spain. Mexico City was built on the ruins of Montezuma's capital, Tenochtitlán, and there Cortés set up administrative headquarters to govern the enormous North American possessions he had won for Spain.

Cortés was riding the crest of popularity. For several years he was Charles's top man. To keep his king happy he sent out several expeditions to discover and add new lands and make

86

the greatest royal domain in history bigger yet. But they discovered neither gold nor riches—and that was what Charles
needed most. Empire building is an expensive business. So luck
began to run the other way for Cortés. His rivals were out to
get him, and Charles, fearing the conqueror's growing power
and ambition, decided to clip his high-flying wings. Moreover,
Cortés himself found that the expedition business was expensive.

Off went the first wing in 1535, when Charles V sent Don
Antonio de Mendoza to Mexico City as Viceroy of New Spain.
Thenceforth the middle-aged conqueror had to share his power
with an uncommonly astute politician and administrator. But
Mendoza, too, had to make good. In 1536 he thought he saw
his opportunity.

In that year four travelers arrived in Mexico with a story so
strange that it spread through New Spain like a prairie fire. It
was a story made to order to stimulate the hot young blood of
several hundred fledgling conquistadores who had nothing to do
around Mexico City but gamble, make love, and get into trouble.
The four, gaunt, bearded travelers were the sole survivors of
Pánfilo de Narváez' abortive attempt to colonize Florida.
Wrecked on the Florida coast in 1528, they had footed the weary,
blistering miles across the continent to Culiacán on Mexico's
western slope near the Gulf of California. For nine years they
had been on their way through the wilderness, and, when
ushered into Mendoza's viceregal presence in Mexico City, they
showed the ravages wrought by six years of complete slavery to
the Indians.

But Mendoza and the eager young Spaniards had little interest in the tales of hardship and endurance told by Alvar
Nuñez, Cabeza de Vaca, and his three companions. They pricked

87

up their ears only at the news that the Indians had described great white cities across the desert far to the north of New Spain. There, Cabeza de Vaca said, doorways were encrusted with rubies and emeralds, and gold was plentiful enough to fill the coffers of Spain forever.

Could these be the fabled Seven Cities of Cibola, which rumor had it were paved with gold and studded with jewels? Mendoza didn't know. As yet no Spaniard had ever seen them or knew just where they were. But the Viceroy meant to find out. And so did Cortés.

Cortés still held a royal license to explore on his own. In order to be first on the spot and to recoup his fortune as well as his sovereign's good will, he pawned his wife's jewels to outfit an expedition to discover Cibola. He meant to lead it himself but at the last moment was prevented from doing so, probably because of the machinations of his archenemy, Mendoza, who never overlooked details. Leadership passed to Francisco de Ulloa, who set sail from Acapulco on July 8, 1539. The three ships under Ulloa's command followed the west coast of Mexico northward into the Gulf of California. Neither riches nor Cibola were found, but, before Ulloa and two of his ships disappeared forever somewhere up the California coast, he made two important geographical discoveries: he found that the supposed island of California was actually a peninsula, and he surmised the existence of a great river at the head of the Gulf. This was, of course, the Colorado.

But that kind of discovery wasn't enough for Charles. It paid no bills. Off went the other wing. Cortés was through flying. The Conqueror who is said to have told his emperor, "I am a man who has given you more provinces than your ancestors

88

...ons of petrified trees in Petrified National Monument, Arizona.

Fossil trilobites in Bright Angel shale, Tont Platform, Grand Canyon.

Petroglyphs on cliff walls near Newspaper Rock, Petrified Forest National Monument.

Bryce Canyon.

View in Bryce Canyon National Park.

left you cities," returned to Spain, where he died in neglect in 1547.

Canny Mendoza's method of stalking Cibola was more cautious. He wasn't going to risk too much on an all-or-nothing gamble. Cabeza de Vaca and his three companions knew the trails to the north, in part at least. Let one of them lead a small party to scout out the land and find just how much truth there was to this Cibola story. If things appeared favorable, then the conquering conquistadores could proudly go forward under the war banners of Spain. It was a careful, well-conceived plan. It deserved to succeed.

But the very name, Cibola, stimulated Spanish ambition, imagination, exaggeration, and downright falsification to such an extent that the Viceroy's reasonable plan led to the most fantastic and improbable series of happenings in the history of exploration.

FORERUNNERS—BLACK AND WHITE

One might speculate on the turn of events had Cabeza de Vaca or one of his two Spanish companions acted as guide. But they had happier things to do than turn around and plunge back into the land of their nine-year travail. So the choice of guiding Mendoza's scouting trip fell on the huge shoulders of the last of the quartet—the Negro slave, Esteban. In him Spanish archives record a unique character: an enormous, blustering, swaggering black man who greedily rushed forward to strut through a page of history to his curious doom.

To accompany Esteban, the Viceroy chose a well-known, ambitious Franciscan friar, Marcos de Niza. He was instructed to bring back all the information he could gather about the peo-

89

ple, climate, soils, plants, animals, and geography of the lands through which he passed. Fray Marcos was to be, in fact, a roving reporter. That he somewhat overdid his assignment will soon become apparent.

So the man of God and the big, black slave left Culiacán, the jumping-off place in the province of New Galicia, on March 7, 1539. With a small number of Indian servants they traveled northward for two weeks, and Fray Marcos industriously made notes of everything he saw.

But friar and slave did not make a smooth, even-pulling team. Esteban wanted his head. Each day he became more impatient to push on to the riches, luxury, and power he was certain waited for him in the north. At the Indian village of Vacapa, Fray Marcos sent Esteban on ahead to scout—probably with a sigh of relief. As Esteban was no man of letters, it was agreed that he would send back fleet Indian runners with verbal messages. They would also bring to the friar wooden crosses varying in size with the importance of the country discovered. And so it came about that the first representative of the white race to enter the region which is now Arizona and New Mexico was a black man. Reveling in his freedom, Esteban was medicine man, chief, and god in the Indian villages through which he passed. With fierce greyhounds at his heels he swaggered at the head of a growing army of awed redskinned followers which eventually numbered three hundred. He shook his feathered gourd rattle, jingled bells at elbows and ankles, and dined off green Spanish dishes, served by an adoring retinue of Indian girls. Esteban's bumptious excursion through the desert wilderness of the Southwest stands alone; nothing like it has been seen before or since.

90

Four days after Esteban's departure, a messenger staggered into Fray Marcos' camp weighed down by a cross as tall as a man. "Come immediately," was Esteban's message. "I have heard that the greatest country in the world is ahead." That was Esteban's last word to posterity.

For the friar, now almost as excited as the slave, was never able to catch up with the speeding black man. Once more Fray Marcos had word of Esteban, who was leaving the last village before crossing the mountain to Cibola. But two weeks later came the unexpected blow which changed Mendoza's scouting party into a hit-and-run affair. The friar met a returning Indian who had been in Esteban's company; then two more, wounded and bloody. They reported that the earthly visit of the black god hadn't impressed the warlike inhabitants of the Seven Cities of Cibola. Esteban and his retinue had been taken prisoners.

All that remains is to put a final period to Esteban's strange, vainglorious odyssey. It was learned later that he died transfixed with Cibolan arrows, and that a piece of his body was sent to each chief of the Seven Cities so that they would know that rapacious strangers would never be led by this black man to conquer their homeland. And the chief of all the Cities inherited two ferocious greyhounds and four green Spanish dishes.

Now comes one of those historical mystery stories which has never been solved to everybody's satisfaction. Whether at this point in his journey Fray Marcos pushed on in the face of danger and looked down upon Cibola from a distance or turned tail and fled Mexico-ward is still a subject for violent controversy four hundred years after the event.

According to his report, the Franciscan friar decided to see

91

the Great White City of the north in spite of his terrified, wailing Indian escorts. Fray Marcos wrote that he crossed the last remaining wilderness and came to a hill from which he looked down upon the first city of Cibola. It surpassed his rosiest expectations. "A very beautiful place, bigger than Mexico City," he reported with enthusiasm. "It seems to me to be the greatest and best of the discoveries." Upon his return he testified on oath to the veracity of his report.

The wondrous city of Fray Marcos de Niza was Hawikuh, largest of the seven villages of Zuñi. Today this New Mexican Indian pueblo looks much as it did then. Anyone who has seen modern Zuñi may well wonder what the friar saw to stimulate a running fever of cupidity and conquest in every Spaniard's breast. However, down the years Fray Marcos has had a host of sympathetic explainers to help him out. "The setting sun transformed the mud and sandstone walls into gold," they say. "Mica particles shone like myriads of jewels. The thin desert air magnified and transformed Hawikuh into a great city." Thus was the simple man of God misled.

But it is very probable that Fray Marcos never saw Cibola, or Zuñi, except in the mind's eye of a thumping imagination. Present-day authorities, using evidence out of the friar's own report, conclude that he could not have come closer than two or three hundred miles from Zuñi. His time schedule inexorably testifies against him. But even stern historians let Fray Marcos down gently. He was so certain that the Great White Cities with jewel-studded walls of gold existed, and that Esteban had seen them, he was tempted to make a good story better by claiming to have been there.

92

CORONADO

At any rate, Fray Marcos returned to Mexico City to find himself the most famous man in New Spain. The news of his discovery of riches beyond the dreams of avarice threw all right-thinking Spaniards into a fever of excitement. Plans for a conquest of the northern country shifted into high gear. The Viceroy immediately started mustering an army. He chose as captain-general of his expeditionary force an impeccable, high-born, young hidalgo of thirty, Francisco Vásquez de Coronado, then governor of New Galicia.

Mendoza, unlike Cortés before him, possessed no royal license to explore and plunder. So the northern expedition was his responsibility alone. The bills were footed by the Viceroy personally and by such of his friends as were not averse to speculating on a sure thing. Even members of the expedition were supposed to contribute—down to the last foot soldier. The King couldn't lose, anyway, for royal prerogatives claimed a fifth of all precious metals and loot captured by any expedition under the Spanish flag. The venture was purely private speculation, but it looked good.

So a brilliant array of several hundred warriors left Culiacán in April and May, 1540. Captain-General Coronado himself, mounted on a prancing horse and gleaming in gilded armor, led the first contingent of some seventy horsemen and thirty foot soldiers. And, of course, well up front near the commander, went the newly-elevated Father-Provincial, Fray Marcos de Niza. On to the conquest of the Seven Cities of Cibola! These

93

were the most stirring times in Mexico since the heyday of Cortés.

But Coronado was no Cortés. He was serious and conscientious, but he lacked the spark to kindle enthusiasm in his followers. Mendoza's proud, plundering foray, organized with all the colorful splendor of sixteenth-century Spain, was a failure. But the two years of disillusionment and bitter frustration in the stark deserts of the north cannot be wholly blamed on Coronado. Guided by the ebullient friar, the confident young men expected to conquer the richest country in the world; what they found were mud villages thinly scattered through a barren land. And, as a crowning humiliation, they even failed to subdue the neolithic natives who lived in them.

Nevertheless, Coronado's unsuccessful quest for the shining Cities of Cibola was of prime importance in the history of the Southwest. His party brought the first cattle and horses to the vast rangelands of Arizona and New Mexico. They explored and made known a sizable slice of North America. They prepared the way for Spanish colonization on the Rio Grande. And, though they were unaware of the fact, they introduced to European exploitation a land which was destined to be one of the world's foremost producers of gold, silver, copper, and other metals. In truth, 1540 was the Great Year in Southwestern exploration. More major geographical discoveries were made in twelve months than ever before or since.

Explorations were made by sea as well as on land. Mendoza was a thorough organizer. Coronado's expedition was to be supported by a fleet of vessels which would carry extra supplies and provisions. The sea party was ordered to assist the land forces in every way. However, it turned out that the two groups

94

never made connections, thus adding one more failure to the dismal list.

The expedition's sea arm of three ships under Hernando de Alarcón sailed northward up the Gulf of California in the summer of 1540. Alarcón went Ulloa one better by actually discovering the Colorado River, and his men made a couple of trips in small boats some two hundred miles upstream from the delta. But he couldn't find so much as a footprint of Coronado's party. So by November he was back in Mexico City, trying to explain why to a displeased Viceroy. Had he but known, Melchor Diaz, dispatched by Coronado, was then marching up and down the lower Colorado looking for him.

Meanwhile the Captain-General and his brave task force arrived in Cibola far in advance of the main army. Eleven weeks on the tough, fifteen-hundred-mile trek from New Spain had deflated their enthusiasm. The bedraggled, bone-weary warriors were near starvation and coveted the Cibolans' food supply far more than their gold. The battle of Hawikuh was fought on July 7. It lasted an hour. Then the swarming white invaders scurried to the food storehouses to gorge themselves. Not a Spaniard was killed, but among the casualties carried from the field was Coronado himself. His wounds kept the conquering Captain-General abed for twelve days.

Stomachs filled, the victors looked about them. Where were the riches, the gold, silver, and jewels of Cibola? Maledictions fell upon the head of Fray Marcos. So bitter was the feeling against the friar that he hurriedly departed, in disgrace, with the first party returning to Mexico. Perhaps we had better leave Fray Marcos at this point with a final statement by a man

95

who was there—Francisco Vásquez de Coronado—who wrote the Viceroy, "I can assure Your Lordship that in reality he has not told the truth in a single thing that he has said, except the name of the city and the large stone houses."

The Captain-General spent five months at the pueblos of Zuñi directing his lieutenants in the exploration of the surrounding region. Still faintly hopeful of finding riches for Spain, he sent Pedro de Tovar to Tusayán with seventeen horsemen and a few foot soldiers. Tovar found there the villages of the Hopis which were discouragingly similar to those at Zuñi —mud and stone instead of gold and jewels. But he brought back word of a great river, flowing south, which the Hopis said was some days' journey to the west. Coronado concluded correctly that the stream should flow into the Gulf of California. By following its banks his men might be able to get in touch with Alarcón and his ships. So he dispatched Don García López de Cárdenas with a dozen horsemen to find the river.

They did. But they never reached its banks. After picking up Hopi guides at Tusayán, Cárdenas and his party crossed the high, arid plateaus of northern Arizona and suddenly came to a dead stop at the South Rim of the Grand Canyon. It is not recorded what the first white men thought when they peered a mile down into this gigantic gash in the earth's crust and saw the thin thread of a river at the bottom. But for three days they followed the South Rim, trying to find a way to descend. A trio of the party's most agile climbers did get a third of the way down but were forced to give up. They came back over the rim, eyes popping, mouths open: some of the pinnacles which looked from the top to be about the size of a man were actually bigger than the Great Tower of Seville! So Cárdenas and his party

96

did not meet Alarcón, but they have gone down in history as the first white men to have had the soul-stirring experience of seeing the Grand Canyon of Arizona. And more than two hundred years were to pass before white men from the young republic on the East Coast came that way.

Coronado, followed a month later by his army, packed up and left Zuñi in November to winter in the warmer, more fertile country along the Rio Grande. The two years of their trials, tribulations, and shabby little battles with ill-equipped natives, ending in a final retreat, empty-handed, to Mexico in 1542, are no part of the story of the Canyon Country. But Coronado's soldiers never discovered gold or riches. They did not even enjoy honor and glory upon their return to Mexico. The Captain-General himself retired to the life of family man, country squire, and minor official. But his journeys bequeathed a Spanish heritage to the American Southwest which is strong there today— four hundred years later.

THE PADRES

For over two centuries after Coronado, Spanish activity in the Southwest was centered in New Mexico and southern Arizona. Indian life in the high, arid plateaus of the north went on much as before the coming of the huge black man and an army led by a white warrior in gilded armor. They passed into legend, but their influence was as evanescent as a flash flood in a dry wash. There were a few other intruders. Antonio de Espejo led a small, private expedition from the Rio Grande into northern Arizona in 1582 and found silver ore at the head of Bill Williams River west of where Prescott now stands. And

97

in 1600 Franciscan missionaries moved in among the Hopis and converted them to Christianity—or thought they did.

The last of the conquistadores to penetrate the lonely mesas and canyons of northern Arizona were Don Juan de Oñate, first governor of New Mexico, and his nephew, Vicente de Zaldivar. Oñate was a rich and distinguished cavalier who had wangled a royal contract to conquer and settle New Mexico. In 1604, with thirty men and two priests, he crossed all of Arizona from Zuñi to the Colorado River and down to the Gulf of California. Fourteen years later Zaldivar, following the same route, became entangled in the rough precipitous country around Marble Canyon and went no farther.

Spanish colonization began along the Rio Grande in 1598, and Santa Fe was founded as capital of New Mexico twelve years later. But in 1680 Spanish rule was violently ended by an uprising of the Pueblo Indians. Some four hundred Spaniards were killed, the rest driven from New Mexico. Even the priests in remote Hopiland suffered martyrdom. So the frontiers of white supremacy retreated down the Rio Grande to El Paso, there to remain for fifteen years.

By the time Don Diego de Vargas, as governor of rejuvenated New Mexico, reconquered the northern provinces and established the capital once more at Santa Fe, Spaniards were again following Coronado's trail from Mexico into southern Arizona. But the newcomers were men of God. The day of the conquistadores was over. Throughout the New World Spain conquered with the cross as well as the sword. Where the soldier went, there went the priest also. The quest to save heathen souls from hell-fire was carried on with as much zeal as the search

98

for riches. And it was the clerics who brought civilizing influences to the raw, new lands the soldiers had conquered. With the crucifix came cattle, livestock, grains, fruits, farming, and the crafts.

The soul-saving pioneer of white civilization in southern Arizona was Father Eusebio Francisco Kino. This versatile, Austrian-born Jesuit priest was one of the great characters in American history. He established headquarters at Mission Dolores in northern Sonora in 1687. From there he carried his missionary labors northward among the Papagoes, Pimas, and Yumas from California on the west to the fringes of the dread Apache country on the east. Kino made forty journeys, or *entradas*, in twenty-four years, blazing trails that have become highways, establishing missions which have blossomed into towns, and opening up a territory almost as large as Spain itself. Colonization followed in the padre's wake, beginning with Tubac in 1752—the first white settlement in what is now the state of Arizona.

Arizona. How did that name happen to be applied to the western part of New Mexico province? Some say that Coronado's men, disappointed in finding no riches, disgustedly called the region of deserts, mesas, and canyons through which they wandered *La Arida Zona*—the dry zone—and usage brought the contraction, Arizona. That, of course, is too simple and glib to suit historians. The usually accepted derivation is that the name is a Spanish rendering of a Papago word, *aleh-zon*, a small spring of water. It was first applied to a creek on the trail northward from Sonora. But, whatever its origin, by 1754 the name Arizona was in general use to designate the entire region.

Regretfully we leave Father Kino, for he was probably the

most remarkable and colorful missionary pioneer of them all. But he never saw the Canyon Country. His journeys, extensive as they were, did not take him north of the Gila River. After his death in 1711, no Jesuit succeeded in extending Kino's frontiers of salvation further into the wilderness. No priest was even big enough to keep the gains he had made. So the brave string of missions slowly crumbled back into the desert. Fifty-six years passed before Kino's Franciscan successor, Fray Francisco Tomas Hermenegildo Garcés, carried the cross far to the north and west. He was the first white man after Zaldivar to become acquainted with the deep tributaries of the Grand Canyon.

In 1767, a high-pressure area in European politics caused squalls in the New World. As a result the Pope suppressed the powerful Jesuit Order throughout the Spanish Empire. The edict exploded like an unexpected bomb. Six thousand Black Robe priests in Mexico were given twenty-four hours to abandon their churches, missions, flocks, and Indian converts. They were forced to flee the country, carrying only their crosses and breviaries.

The results of two centuries of Jesuit labor fell to the Franciscans. And it was Father Garcés who was assigned to Kino's mission of San Xavier del Bac, near Tucson. He found the buildings run down and the Indian converts destitute. But things did not remain that way for long. Another spiritual empire builder had arrived at last.

Garcés did not have the greatness of Kino. He was a simple man, pious, sincere, and great-hearted. His whole life was consecrated to bringing Catholic salvation to the natives in the wilderness. Garcés loved them, and they returned his affection, unusual as it was. Faith, holy zeal, and a rawhide tough constitution combined to make Garcés the right man for the job before him.

He made five lengthy *entradas*, seeking missionary possibilities among the Indians. Many of these journeys led the intrepid padre into wilderness where no white man had been before. When the powers in Mexico City realized they had a superlative pathfinder up on the northern frontier, they began using Garcés regularly to ferret out routes between distant outposts. He might save all the souls his heart desired so long as they were on the main arteries of a growing Empire. So there came orders from Viceroy Buccerelli to explore routes from Santa Fe to Monterey on the California Coast. This was such a large order that no Spaniard had ever been found big enough to fulfill it. But Garcés responded with characteristic alacrity. He plunged into the wilds to the north and west again and again. Each time that he returned to San Xavier the padre must have had a beatific smile on his face—for he discovered thousands of redskinned pagans ripe for salvation.

In October, 1775, Garcés guided Juan Bautista de Anza and 240 colonists bound for San Francisco Bay. They left him at the Colorado River. The padre had his usual double orders, clerical and secular. He was to carry on missionary work among the Yuma Indians and to continue the search for a New Mexico-California route. He wintered on the Colorado, but by early spring left on his fifth *entrada*—one of the most remarkable one-man expeditions ever made.

For Garcés traveled alone except for Indian guides. He jogged along on muleback from one native village to the next, through heat and cold, over deserts and mountains, across rivers and arroyos. He ate whatever food the natives gave him or none at all, slept where he could, and everywhere talked of his God to whoever would listen. His banner was emblazoned with the Madonna and Child on one side, a lost soul in torment on the other.

Altogether Garcés was absent from San Xavier eleven months and covered something like twenty-five hundred miles. By April he was far into California. In June he visited the Mojaves near the present site of Needles, California. Then he struck off east into northern Arizona with the double purpose of visiting the Hopis and scouting a route to Santa Fe. Following Hualpai guides, Garcés descended into Cataract Canyon to enjoy the hospitality of the Havasupai in their remote, miniature paradise nestled between red cliffs three thousand feet high. The People of the Blue Water liked the white padre. They begged him to stay with them, even offering to provide a suitable bride. But celibate Christian duty called. After five days Garcés climbed out of the Canyon and faced east once more.

He skirted the South Rim of the Grand Canyon—the first white man to have done so in 236 years—crossed the edge of the Painted Desert, and rode into the Hopi country on July 4, 1776, the first Independence Day of the United States of America.

The Hopis were Garcés' first failure. But other Spaniards were to blame, not he. Back in the days of the swashbuckling conquistadores the Hopis had become thoroughly fed up with white intruders who talked of heaven and salvation, but who practiced rape, pillage, and murder. They had not forgotten. Since the Pueblo uprising of 1680, no Spaniard had been permitted to enter a Hopi town. The chiefs and medicine men accepted nothing from Garcés, gave him nothing, and bade him

102

be on his way. So on September 27, 1776, the indefatigable priest-explorer finally rode into the home corral at San Xavier.

Five years later Garcés was killed by the Yumas. Again other Spaniards were to blame. For Padre Tomas died as he had lived, in self-effacing humility, uncomplaining and undismayed.

But Garcés was not alone in the search for a route from New Mexico to California. While he was returning from the Hopi towns to San Xavier, two Franciscan Fathers led an *entrada* from Santa Fe north and west. It proved to be the last great journey of Spanish missionary priests in the Southwest.

The narrative of this notable expedition relates that

On the 29th day of July, in the year 1776, under the protection of Our Lady the Virgin Mary, conceived without original sin, and under that of the most holy Patriarch, Joseph, her honored spouse; we, Fray Atanasio Dominguez, the actual visiting delegate to this district of the Conversion of Saint Paul of New Mexico, and Fray Francisco Silvestre Vélez de Escalante, teacher of Christian doctrine in the Mission of Our Lady of Guadalupe of Zuñi,

together with five hard-headed businessmen and three packers,

having invoked the Holy Eucharist, departed from the Villa of Santa Fe, Capital of New Mexico.

Actually the nominal leader was Father Dominguez, but Escalante was the dominating influence. He planned the trip and succeeded in persuading the governor to sponsor and finance the expedition. Furthermore, Escalante submitted a diary upon his return which has made him by far the most famous of the ten men.

The expedition was a brilliant failure. The gentlemen rode around a twelve-hundred-mile circle right back into Santa Fe, having discovered absolutely nothing practical except how dif-

103

ficult it was to travel in the wilds of Utah. It is recorded that not one of these trailmakers was under sixty. If so, such a trip was solid testimony to the virility of eighteenth-century Spanish middle age, for the going was of a kind to try the mettle of the Notre Dame backfield. But the advanced years of the members of this last famous *entrada* were symptomatic, too. The Spanish Empire, long past the Golden Age, was beginning to show signs of palsy in its farthest extremities.

It has never been explained why Escalante chose a northern route in seeking Monterey, except that he vaguely felt it would be easier. The trail into Colorado was known as far as the junction of the Grand and Gunnison rivers, while one man, Fray Alonso de Posada, had reached the Green River in Utah ninety years before. But beyond that the route to the west was completely unknown.

With little difficulty, Escalante and company arrived on the banks of the Green River by the middle of September. They crossed the river, which the padres named San Buenaventura, then ascended the Uinta Valley, crossed the Wasatch Mountains, and entered Salt Lake Valley by way of Spanish Fork Canyon. The party stayed a few days among the friendly Utes on the shores of Provo Lake but were not curious enough to explore the great salt lake which the Indians said lay a few miles to the north.

At this point one would naturally suppose that an expedition bound for Monterey would take a deep breath, see that the water supply was adequate, then strike off due west across the Great Salt Lake Desert. But Escalante's party did no such thing. The ten men turned south and traveled down through central Utah.

104

There were several reasons for this erratic quirk in the Monterey route. Decidedly things were not going well. Escalante wrote: "Winter had set in with great cold, and all the mountains which we began to perceive in all directions were covered with snow." The weather was changeable and raw. Moreover, provisions were running dangerously low. Under these conditions the deserts to the west appeared singularly uninviting.

On October 8, the expedition reached a point south of the present Mormon town of Milford, Utah. Monterey still seemed as far distant as the moon. The food problem had become acute, while grumbling and dissension had reached the danger point. Some of the party wanted to return to Santa Fe; others insisted on California, whatever the consequences. Escalante and Dominguez won over the majority, and it was decided that retreat was the only sensible course.

Escalante's clear-headedness is shown in his estimate of the situation. If they continued, he reasoned, they might well be snowed in for the winter on some remote mountain range with little food or shelter. The provisions were nearly exhausted, so if they persisted in bucking the unknown they would perish of hunger if not of cold. In this argument Escalante was prophetic of the fate of later American immigrant parties. Unconsciously the padre seemed to sense the winter snow-bound Sierra Nevada which forms an icy barrier four hundred miles long, blocking the eastern gateway to California.

But three of the party still did not relish returning to Santa Fe with nothing to show for their journey. They were businessmen, and they wanted results. "Everything was extremely vexatious to them, and everything frightfully troublesome," Escalante wrote. So, on the evening of October 11, while camped near the site of Cedar City, Father Dominguez gave the dissentients a good, plain talk. Then he proposed that they accept God's will by casting ballots to determine whether to push forward or to retreat. The party agreed. Santa Fe and the priests won again. "We all accepted this decision, happily and willingly, thanks to the Lord," Escalante recorded. This was not the exact truth, but we can allow the diarist some leeway for literary effect.

Following the priests, the party now struck out across the wildest part of northern Arizona, traversing a section which is today still largely uninhabited desert. Hardships multiplied. Their food supply gave out, and they resorted to piñon nuts and whatever edible herbs could be found. Finally they slaughtered the packhorses, one by one. But steadily the little party made headway across the stern terrain. From the vicinity of Zion Canyon they pushed south to Kanab Creek, where they were within twenty miles of the Grand Canyon. Then, avoiding the climb over Kaibab Plateau, they cut northeast to the Paria River. And on October 26, the party reached the Colorado.

They now faced the most difficult problem on the entire journey—how to cross the river. For twelve days the men scrambled up and down the precipitous side gorges and among the vertical sandstone walls of Glen Canyon, searching for a practical fording place. It is a tribute to the geographical sense of Escalante and Dominguez that they found a vulnerable spot at all. But cross they did, at a point in Glen Canyon a few miles north of the present Utah-Arizona line now known as the Crossing of the Fathers. Those who visit this still roadless, uninhabited wilderness today may see the steps cut into solid rock which the Escalante party made to enable them to get their remaining animals down the steep bluffs to the river. Baggage was lowered with ropes to the fording place. Fortunately the water was low, so by 5:00 p.m. on November 7, 1776, after a full day's work, all were on the home side of the river. "We praised the Lord Our God," Escalante exulted, "and fired off some shots as a sign of the great happiness which we all felt at having overcome such an enormous difficulty which had cost us so much trouble and delay."

From this point the party made straight for Zuñi, then followed the familiar road to Santa Fe, where they arrived New Year's Day, 1777.

The Dominguez-Escalante expedition proved nothing, conquered nothing, and left no lasting trace. But these ten elderly men had the distinction of carrying Spanish land exploration in America to its most northerly point. After them, the Empire retreated southward, leaving much of the vast, empty Southwest as it had been when Coronado's army proudly marched northward to conquer mythical Cibola over two hundred years before. The Southwest was a hard geographical and climatic nut to crack. It was now the turn of the lusty, young United States to have a try from the East.

CHAPTER FIVE

INDIAN LIFE—PAST AND PRESENT

By Harold S. Colton

THE FIVE TRIBES

When the first white explorers entered the Canyon Country in the sixteenth century, few Indians occupied the area. Although the land was dotted with the crumbling walls of abandoned towns, permanent settlements, except for a few villages of Hopi Indians, were rare. In the canyons empty cliff dwellings looked down on the temporary gardens of the nomadic people who spent most of their time gathering the seeds of wild plants and hunting deer and antelope.

Of the five Indian tribes that the early explorers encountered in northern Arizona, the Hopi were by far the most advanced in culture. When visited in 1540 by one of Coronado's captains, Pedro de Tovar, they were living in large masonry "apartment houses" in five or possibly seven villages on the southern tip of Black Mesa, in much the same way that they are living today. Of the twelve present-day pueblos, Walpi, Shungopovi, and Oraibi are the best known. The last, which was settled in the twelfth century, is the oldest continuously occupied town in the United States.

The name that the Hopi call themselves means Peaceful

People, and they live up to a Quaker tradition of passive resistance, as all persons from the Spanish conquistadores to members of the Indian Bureau have found out. Although they have protected their homes with force of arms, they have seldom been aggressive, and, when they have, they have worried over it.

The Hopi man is an industrious dry farmer and something of a stockman, while his wife, in addition to her household duties, tends the vegetable garden, makes pottery, and weaves baskets and plaques. In the winter many men weave textiles or work on silver jewelry. The Hopi have more different kinds of crafts than any other Indian tribe in the United States.

The Hopi are deeply religious, and their colorful dance ceremonies, centering about the "kiva," an underground ceremonial chamber, are very beautiful, with ever-recurring symbols of rain, clouds, lightning, and the growth of corn. Although the principal part of the ceremony may take place in the kiva, visitors to the Hopi country in the spring and early summer may witness a public *kachina* dance in the village plaza, or in the late summer see the famous Snake Dance. When a dance is held in a village every family keeps open house.

Unlike the Pueblo Indians of New Mexico, the Hopi never received one of the land grants from the Spanish Government which, under the Treaty of Guadalupe Hidalgo, was guaranteed by the United States Government. Although they have occupied the land of their ancestors for over a millennium, the only title they hold is an executive order of President Arthur, in 1882, which sets aside a reservation of 2,472,320 acres, today mostly overrun by Navajos. As this executive order can be repealed by the whim of any president, the Hopi do not feel secure in the ownership of their lands and homes.

112

Although the Hopis have been crowded off three-fifths of their reservation by the aggressive Navajos and are subject to the same economic stresses that have brought distress to their neighbors in the late 1940's, yet they are, on the whole, much better off. For two generations most Hopis have had some schooling, and nearly all of the younger generation, as well as their parents, speak English, so that they can find work in a white man's world off the reservation. Since many Hopis work in the shops of the Santa Fe Railroad, Winslow, Arizona, is now the largest Hopi pueblo.

The Paiute Indians, who speak a language somewhat similar to that of the Hopi, dwell north of the Grand Canyon. When Father Escalante passed through their country in 1776, these Indians were food gatherers who practiced little agriculture and procured most of their food from game, the seeds of some wild plants, and the roots and leaves of others. Their habitations were simple, often only brush shelters. As wild food is usually scarce and hard to find in the semiarid country of the Southwest, the Paiutes had to scatter in small bands over a wide territory and thus had little time for elaborate religious ceremonies or for indulgence in artistic expression. Compared to the Hopi, their standard of living seems to us very low. At the present time the Paiutes dwell on the Pipe Springs Reservation, north of the Grand Canyon, and many other small reservations in Utah and Nevada.

On the south side of the Grand Canyon, facing the lands of the Paiutes, live the Havasupai, Walapai, and Yavapai Indians, who all speak related languages called Yuman. They were food gatherers like the Paiutes but also practiced some agriculture.

Of the three Yuman groups, the Havasupai, first visited by

113

Father Garcés in 1776, are the most advanced. Living a semi-sedentary life by the springs and streams in the deep canyons tributary to the Grand Canyon on the south, they irrigated small plots of ground and thus supplemented their meager rations with cultivated plants. As far as we know, their numbers have always been small. At present about two hundred occupy a small reservation in the bottom of Havasu Canyon on the west edge of the Grand Canyon National Park. Although the Indians raise a few crops in the Canyon, most of their support comes from outside sources. Many Havasupai run cattle on the Canyon rim, and others work at the Grand Canyon National Park or for the Santa Fe Railroad.

The Walapai, a small tribe very closely related to the Havasupai, occupy a good-sized reservation just west of the latter on the South Rim of the Grand Canyon. Although their recent ancestors were food gatherers living in brush shelters, the present-day Walapai are cattlemen, and many now have comfortable little homes. After a long legal struggle with the Santa Fe Railroad, they have recently received title to their reservation lands.

South of the country of the Havasupai and the Walapai, in the vicinity of Prescott and in the Verde Valley, lived small bands of Yavapai, first visited by Espejo in 1583. Although principally food gatherers, the Yavapai irrigated small gardens by springs and small streams. In the 1860's the country of the Yavapai was invaded by prospectors and miners, who had no compunction about appropriating the water sources of the Indians and taking pot shots at the owners when they objected. As the Yavapai were naturally warlike, they resented this treatment and retaliated, making life miserable for the invaders until the United States Army was called into action to round up the

114

Indians and place them on a reservation in central Arizona with the Apaches. Now some of the few surviving Yavapai occupy a small reservation in their old country, while others work in Yavapai County towns like Prescott and Camp Verde, on the outskirts of which the visitor can see their rather unkempt brush wickiups.

The Navajo Indians, a sixth Indian tribe of the Canyon Country, penetrated northern Arizona from New Mexico in the last two hundred years. At the time the Spaniards first mentioned these people they seem to have been a small, more or less agricultural group occupying the region northwest of Santa Fe. Stealing horses and sheep from the Spanish settlers, the Navajo changed their way of life, abandoning agriculture as a major industry and living off their flocks and herds. Today the Navajo, who number sixty thousand and are the largest Indian tribe in the United States, have surrounded the Hopi and have displaced the Paiutes from much of their old range east of the Colorado in northern Arizona.

Throughout northern Arizona, the Navajo dome-shaped houses, called "hogans," built of logs and covered with earth, are familiar and characteristic features of the landscape. As the Navajo family with its herd of sheep has to follow the grass with the seasons, each family owns several hogans, which gives to the uninitiated a false impression of the number of families in a neighborhood.

The Navajo are the most famous craftsmen of the Southwest; the women weave fine blankets and rugs, and the men are expert silversmiths. Besides textiles and silver, Navajo art has another form. Sand painting holds an important place in their ceremonies. Symbolic designs combined with mythological figures are laboriously worked out in great detail with different colored sands, only to be destroyed before sunset of the day they are made. Not only are the Navajo expert craftsmen, but they have a poetic streak as well. Their songs are full of deep feeling for the beautiful country in which they live, the mountains, the animals, the birds, and the trees.

During the past seventy years, since 1868 when they returned from five years' internment at Bosque Redondo in New Mexico, they have increased in numbers very rapidly, at the same time multiplying the number of their sheep, goats, and horses, the principal form of their wealth, so that by 1930 their lands were so seriously overgrazed that large areas, with all the topsoil eroded, became useless. To prevent further deterioration of the land, the government required the reduction of the numbers of livestock to meet the conditions on the range, thus removing the main economic prop of the tribe. During the New Deal in the 1930's, the shock of this reduction in livestock was partially absorbed by Federal Aid Projects, such as the building of roads, schoolhouses, and administrative centers, and water development. During the war these projects were discontinued, but in a few years soldiers' allotments and war work made up the difference so that the Navajo got along. With the end of the war and the cessation of benefits, many families have had to eat up their principal, their sheep and goats, and for many families the principal is nearly gone.

Since relatively few Navajos have had an opportunity to go to school, few can talk English, and few can adapt themselves to our way of life—thus we have a Navajo problem.

116

STUDYING THEIR PAST

All over the Canyon Country we find the remains of the homes of early Indians. The visitor usually does not have to go far to observe little piles of rock, areas covered with broken pottery, cliff dwellings, and drawings painted or pecked on the walls of the canyons. Archaeologists have given these remains much study. They have mapped the sites, collected the pottery scraps, and, in a few cases, excavated the ruins.

From all of these studies we can write a history of the Indians of the Canyon Country covering a period of many centuries, for we now have at our service two essentials of a history: a chronology in years of our era, and the ability to recognize several prehistoric Indian tribes and map their boundaries at different time periods. Thus we can reconstruct the history of each of these ancient Indian groups for periods of several hundred years; indeed, for one tribe we can trace its history for over sixteen hundred years. In no other part of the United States do we have so complete a story.

The method of dating prehistoric sites by tree rings is a product of the Canyon Country, for it was on the plateau of northern Arizona that Dr. A. E. Douglass, an astronomer interested in the relation of sunspots to climate, made his fundamental studies. One would think offhand that it was a far cry from sunspots to tree rings, but Dr. Douglass made the relationship clear. When there are many sunspots, more cyclonic storms appear on the earth and thus more rainfall; with more rainfall trees grow more rapidly, a fact which is particularly evident in our semiarid Southwest.

117

Tree-ring dating, as developed by Dr. Douglass and his students, is based on the following principles: When we look at a cross section of a tree trunk, we notice rings of light and dark material. Botanists tell us that the light ring was formed by the rapidly growing wood of spring and summer and that the dark, denser wood was produced in the fall and winter. The distance between two contrasting dark rings of the denser winter wood we call a tree ring, and it represents one year's growth of the tree.

In a semiarid region, where trees are entirely dependent on fluctuating rainfall, the width of the tree ring varies according to the amount of precipitation. If we compare the rings of two trees growing at the same time in the same area we will see that the wide rings and the narrow rings will have the same relationship to one another, so that we can match the rings of one tree with those of another. Sometimes the order of wide and narrow rings, during a given period, shows such a characteristic pattern that Dr. Douglass has called it a "signature." Such "signatures" can be memorized and are an important aid in dating.

Dr. Douglass found not only that the rings of trees growing close together could be matched, but that trees growing hundreds of miles apart showed similar patterns of wide and narrow rings. For example, if we start with one of the oldest ponderosa pine trees, which was cut down in 1938 at Flagstaff, we can measure the width of the rings back to 1313 A.D., when the tree began to grow, noting the sequence of wide and narrow rings. In the old houses of the Hopi pueblo of Oraibi, a hundred miles northeast of Flagstaff, are many old roof beams. Dr. Douglass has studied sections of these, and he has found that the outer rings of these beams match the inner rings from the present Flagstaff trees. The inner rings of the Oraibi beams are much older than those of the Flagstaff trees, so that we can carry the series of wide and narrow rings back to the 1200's. The later rings from the timbers found in the cliff dwellings in Tsegi Canyon match the earlier rings at Oraibi. This method of cross dating trees, and thus carrying back the chronology, Dr. Douglass calls the "bridge method," and he has now pushed the tree-ring chronology back to about 11 A.D.

When timbers are from a prehistoric ruin, the pottery fragments associated with the ruin became dated also. Because the styles of pottery made by the prehistoric women of the plateau changed from generation to generation, and because decorated pottery was widely traded, it is now possible to date ruins over a broad area without ever studying a single tree ring. With this technique in the hands of a competent archaeologist, a history of the area can be prepared.

An archaeologist can distinguish one prehistoric Indian tribe from another by the kinds of objects that he finds in the ruins, but he does not know by what names the tribes were called either by their members or their neighbors, so if he wishes to talk about them he must name them himself. For this reason archaeologists call these ancient tribes by some geographical name in their territory. The tribe with the longest history we call "Kayenta," after a trading post in northern Arizona.

Archaeologists digging in dry caves found traces of a people who did not make pottery and who lived very much as the Paiute Indians lived a hundred years ago. Although they grew corn, squash, and beans, they gathered much of their food. As their houses were made of perishable materials, we know little about their structure. Although these people made no pottery, archaeologists found many well-made baskets in the dry caves and so have called them "Basket Makers." By 500 A.D., the Basket Makers learned to make crude pottery and build pithouses, structures very much like the present-day Navajo hogan, with the floor below the surface of the ground. By 800 A.D., the sedentary agricultural way of life, which we associate today with the Pueblo Indians, was well established with many special features, among which was the kiva, a specialized circular underground chamber for religious observances. During the eleventh century, the people abandoned their pithouses and built masonry dwellings with contiguous rooms on the surface of the ground; we call these habitations by the Spanish name for village, "pueblos."

Although most of the Indians built their pueblos in open valleys and on mesa tops, yet some found in the canyon walls shallow caves spanned by great arches, which furnished a more perfect shelter from the rain and snow. In these protected caves the Indians built large and small villages that we call cliff dwellings; those at Mesa Verde National Park, Betatakin and Kiet Siel in the Tsegi, and Montezuma Castle on Beaver Creek furnish the finest examples.

About the time William of Normandy invaded England in 1066, the Indians that dwelt in and about the San Francisco Mountains witnessed the eruption of an explosive volcano, just as some Mexican Indians saw the birth of Paracutín in 1943. In a few months Sunset Crater grew to the height of a thousand feet, red-hot lava filled the neighboring valleys, and black volcanic sand rained on a thousand square miles of northern Arizona. A disaster for a few Indians proved a godsend to the many, for, where the ash was not too deep, it formed a mulch

120

Havasu Falls in Havasupai, Arizona.

The Prince and Princess, guardians of the Havasu rise above the fields of Havasupai.

Hawa of Havasupai Indian in Havasu Canyon.

On south rim, Grand Canyon National Park.

which preserved the moisture in the soil so that crops could be grown in an area where no crops had been possible before.

After the volcano had ceased its activity, and the lava had cooled, hundreds of Indians from neighboring areas rushed into the area of black sand and staked out their fields, forming dozens of small communities such as Winona Village, twenty miles east of Flagstaff, which was settled by people from the Verde Valley, and the community about the Citadel on the Wupatki National Monument, settled by the Kayenta from the north. For a hundred years a couple of thousand people lived in the region of the ash fall, but their days were numbered because the fine black sand, continually disturbed by the agricultural activities of the Indians, was carried away by the high winds of the spring and deposited in great dunes in the canyons and behind the mesas and lava flows. When most of the land was stripped bare of the ash mulch, the people had to seek other agricultural areas or starve. By the end of the great drought which lasted from 1276 to 1299, only one community in the San Francisco Mountains survived, and it, too, was soon abandoned.

The great drought, recorded in the tree rings, affected not only the people of the ash-fall area but all the people of the Southwest. As tree rings recorded only the winter precipitation, we do not know whether or not there was a diminution of summer rainfall in the last quarter of the thirteenth century. While summer rains make agriculture possible, it is the winter rains and snow that supply the springs, and the springs supply the permanent domestic water supply of the Indians. We do know that at this time there was an extensive redistribution of the population, a redistribution which is revealed by the great growth, after 1300, of the Hopi pueblos and the pueblos of the

Verde Valley, areas which had permanent water. It seems quite evident that the Hopi Indians of today carry the blood and have preserved the culture of the Kayenta of the distant past.

In addition to the history of the Kayenta, we know the history of some other prehistoric tribes, but we know nothing of their descendants, for they disappeared several hundred years before the white man came to the region. Thus it is still impossible to demonstrate a connection between these prehistoric tribes and the Indians now occupying the same areas. Archaeologists have work laid out for many years to come to determine these points.

Rock drawings that appear here and there on the canyon walls present an evidence of prehistoric life that intrigues the visitor to the Canyon Country. Pecked, incised, or painted, they depict men, animals, plants, sun, stars, and geometrical figures. Many attempts have been made to interpret these drawings; some persons even try to read into them a story, but this is speculation. It is probable that some drawings are mere doodles made to pass the time away, while others are fetishes, such as a picture of an animal about to be hunted, a "prayer" to make the outcome of the hunt more certain.

We are sure, however, that certain pictures carved on the rocks represent the signatures of Indians who wished to let others know that they had passed that way. We know this to be true in certain cases because the Hopi Indians are doing it today. Each Hopi Indian of northern Arizona belongs to a clan, which is another way of saying a family. Suppose that your name is Smith, that you cannot read or write, and that you are making a long and dangerous journey. To let others know that you have passed, you select some conspicuous landmark, such as a large red rock beside the trail, and carve your family

122

symbol on the rock. If your clan is Smith, the symbol might be a hammer or an anvil. A Hopi of the Cloud clan would carve a cloud symbol, and a member of the Sun clan, a picture of the sun. A present-day traveler is often tempted to pull out a pencil and write his name on one of the benches at the Grand Canyon, for to record a visit seems to be human nature. For this reason visitors' books are available at National Parks and Monuments, so that a visit can be recorded without defacing the landscape.

THEIR TRADING

The Indians of the Plateau have always been in business, with some men and women producing goods and other people engaged in exchanging them. We call that trade or commerce. From early times three major trade routes crossed the Canyon Country. A trail from the Pacific coast originated in the neighborhood of Los Angeles and crossed the Mojave desert to split near Barstow. One branch passed north of the Grand Canyon through Nevada and Utah, and the other crossed the Colorado River above Needles to follow the South Rim of the Grand Canyon through the country of the Mojave, Walapai, and Havasupai Indians to the lands of the Hopi. This trail continued east to Zuñi and thence to Acoma and the Rio Grande Valley near Albuquerque. The third trail ran from the Gulf of California to the region of Phoenix, then north through the Verde Valley, to the Hopi country in historic times, and as far as Kayenta in the prehistoric past. ·

The movement of goods from one part of the country to another is an intriguing subject. Economics, religion, and esthetics furnish the driving force, and transportation a romantic inter-

123

mediary. As trade plays such a lively part in our own lives, we may wonder about trade in pre-Columbian times. Notwithstanding the fact that the study of prehistoric trade demands the most highly technical services of any branch of archaeology, yet the archaeologist now has a considerable fund of information at hand.

Whenever an archaeologist takes up the subject of trade he shortly runs into problems that he himself is unable to solve with archaeological techniques, so he must call on some person trained in some other fields of science. He may need the services of a petrographer, a chemist, a botanist, a zoologist, or some other specialist. The progress that has been made in the study of prehistoric trade in the Southwest furnishes a splendid example of co-operation in science.

To give some idea of this Indian commerce we will mention two historic examples, examples that seem to have their roots in deep antiquity. Until 1882 and the coming of the Atlantic and Pacific Railroad, the Indians of northern Arizona were little affected by white men. Although the Apache had, more or less, dislocated all commerce to the south, yet the east-west commerce across northern Arizona was still much as it had been in prehistoric times, and some men living today had a part in it.

Over a thousand miles of trail, from the Pacific coast to the Rio Grande Valley, shells from the ocean passed to points on the Plateau, and along the route locally other objects passed east and west. Spier reported how the Walapai Indians killed deer or mountain sheep and traded the hides with the Havasupai for woven goods procured from the Hopi. The Havasupai tanned the hides and traded them with the Hopi for woven goods and pottery. The Hopi manufactured the buckskin into white

124

boots for their women or traded the hides or boots with the Zuñi or Rio Grande pueblos, receiving in return turquoise from Santo Domingo, Mexican indigo from Isleta, and buffalo skins from the plains.

This old trail was in active use in 1776, for Father Garcés saw abalone shells from the Pacific, Hopi textiles, and Spanish textiles from Santa Fe at Walapai settlements in western Arizona. He describes a Hopi man and woman on a trading expedition to the Mojave. This famous old trail is now abandoned, but the trade between these Indian tribes is still quite active, now passing over U. S. Highway 66.

Probably the most interesting story of aboriginal trade is that of a curious red paint, a particularly greasy red ochre, procured by the Havasupai Indians from a cave in the Grand Canyon near the mouth of Havasupai Creek. This paint is in great demand by the Hopi and other Indians for face decoration. It is red, yet has a metallic sheen. The Hopi Indians purchase the paint from the Havasupai for five dollars a pound, write up the price, and peddle it to other Indians, even as far as the Rio Grande, for twenty-five cents a teaspoonful. This red paint is considered by the Indians of the Southwest a very superior cosmetic.

The trade in red paint is of long standing and formed the basis of an inquiry called by the Spanish viceroy of New Spain near El Paso in the year 1691. As mercury ore, in the form of red cinnabar, was badly needed in Mexico for the refining of silver, and was at that time all imported from Peru or Spain, the finding of mercury ore in New Mexico would have been of great economic importance. Therefore the viceroy ordered Governor De Vargas of New Mexico to interrogate witnesses under oath as to what they knew about the red paint. An investigation was held

125

to which De Vargas called military men, padres, and others who had lived in New Mexico. During the investigation the witnesses told how this red ore was gathered from a cave four days' travel west of the Hopi pueblo of Oraibi. Although not one of the Spaniards had seen the cave they mentioned friends who had visited it. They confirmed the data in the viceroy's letter that Hopi traded the paint at Santa Fe, where the Spanish ladies preferred it to all other kinds of rouge. On the strength of this testimony De Vargas was ordered to take an expedition into New Mexico. This he did and reached the Hopi town of Oraibi, where he purchased a burro load of the ore. He sent it on to Mexico City, where it was assayed, but it proved to be iron ore and not mercury. This little incident shows how old the commerce in Havasupai red ochre is. We have, therefore, documentary evidence that it was just as important as an article of trade before 1691 as it is today.

Marine shells form one of the best sources for the study of Indian trade, because marine shells were used for ornaments and have been excavated from prehistoric sites all over Arizona and New Mexico. A trained conchologist or malacologist can tell the archaeologist whether the shells came from the Gulf of California or the Pacific coast of California.

To determine the source of stone objects and the stone used in pottery for temper requires the services of a petrologist, who makes thin sections for examination under polarized light and determines the specific gravity and other physical characteristics. It takes a highly trained man or woman to do this and to interpret the results for the archaeologist.

In prehistoric Indian commerce, we must remember, there were

126

no beasts of burden. Everything had to be carried on the backs of men, and only goods of little bulk and high value, such as dyes, pigments, fine textiles, ornaments, and small attractive pottery vessels constituted this commerce. Necessaries which had bulk, although desired, could not be transported far. This was true also in the Orient, where overland caravans carried objects of high worth and little bulk, such as silks and spices.

We know nothing about the organization of prehistoric Indian trade. Were objects traded from village to village, or were trading expeditions organized? We do know, however, that the Southwestern Indians traded as individuals and at times have organized armed bands for the purpose of trading with distant centers. The Aztecs organized such expeditions; the Pima, Hopi, and other Southwestern tribes sent out trading parties to visit faraway people. We can reason by analogy that the ancient people did the same.

The study of man in the Canyon Country has unfolded many fascinating stories. In few parts of the United States can we observe so many remains of the prehistoric inhabitants and also have living Indians to explain the ways of life of those long dead. Because the archaeological evidences are so conspicuous and well preserved, they are subject to damage by curious persons who dig as one would dig for treasure. For this and other reasons it has become necessary to protect our archaeological remains and allow only trained students, who can fully record the data and can interpret what is found in the ruins, to excavate. A ruin once excavated is forever destroyed. Excavation by untrained and ignorant persons will, therefore, destroy historical evidence that can never be recovered. For this reason all sites on Federal lands are protected by law, and only educational institutions such as colleges and museums are given permits to dig. If you are one of those with the prairie-dog instinct, we hope you will understand and ask your favorite museum for a place on its next field expedition in archaeology.

CHAPTER SIX

THE AMERICANS COME

By Weldon F. Heald

THE TRAPPERS

The brash, pushing, restless Americans were more successful than senile Spain, which, after two and a half centuries of heroic effort, barely maintained a feeble and tenuous hold on the American Southwest. In just sixty-six years from the founding of the Republic, continental United States stretched from the Atlantic to the Pacific with an area of three million square miles!

However, throughout this amazing American expansion westward, the Arizona-Utah Canyon Country remained a historical backwater. No battles were fought in that forbidding land; not one flourishing city was founded. The tide of western immigration flowed around the formidable complex of gorges, canyons, mesas, and plateaus, leaving a geographical vacuum large as New England right in the center of our fast-growing western empire. The Americans, like the Spaniards before them, found the region a hard nut to crack. Today one of the Canyon Country's greatest charms is that it is the last remaining major area in the country with any pretensions to being a wilderness.

So our story is one of explorations and the doings of individuals rather than the usual chronicle of mass movements and large-scale trends. But the story lacks nothing of color, romance, or interest for being apart from the broad stream of national history.

Furs were the lure which brought the first Americans to the shining land between the Rockies and the Pacific. The fur resources of the Far West were incalculable. Every river, creek, and rill teemed with beaver, while the mountains, plains, and deserts were the most extensive natural fur farm the world had ever known. At the beginning of the nineteenth century, a great fur industry grew up suddenly and thrived prodigiously. Fortunes were made in a few years by the owners of the big fur companies, which hired hundreds of trappers and dominated areas large as European countries.

The era of the fur trade was one of the most romantic in the history of the country, and it bred a unique race of men—tough, hard, self-reliant, and independent. These "Mountain Men" were the true discoverers of the West. The dangers, hardships, and suffering which they endured make an epic story which still stimulates the imagination. American trappers left few areas of the Far West unvisited, but they were searching for furs, for adventure, for fortunes; the geographical knowledge they left to posterity was meager and fragmentary. Undoubtedly many Mountain Men penetrated the unknown fastnesses of the Canyon Country, but only one left a written record. That was James Ohio Pattie of Kentucky.

In his *Personal Narrative,* published in 1831, Pattie told of a remarkable trapping journey from central Arizona to the Yellowstone. In 1825, with his father, Sylvester, he trapped the Gila, Salt, and Verde rivers, then cut across west to the Colorado. Father and son traveled north along the river, trapping as they went. From then on the exact route becomes vague, but for thirteen days they followed the rim of the Grand Canyon. North or South Rim, no one can make out from the description, but the Patties were unable to reach the Colorado at any point. At last they arrived "where the river emerges from these horrid mountains, which so cage it up as to deprive all human beings of the ability to descend to its banks and make use of its waters." The Patties' journey appears to have been exceptionally "horrid" from beginning to end, for James Ohio worked the adjective overtime to describe his feelings about the country. After trapping the Grand River they crossed the Continental Divide and went on to Wyoming—the first Americans to have made a traverse through the heart of the Canyon Country.

That same year, farther north, General William H. Ashley, founder of the Rocky Mountain Fur Company, made the first attempt by a white man to navigate the Green River. His boat was wrecked in the raging rapids, and several of his companions were drowned. Ashley quit the region in disgust. "The river is bounded by lofty mountains heaped together in the greatest disorder, exhibiting a surface as barren as can be imagined," was the general's verdict.

Other Mountain Men skirted the edges of the Canyon Country. Jedediah Smith, the Bible-reading "knight-errant in buckskin," one of the West's greatest explorers and frontiersmen, followed Escalante's trail southward through Utah on his way to southern California in 1826, and again a year later. Kit Carson, trapper, scout, and Indian fighter, most famous of the early pioneers, saw the Grand Canyon in 1829 and knew the Southwest perhaps better than any man of his day. Then there

133

was "Old Bill" Williams, "long, sinewy, and bony," always playing a lone hand. He trapped Western streams with phenomenal success from Canada to Mexico. Undoubtedly Old Bill knew the gorges of the Canyon Country, but he talked little and wrote nothing. A town, a mountain, and a river now bear Old Bill Williams' name.

But after forty years the heyday of the fur trade was over. Every stream in the Far West had been denuded of beaver. Bear, deer, racoon, martin, and all other animals unfortunate enough to have fur coats were slaughtered by the millions. The first great resource of the shining land between the Rockies and the Pacific was stripped in a generation.

EXPLORERS

But Americans had seen enough to know that the West held other riches. Yankee pioneers had found gold in the hills, timber in the mountains, and lush bottomlands along the rivers. Mexico became a free, independent state in 1821, but its hold on the northern frontier provinces was as feeble as had been Spain's. The United States coveted these provinces and invented a "Manifest Destiny" to justify seizing them. A clash with Mexico was inevitable.

After a series of incidents involving the annexation of Texas by the United States, President Polk announced on May 13, 1846, that a state of war existed with Mexico. The Army of the West, under Colonel Stephen W. Kearny, marched into Santa Fe three months later and raised the flag of the United States over the Palace of the Governors. The invasion was all very friendly and cordial. The Americans were welcomed by the

134

New Mexican governor and honored by a salute of thirteen guns—the only shots fired. Not all engagements were as simple as the conquest of Santa Fe. But in 1848 the United States got what it wanted: California, the area now included in Nevada and Utah, Arizona, and New Mexico. Manifest Destiny had been achieved.

The first official survey parties were sent West primarily to locate railway and wagon routes to the newly discovered California gold fields. Captain Lorenzo Sitgreaves led an expedition across northern Arizona in the fall of 1851. He gave a vivid topographical description of the country, but the personal record was one of pure misery with overtones of thirst, hunger, and cold. A second survey during the winter of 1853-1854 was made under Lieutenant A. W. Whipple. Besides a command of soldiers, he was accompanied by twelve civilian specialists who described minutely the geography, plants, and animals, as well as the manners and customs of the Indians. The thoroughgoing Whipple Report, illustrated by maps and drawings, fills several large volumes of *The Pacific Railroad Explorations*, printed by the government.

But it was Edward F. Beale, Mexican War hero and friend of Kit Carson, who first blazed a practical route for a wagon road across northern Arizona. In 1857 Beale discovered the line of least resistance which is now followed by U. S. Highway 66 and the Santa Fe Railroad. The expedition used forty-seven War Department camels as pack animals from Fort Defiance in northeastern Arizona to the Colorado River. Beale's report brims with glowing praises for the African and Asian Ships of the Desert, but he appears to have been alone in his love for dromedaries and bactrians. After Beale's expedition the camel experiment languished, and the animals were turned loose to wander the Western deserts for many years.

These three government survey parties passed south of the Canyon Country. But the War Department next turned its attention to the Colorado River itself. In 1857, Lieutenant Joseph C. Ives was authorized "to ascertain the navigability of the Colorado" from the Gulf of California as far as a steamboat could be taken. Inasmuch as two steamboats were already plying the lower river at that time, it would seem that Ives had a simple assignment. However, the lieutenant and the War Department preferred to do it the hard way, and it was three years before the world saw Ives's engaging *Report Upon the Colorado River of the West.*

A fifty-foot steamboat, built in sections at Philadelphia, was shipped via the Isthmus of Panama to San Francisco, thence by sea to the head of the Gulf of California. The boat was assembled in December, 1857, christened the *Explorer*, and launched on the Colorado. Then trouble started. The poor *Explorer* was never at home in the swift, shallow Colorado; she shipped water and ran aground on sand bars, and her engine was too weak to buck the rapids. The men often had to tow her upstream with lines from the banks.

But for two months the Ives party laboriously inched their way three hundred and fifty miles up the temperamental Colorado. Then they suddenly reached the head of navigation—at least as far as the *Explorer* was concerned. On March 6, 1858, they entered the mouth of Black Canyon, where Hoover Dam now bars the way. Lieutenant Ives wrote: ". . . We were shooting swiftly past the entrance, eagerly gazing into the mysterious depths beyond, when the *Explorer*, with a stunning crash,

136

brought up abruptly and instantaneously against a sunken rock. For a second the impression was that the canyon had fallen in." Several men were thrown overboard, and Ives was pitched head foremost into the bottom of the boat. In three days the damaged *Explorer* was repaired. However, the lieutenant judiciously preferred to seek the actual head of navigation in a skiff, although river pilot Johnson in his hundred-foot steamer *Colorado* had ascended twenty miles above Black Canyon.

Ives's discoveries so far had resulted in nothing but beautiful descriptions of the scenery. But it was the second part of his explorations which made Canyon Country history. Ives led the first party since the Patties, thirty-three years before, to see and explore the Grand Canyon—or Big Canyon, as the lieutenant called it.

At the end of March, 1858, the Ives party started overland in a northeasterly direction, guided by a friendly Mojave Indian named Ireteba. Although he was willing and able, for some reason additional Hualpai guides, some with "features like a toad's," were daily hired, fired, disappeared with Ives's mules, and reappeared with nothing much in particular. But, in spite of erratic Hualpai guidance, the party descended Diamond Creek to the Colorado and on April 5 became the first white men known to have reached the bottom of the Grand Canyon.

Next they climbed down into Cataract Canyon almost to the oasis of the Havasupai Indians, where Garcés had spent five days in 1776. A broken ladder on the final pitch to the floor of the canyon prevented them from being the first American party to visit these remote Indians. The expedition's artist, F. W. Egloffstein, did descend rather precipitately, taking most of the ladder down with him. He had to be pulled back up again with a line

137

made by knotting together the slings from the soldiers' muskets.

From Cataract Canyon Ives's party crossed the high Colorado Plateau. There, lack of water caused considerable suffering, and several mules were lost. Ives was harassed, but he could always forget his troubles by describing the scenery. He writes: "Fissures so profound that the eye cannot penetrate their depths are separated by walls whose thickness one can almost span, and slender spires that seem tottering on their bases shoot up thousands of feet from the vaults." That was the first serious effort to describe the Grand Canyon. How many hundreds have tried since Ives's time—and failed?

The party backtracked away from these "gigantic chasms," cut south to Beale's trail, then pushed northeast across the Painted Desert to the Hopi towns. Ives reached Fort Defiance on May 22. The lieutenant's conclusion was that "the region explored after leaving the navigable portion of the Colorado— though in a scientific point of view, of the highest interest, and presenting natural features whose strange sublimity is perhaps unparalleled in any part of the world—is not of much value. . . . Ours has been the first, and will doubtless be the last party of whites to visit this profitless locality."

War clouds were gathering in the East, and official interest in the Far West declined. One more government expedition, under Captain Macomb, explored the region around the junction of the Green and Grand rivers in 1859. But, when guns barked at Fort Sumter, Civil War engulfed the country. For four years military men were engaged in grimmer expeditions than could be found in the gorges of the Colorado River Basin. So the Canyon Country was left once more to the sun, the winds, the storms, and the red men for a full decade.

138

In the three and a quarter centuries since Cárdenas had looked down upon the Colorado River from the South Rim of the Grand Canyon, many white men had come, had seen, and had gone away again. But their visits to the Canyon Country had been peek-and-run affairs. Both Spaniards and Americans had so far failed to make a permanent mark, leave a lasting trace, or even conduct a thoroughgoing examination. At the close of the Civil War, fully ten thousand square miles of the Colorado River Basin was a blank, white place on the map, marked "unexplored."

In just three years—1869-1872—Major John Wesley Powell filled in the gap. His two daring expeditions down the Green and Colorado rivers by boat, and his thorough survey of the surrounding region, are epic stories in the history of exploration. Major Powell was the real discoverer of the Canyon Country, and his journeys were so important that they are treated more fully in Chapter Seven, "The Colorado River."

THE SETTLERS

In 1847, the Mormons, under their great leader, Brigham Young, slowly moved westward across the plains, taking all their worldly possessions with them. In July the caravan topped the Wasatch Mountains and wound down into Utah's Great Salt Lake Valley. "This is the place," Brigham Young said. So, there, in that desert wilderness valley, a thousand miles from the nearest American settlements, the Mormons founded Salt Lake City. Ever since it has been the Mormon Rome, fountainhead of their Church of Jesus Christ of Latter-Day Saints.

The early Mormons were remarkable and determined colonizers. Far from sources of supplies, and without manufactured goods, they planted crops, constructed irrigation systems, built log or adobe forts and towns. The Saints rapidly spread out from Salt Lake City, colonizing the desert valleys of Utah one after another. In spite of frontier hardships, Indian troubles, grasshopper plagues, droughts, and floods, it is estimated that by 1856 there were fifty thousand people in the Mormons' Western "kingdom." And, thirty years after Brigham Young led his people into the new, empty land beyond the Rockies, the Mormons had completely ringed the Canyon Country with settlements.

The Saints were explorers and discoverers, too. Brigham Young sent a party in 1856 to explore the Colorado River region and to make a peace treaty with the Navajos. Zion Canyon was discovered in 1858 by a Mormon pioneer named Nephi Johnson, and several families had farms in the canyons during the 1860's. The non-Mormon Powell on his second expedition visited the upper Virgin River in the winter of 1871-1872 while triangulating for the first map of the Colorado River country. The Major named the canyon Parunuweap—Ute for Roaring Water. But Bryce Canyon was a Mormon discovery. Settlers ran cattle on the plateau above in the early 1870's, and Ebenezer Bryce took up a homestead there in the fall of 1875. The one remark this practical Mormon farmer left to posterity about the rainbow-hued canyon named after him was, "It's a hell of a place to lose a cow."

But no man ever knew the Canyon Country better than Jacob Hamblin. Appointed Mormon missionary to the Indians in 1857, he skillfully maintained a good-neighbor policy between white man and red for thirty years. With zeal and devotion to his task, Hamblin crossed and crisscrossed the Canyon Country a score of times, enduring hunger, thirst, heat, and cold with equal stoicism. Late in life he summed up his creed in two sentences: "I had been appointed to a mission by the highest authority of God on the Earth. My life was of but small moment compared with the lives of the Saints and the interests of the Kingdom of God." Jacob Hamblin was one of America's truly great.

But the first man to settle in the Canyon Country was a murderer and fugitive from justice. John Doyle Lee, a Mormon pioneer, was accused of taking a leading part in the infamous Mountain Meadows Massacre which occurred in southwestern Utah in 1857. Mormons said to have been disguised as Indians attacked a westbound wagon train of immigrants and killed over a hundred men, women, and children. For thirteen years Lee roamed around Utah and northern Arizona just a jump ahead of the law. About 1870, he and several of his wives settled in the remotest spot they could find—the Colorado River at the mouth of the Paria. Here Lee maintained a ferry until federal authorities finally caught up with him. He was tried, found guilty, and shot at Mountain Meadows in 1877.

After Lee's death, the ferry was operated for several years by Emma Lee, one of his widows, and afterward was run continuously by the Mormon Church and then by a cattle company until Navajo Bridge was built across the Colorado in 1929.

Early Mormon leaders frowned upon the development of mineral resources, but the Church became interested in the great cattle ranges of the Canyon Country in the 1870's. Several Mormon cow towns were founded on the plateaus and in the valleys west of the Colorado River. All of them were small,

141

remote outposts in the wilderness. But one, the hamlet of Boulder, population 216, kept the distinction of being the last "pack-horse town" in the United States until 1935, when a road was built connecting it with the outside world.

The then rich grasslands of northern Arizona led to Mormon colonization of the Little Colorado River Valley in 1876. And it was near the present town of Flagstaff that the Mormon Church owned the Moroni Cattle Company. John W. Young, one of Brigham's forty-seven children, managed the outfit, efficiently building up a herd of ten thousand cattle and two thousand horses.

But in the history of Mormon colonization the most heroic saga of hardship and privation endured because of faith and strict adherence to a creed was the story of the San Juan settlement. In 1879, 225 Saints were "called" to colonize the wildest, most barren section of Utah—the San Juan country. In December, without sufficient preliminary exploration, seventy families, with eighty-two wagons and hundreds of horses and cattle, struck out directly east from Panguitch into some of the roughest country on the continent. At Hole-in-the-Rock, the caravan halted two weeks while the men of the party labored ten hours each day to make a passable wagon track down the two-thousand-foot ledges to the Colorado River. Then the colonists, animals, and wagons went down over the rim and crossed the muddy stream. The men and animals swam, while the wagons were floated over. Two more weeks were consumed building a road up the east wall of the canyon. On February 10, 1880, the party set out from the Colorado and arrived at the site of Bluff in the San Juan country on April 5—almost two months to cover an airline distance of seventy-five miles!

How these ardent Saints brought wagons and animals across the intricate maze of canyons, domes, and ridges of slick sandstone north of the San Juan River is one of the miracles of Mormonism. The San Juan colonists chalked up a higher score in hardships, privations, and foot pounds of energy expended than any Spanish or American party before them. By comparison, the overland journey to the Pacific was a long, level boulevard.

And thus the indomitable Saints built their "kingdom," tamed the desert, and brought civilization to the fringes of the Canyon Country.

BANDITS, MINERS, AND TOURISTS

The coming of the railroads brought new men and new ways to the Shining Land beyond the Rockies. Modern times began when the first locomotive whistle echoed in lonely desert canyons.

The Atlantic and Pacific Railroad, now the Santa Fe, was pushed across northern Arizona in 1881-1882. Its lines tapped the rich resources in cattle, timber, and mines along the route Beale had surveyed a quarter of a century before. The Denver and Rio Grand Western followed in 1883 with a line from Grand Junction, Colorado, to Salt Lake City. Its rails reached northern Utah's extensive coal deposits.

Along these railroads new towns sprang up: Holbrook, Winslow, and Ashfork on the A. & P.; Greenriver, Utah, and the coal towns of Price and Helper on the D. & R. G. W. The railroads gave new life to some of the older towns, too, such as Flagstaff and Williams, which had been settled in the late 1870's. The name Flagstaff, by the way, came from a tall pine

143

tree which was stripped of bark and branches to serve as a flag-pole during a Fourth of July celebration in 1876. Helper stems from the use of helper locomotives to pull trains up the steep east slope of the Wasatch Mountains.

The railroads brought new activities, both legitimate and irregular. Rustling, train robbery, murder, and general hell-raising became a specialty with some of the newcomers. An Atlantic and Pacific train was held up at Canyon Diablo by four bandits in 1889. They fled north with the express company's strongbox, a sheriff's posse hot on their heels. The robbers were captured in southern Utah, and the money recovered. But such swift justice was hardly a characteristic of the early West.

Farther north, banditry developed into a profession. Hanksville, Utah, during the 1880's and 1890's, became headquarters for the Robbers' Roost gang. For thirty years this organization of early gangsters terrorized the entire West—robbing, holding up trains, and rustling cattle. The best-known leader of Robbers' Roost was Butch Cassidy. This super-bandit, who started from the cradle with the inoffensive name of George LeRoy Parker, was reputed never to have killed a man. Some say he ended up in South America as a cattleman; in any event the law never caught up with Butch, and presumably he died in bed with his boots off.

The Mormon disapproval of mining meant nothing to the thousands of newcomers. Prospectors roamed the country, speculatively tapping rocks, their eyes peeled for ledges and floats. Hardly a canyon, gulch, or mountainside was missed. Rumors of rich gold in the sand bars of the San Juan started a minor gold rush in 1892-1893. Nearly two thousand men tried their luck and found it all bad. Two years later Cass Hite, a hermit pros-

144

pector who had settled beside the Colorado in the wildest part of the Canyon Country, started a story that there was a coarse-gold bonanza in the riffles of Glen Canyon. This "news" brought on another stampede. At one time, it was said, the Colorado from the San Juan to Lees Ferry was as busy as the Grand Canal in Venice, with boats, scows, and dredges full of men looking for gold which wasn't there. Mr. Hite wisely disappeared for two years until trigger fingers had relaxed somewhat.

The Grand Canyon had been prospected for some years, even by Mormons, and several mines were located there as early as the 1870's. Seth B. Tanner, a Mormon, worked a gold mine at the bottom of the Canyon near the mouth of the Little Colorado. And John D. Lee, while hiding out from the federal authorities, was supposed to have developed a rich Grand Canyon mine in which he cached seven cans of almost pure gold. These pots of gold have never been found, and Lee's claim has become one of the romantic lost mines of the West.

As a result of miners' stories and government reports, the world began to hear about the wonders of the Grand Canyon. A few came to see, riding horseback to the South Rim and camping among the pines. Each enthusiastic visitor upon his return rushed into print in an effort to outdo his predecessors. One lyrical gentleman, signing himself "Fitz-Mac," hit an all-time literary high. In a newspaper article on the Grand Canyon entitled, "The World is Cleft," he wrote: " . . . the massive, the gorgeous, the magnificent, the sensuous, the brilliant, the mellow, the tender, swept and swirled by great Nature's unerring brush into a ravishing, harmonious, chromatic maze that bursts upon the view with an effect as if the skies had opened and all the choirs of heaven had broken into a grand and joyful

145

overture, an allegro through which runs a penetrating minor chord of tragic sadness." What self-respecting nineteenth-century globe trotter could resist this clarion call? The tourist business began suddenly in the late 1880's.

But visitors flocked in before the Canyon was ready for them. The few miners and South Rim settlers found themselves dude wranglers whether they liked it or not. John Hance liked it. In fact he blossomed into a professional Grand Canyon character. Hance, self-styled "guide, storyteller, and pathfinder," owned an asbestos mine in the canyon below Grandview Point. He accommodated tourists at his camp on the rim above and led palpitating visitors down the dizzy trail to his mine. That is about the extent of John Hance's guiding and pathfinding, but his stories grew in breadth, scope, and incredulity until he proudly earned the title of the Munchausen of the West. When the Santa Fe Railroad took over the tourist business at the South Rim in 1904, Hance was retained board-free as a unique attraction, second only to the Canyon itself. His most famous story related his experiences snowshoeing across the mile-deep gorge from rim to rim on top of the fog. So many variations of this masterpiece of mendacity exist that a collecter of Hanceiana could probably make a book of them.

William Wallace Bass, another early Grand Canyon character, was, unlike Hance, a serious student and explorer of the region. He became interested in the Havasupai Indians and was instrumental in persuading an apathetic Indian Service in Washington to establish a school and send a farm expert to their remote canyon. Bass maintained a tourist camp on the South Rim near Havasupai Point and had a road surveyed and built in from Williams. Although he had originally come to Arizona as a

146

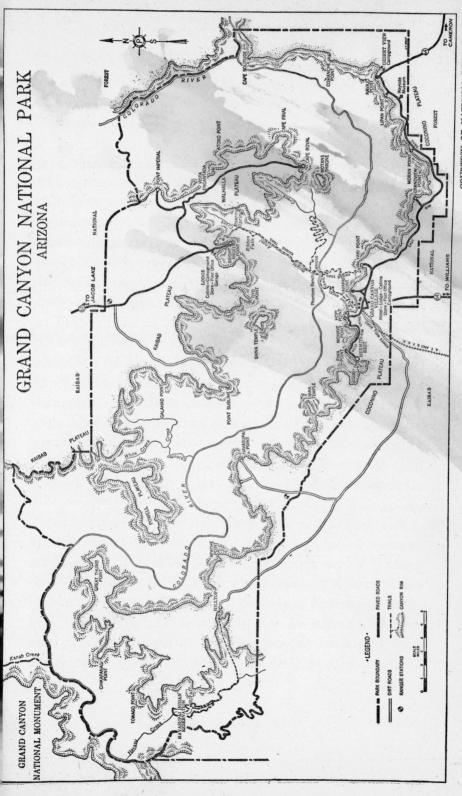

GRAND CANYON NATIONAL PARK
ARIZONA

GRAND CANYON
NATIONAL MONUMENT

FOREST

COLORADO RIVER

CAPE SOLITUDE

DESERT VIEW
Campground

COMANCHE
POINT

NAVAJO

Wayside
Museum

LIPAN POINT

PLATEAU

CAPE FINAL

COCONINO

FOREST

CAPE ROYAL

VISTA
ENCANTADA

WOTANS
THRONE

ATOKO POINT

POINT IMPERIAL

WALHALLA
PLATEAU

MORAN POINT

GRANDVIEW
POINT

TO
CAMERON

EAST RIM

NATIONAL

TO
WILLIAMS

NATIONAL

TO
JACOB LAKE

Ribbon
Falls

BRIGHT ANGEL POINT

LODGE
Cabins—Campground
Store—Post Office
Garage

KAIBAB

PLATEAU

SHIVA TEMPLE

KAIBAB

KAIBAB

TRAIL

Phantom Ranch

ZUNI POINT

YAKI POINT

MOHAVE POINT

HOPI POINT

GRAND CANYON VILLAGE
Hotel—Lodge—Cabins
Store—Post Office
Campground

PIMA POINT

HERMITS REST

KAIBAB

COCONINO
PLATEAU

A.T. AND S.F. R.R.

GALAHAD POINT

POWELL PLATEAU

POINT SUBLIME

White Creek

Shinumo

HAVASUPAI POINT

Creek

COLORADO RIVER

GREAT THUMB POINT

HILLTOP

KAIBAB PLATEAU

KAIBAB

Kanab Creek

CHIKAPANAGI POINT

TOPOCOBA
POINT

HAVASUPAI INDIAN
RESERVATION

Creek

Havasu

•LEGEND•

PARK BOUNDARY   PAVED ROADS

DIRT ROADS   TRAILS

RANGER STATIONS   CANYON RIM

SCALE
MILES
0   1   2   3   4   5   6

health-seeker in 1883, Bass lived an active, strenuous, and useful life at the Grand Canyon until his death in 1933 at the age of eighty-four.

Pete Barry, a third old-timer who owned a copper mine in the canyon, built the first hotel at Grandview Point in 1892. A road was scratched across the Coconino Plateau from Flagstaff, over which stage coaches, enveloped in clouds of dust, jolted passengers through ". . . what is perhaps the most beautiful scenery in Arizona or elsewhere. . . ." Advertisements of the Grand Canyon Stage Line stated that ". . . the drive is sixty-five miles long, which is easily accomplished in ten hours, there being four relays of horses for the journey. . . ." In the words of the general manager, the Grand Canyon was no longer a "terra incognito."

At the turn of the century there was a lively battle for Grand Canyon tourist trade. Even William Randolph Hearst tried unsuccessfully to stake out a claim in this rich new bonanza. Santa Fe's Fred Harvey won. A branch railway line was extended from Williams to the South Rim in 1901, and Harvey showed his capabilities by opening the luxurious El Tovar Hotel three years later. President Theodore Roosevelt proclaimed the Canyon a National Monument in 1908. But there followed a long period of litigation and involved extinguishment of private claims before the area could achieve Park status. Finally, in 1919, Grand Canyon National Park was established. Its 1,009 square miles include about half of the canyon. However, in the 1930's a new Grand Canyon National Monument and Boulder Dam National Recreation Area were formed to the west. So today these three adjoining government reservations, with a combined area of four thousand square miles, include the en-

147

tire Grand Canyon and stretch along the Colorado River for a distance of nearly three hundred miles.

Development on the North Rim and at the other canyons came much later. Kaibab Forest was a remote wilderness when Theodore Roosevelt hunted there in 1913. "Uncle Jimmy" Owens, the famous "lyin' lion hunter," acted as guide and host to the few hardy parties who packed in for deer, bear, and mountain lions. Owens himself killed fabulous numbers of cougars and established a herd of buffalos in House Rock Valley for the Arizona Game and Fish Commission. Uncle Jimmy has now passed on, but his bison have thrived and multiplied. Permits to hunt them are issued annually both to resident and nonresident applicants. Each buffalo-hunter is allowed the head, hide, and one quarter of the animal he kills.

The first road to cross the virgin pine, spruce, and aspen forests of Kaibab Plateau was built in 1926. Tourists followed two years later when the Union Pacific Railroad opened a magnificent resort lodge on the North Rim near the head of Bright Angel Creek. The North and South Rim settlements are twelve miles apart; their lights wink at each other across the black chasm each night; they are connected by a foot and horse trail which crosses the Colorado on a swaying suspension bridge. But until Navajo Bridge was built near Lees Ferry in 1929, the shortest distance between North and South rims by road was over seven hundred miles. Even today, to drive from one rim to the other is a trip of 215 miles! Modern times have not yet tamed the Grand Canyon.

Zion and Bryce canyons, together with neighboring Cedar Breaks, remained little known, even to residents of Utah, until the Union Pacific Railroad developed the areas for tourist traf-

148

fic in the late 1920's. Back in 1909 President Taft included Zion Canyon in the Mukuntuweap National Monument. The name was changed to Zion in 1917, but the Canyon did not achieve Park status until 1929. Zion National Park contains 94,888 acres, while, adjoining it on the west, a new Zion National Monument protects eight canyons, among which is Kolob, almost as spectacular as Zion Canyon itself.

Interest in Bryce Canyon was stimulated by photographs of its outstanding features published in 1916. A road was built through Red Canyon to the rim in 1923, and a lodge opened two years later. Bryce became a National Park in 1928 but was greatly enlarged by President Hoover to its present area of 35,240 acres.

After four hundred years the Arizona-Utah Canyon Country remains a relatively undeveloped island. Its greatest sources of revenue to the industrial civilization which surrounds it are not in timber, ore, or water. The resources of the region are its unique beauty, natural wonders, and archaeological wealth. With three National Parks, eighteen Monuments, and a National Recreation Area to be visited, people will continue to come from all parts of the world to revel in these wisely preserved bits of unspoiled wilderness—perhaps for another four hundred years.

As long as a warm desert sun shines down into deep gorges as in Cárdenas' time, the wind and clouds play over the mesas as they did in Pattie's day, the river roars with the same thunder that Powell heard, people will continue to sense the strange, compelling fascination of the Canyon Country and to feel the irresistible urge to climb down the Inverted Mountains to their summits in the bowels of the earth.

149

CHAPTER SEVEN

THE COLORADO RIVER
By Weldon F. Heald

Except to their mothers, all babies resemble each other. They may differ in temperament, but they betray no sign of their destinies. So it is with rivers. Whether born of mountain snow-banks or in springs upon a forested plateau, they give no hint that some are potential Mississippis while others will lose themselves in desert sands.

Thus the Colorado River is conventionally born high among the snowy peaks of Colorado, Utah, and Wyoming. It starts in a thousand sparkling trout streams cascading down mountain valleys between banks of spruce and pine. Not until the arid interior basins are reached is there a suspicion that the Colorado in maturity will become the most tempestuous and inhospitable, yet the most fascinating, of all our rivers.

The Colorado's antisocial tendencies appear early in life. Each little childhood stream, upon leaving the high mountains, burrows into a canyon. These canyons join larger canyons, which deepen and are gathered together into stupendous barren gorges pouring their flood waters into the main channel of the river

153

thousands of feet below the surface of the surrounding plateaus. There, at last, the full-grown Colorado River of the West reveals itself—an incredible giant, resembling no other river on earth.

With irresistible power and violence this colossus has torn a gash in the surface of the earth a thousand miles long. Between its youthful upper reaches above the town of Green River, Wyoming, and a placid, but still vigorous, old age below Parker Dam on the California-Arizona border, the Colorado has cut a rugged, almost inaccessible course through nineteen tremendous gorges. The greatest of these is the Grand Canyon. Including Marble Canyon, directly to the north, the Colorado here flows for 278 miles between continuous walls of naked rock, 3,000 to 6,000 feet high.

Although geologists tell us that this same giant has been cutting, gouging, and excavating for seven million years, it shows no trace of weariness. More than a thousand rapids thunder and rage deep in the hearts of the canyons, while treacherous whirlpools and sand waves constantly form and disappear on the river's restless surface. With relentless, determined energy the Colorado is still attacking the sandstone, limestone, shale, and lava in its bed and, in the Grand Canyon, is sawing through glasslike granites of the Archean Era—some of the earth's oldest rocks. Rains, snows, frosts, winds, and rock-decay are the river's allies, helping to widen the canyons and carve the land into a fantastic labyrinth of gorges, cliffs, buttes, and mesas.

Inch by inch, century upon century, the river wears away the rocks, sweeping them down its turbulent flood as boulders and silt. These billions of abrasive particles form the sharp edges of

154

mammoth cutting tools; thus the rocks themselves furnish the means to their own destruction. The vast load of sediment transported by the Colorado is probably greater today than when Coronado's man, Cárdenas, first beheld its muddy waters four hundred years ago. For man has aided the forces of destruction, accelerating erosion by deforestation and depletion of range land. Careful tests made by the United States Geological Survey in the Grand Canyon show that the river carries almost a million tons of sand and silt past any given point every twenty-four hours—enough material to fill four hundred freight trains of a hundred cars each!

The billions of tons of water required each year to cut such gigantic canyons and to sluice away the debris stagger the imagination. Yet, paradoxically, the Colorado is a desert river flowing for nearly two thousand miles through a land of little rain. Were the river dependent upon its immediate surroundings for water, the result would be a puny weakling of intermittent flow and sand-choked channels. Such is the fate of most desert rivers. But this roaring, raging giant is an example of heredity's winning out over environment—the Colorado derives strength throughout its life from its vigorous, noble birth. Its blood and sinews come from the ring of lofty ranges—the Rockies, Wasatch, Uinta, and others—which form an almost continuous border around the outermost rim of the Colorado River Basin. The basin itself, although constituting fully three quarters of the river's drainage area, is a region of deserts and semiarid plateaus. It contributes an undependable and fluctuating water supply derived principally from summer thunderstorms. These afternoon convection showers are usually of short duration, but they sometimes reach cloudburst proportions, turning dry washes

155

into rampaging torrents and pouring their flash floods in ephemeral waterfalls over the canyon rims into the river and its tributaries. Even in little things is this giant violent and threatening.

Winter is the time of low water in the Colorado. As spring arrives the mountain snowpack begins to melt, slowly at first, but with increasing rapidity until by late May or early June a deafening red-brown flood pours through the narrow canyons, forty to sixty feet above low watermark. A sharp drop follows the spring peak; then, with many minor risings and fallings, the waters slowly recede to the low-water stage of winter.

The annual average runoff of the Colorado is thirteen million acre-feet. But its flow has varied from a low of three thousand cubic feet per second to over two hundred thousand. This means that in spring the river may carry sixty-five times more water than during the low stage of winter.

Twice in the past century the Colorado has almost run dry, and stories are told of men exploring its remote gorges on horseback. Twice in a hundred years the task of canyon cutting has been suspended, the tools abandoned, the rapids silenced as the mighty excavator took well-earned vacations.

Major Powell in his classic report, *Exploration of the Colorado River of the West, 1869-1872*, began page 1 with the terse sentence, "The Colorado River is formed by the junction of the Green and the Grand." Strangely enough, this is no longer true. Although there have been no earth-shaking geological disturbances in the region for the past seventy years, the Grand River has disappeared. But Congress, not nature, was responsible.

A resolution presented by the state of Colorado was passed by both houses in 1921. It declared that the Grand River should

156

thenceforth be known as the Colorado. Up to that time the
Colorado nowhere flowed within the boundaries of the state of
that name. But the Grand, its eastern branch, was strictly a
Colorado affair. So, by a stroke of the legislative pen, the ingenious Coloradans captured their namesake river and placed
its official birthplace at Lulu Pass in the Rocky Mountains west
of Denver. But the Green was a much longer branch than the
Grand, and, though the shorter tributary has usurped the title,
old-timers will continue to consider the Green as the logical
upper continuation of the Colorado.

The length of the Colorado measured up its Green branch is
exceeded among the rivers of the United States only by the
Missouri, Mississippi, and Rio Grande. From the headwaters
of the Green, amid the glaciers of the Wind River Range in
Wyoming, to the mouth of the Colorado at the Gulf of California is nearly seventeen hundred miles—equal to the distance
from New York to Denver. The total area drained by the Colorado and all its tributaries is 244,000 square miles, or one thirteenth the area of the United States. This river empire com-
prises a large part of the states of Wyoming, Colorado, Utah,
and Arizona as well as portions of southern Nevada and California, and it is larger than all New England and the Middle
Atlantic States with Maryland and Virginia thrown in for good
measure.

And so this incredible giant, although unique, is no freak or
accident to be dismissed lightly. Rather the Colorado is one of
our greatest rivers. Its barren and uninhabited reaches are un-
sung and unfabled, but it exerts a powerful fascination upon
the few who have felt its mystery and explored its secrets.

157

THE COLORADO IS STILL WILD

It would be strange indeed if this exceptional river had not notably affected the western advance of white civilization across the continent. As a matter of fact, the Colorado has proved to be a more effective obstacle to western migration and routes of travel than all the mountain ranges and deserts of the continent. Other rivers have been pathways of exploration, arteries of travel, highways of commerce; they have contributed to the development of the country. But not the Colorado. It alone has stood like a barrier across the Far West, preventing expansion, hampering communications, detouring commerce far to the north and south. The hard-riding Spanish conquistadores and zealous priests, American pioneers and settlers, railroad builders and modern highway engineers have all been successively turned back from the Colorado River country. The tide of humanity has flowed around the obstruction, leaving a land which is, even today, the West's last great wilderness. Fewer than a hundred white men have seen the innermost recesses of the Colorado's nineteen mighty gorges, while scores of side canyons and cliff-guarded mesas remain unknown. The Colorado today roars down through its lonely mile-deep canyons exactly as it did in the days of the Spaniards—sullen, treacherous, inimicable to man.

Rivers usually bring to mind shady, tree-bordered banks, sleepy waterside villages, fishing along quiet sunlit reaches—or, perhaps, some lordly stream churned by busy steamers and barges plying between prosperous, smoky cities. But we are forced to revise our ideas when we study a map of the Colorado.

158

It has, to be sure, sleepy, even languorous, villages on its banks—seven of them, to be exact, if we do not include the practically lifeless Mormon town of Hite, Utah—population 1. But there is only one city with more than ten thousand inhabitants, and that, Grand Junction, is situated on the more hospitable stretch of the one-time Grand River in Colorado. Four more communities, ranging from Yuma's 5,325 to Blythe, California, and Green River, Wyoming, with 3,000 apiece, complete the roster of urban centers in a stretch of almost 2,000 miles. It is doubtful if the most conscientious census taker could find more than fifteen thousand citizens—fewer persons than live in Glens Falls, New York—who call the banks of the Green and Colorado home. And yet these two together form the fourth longest river in the United States.

The map also plainly shows the remarkable part the Colorado River has played in diverting travel and settlement around the borders of its rugged wilderness. Between Greenriver, Utah, and Boulder City, Nevada, are no towns, villages, or scarcely a settlement in a distance of seven hundred miles. Hite, Lees Ferry, and the tourist lodge at Bright Angel Creek in the Grand Canyon are the sole human outposts which have breached the Colorado's guarded ramparts. Even modern engineering has found but five locations in fifteen hundred miles suitable for spanning the river with highways and railroad bridges.

A further study of the map reveals that the regular western march of transcontinental railroads and highways is suddenly interrupted east of the Colorado River region. The more northerly route of the Denver and Rio Grande Western, with U. S. Highway 50, trends sharply still farther north in Utah, while the Santa Fe, paralleled by U. S. 66, is forced southward from

159

Colorado into New Mexico. In eastern Colorado these two transcontinental traffic arteries are barely sixty miles apart, but when they finally cross the river a gap of four hundred miles separates their bridges.

But the map of the Colorado River country tells much more than mere facts concerning towns, roads, and bridges. There are also long wavy lines of cliffs upon it, mountains and sweeping, sky-wide plateaus, complicated canyon patterns, and blank spaces where cartographers have never been. Names, too, are on the map—laconic names of the pioneers with the tang of the West in them, and strange, remote names of Indian origin savoring of some long past, unknown civilization. It is the map of a country which calls to the explorer in each of us—to come and see what the world was like before man's time.

We need such places. As the pressure of modern life increases we should jealously guard our fast vanishing wilderness, not destroy it utterly as we are now endeavoring to do. A completely humanized world would be a catastrophe, a sterile and dreary end to man's struggle to change and mold his environment into a likeness of himself.

But perhaps it is inevitable that our last great wilderness should succumb. Too long has it defied man's restless urge to put his stamp of ownership everywhere upon the face of the earth. And so, after seven million years, the wild, lawless days of the Colorado are numbered. Already Hoover Dam has drowned its strident voice in the depths of man-made Lake Mead. Parker Dam has been thrown across the lower part of the river, while surveys have been completed for seven future damsites at intervals along the Colorado's course far up into northern Utah.

Electric power to light distant cities is now produced by the shackled river giant, and thousands of desert acres are irrigated by its waters. The cities of southern California have forsaken the sparkling mountain streams of the Sierra Nevada to draw their main water supply from the Colorado through an aqueduct two hundred and forty-two miles long. Although tremendous future power can be developed by the building of these dams, their principal purpose will be to hold back the silt from filling Lake Mead and thus rendering Hoover Dam useless. Unless some means are found to check the daily million-ton load of sediment, engineers estimate that the 120-mile Lake Mead will be an arid sand flat in less than 250 years.

The first of the new dams to be built will probably be in Glen Canyon in southern Utah. There it is planned to establish a recreation area on the shores of the canyon lake impounded by the dam. So, perhaps, not many years hence, trim boats will skim across blue waters under a brilliant desert sky, their sails outlined against multicolored cliffs; the putt-putt of outboard motors will echo from canyon walls where once a few men braved a mighty river—some never to be heard from again.

Those who love the plain, undecorated earth they live on must bow to the urge to reduce stimulating and varied environments to a dead level of human acceptability. This is called progress, and the people who deplore it are in a minority. But the few who know the Colorado will regret its passing as they would mourn the loss of a unique and irreplaceable friend.

CHALLENGE

WASHINGTON, D.C., June 16, 1874

SIR: I have the honor to submit herewith my report of the exploration of the Colorado River of the West and its tributaries,

161

and respectfully request that the same may be forwarded to Congress.

I am, with great respect, your obedient servant,

J. W. Powell

To: Prof. JOSEPH HENRY,
      Secretary, Smithsonian Institution,
      Washington, D. C.

With these words Major John Wesley Powell gave to the American people the first full account of his epoch-making journey in 1869 by boat down fourteen hundred miles of the Green and Colorado rivers.

Until Powell's explorations the mysterious Colorado River of the West was virtually unknown. The Spaniards, master explorers and colonizers, had failed to make the savage river's acquaintance in their usual thorough manner. Alarcón, sailing up the Gulf of California in 1540, discovered the wide mouth of the river and ascended with twenty of his men in small boats for a distance of two hundred miles. In the same year Cárdenas looked down from the South Rim of the Grand Canyon upon the turbid waters of the "Big River" a mile below him. And in 1776 Father Escalante crossed the Colorado in what is now southern Utah on his return to Santa Fe after an unsuccessful attempt to discover a short route to California. But that was all. And so during the three hundred years of Spanish and Mexican occupation of Western America the Colorado kept its secrets.

Nor were the Americans much more successful in penetrating the maze of canyons and steep-walled plateaus which had turned back the Spaniards. In 1857, as we have learned, Lieutenant Ives of the United States Corps of Engineers assembled a wheezy Philadelphia-built steamboat, in which he chugged precariously

162

up the river to Black Canyon where Hoover Dam now bars the way. The next year Lieutenant Ives endeavored to explore the Grand Canyon but found little except difficulties and hardships, as did Captain Macomb, who was sent to examine the junction of the Green and Grand rivers in 1859. These two expeditions ended all official attempts to solve the riddle of the Colorado. Lieutenant Ives reported, "It seems intended by nature that the Colorado River, along the greater portion of its lonely and majestic way, shall be forever unvisited and undisturbed." The United States Government, becoming increasingly concerned over the growing friction between the North and South, apparently was inclined to let it go at that.

Meanwhile unofficial activities had been gnawing away little chunks of the unknown on the upper river. Trappers followed the profitable beaver into the canyons of the Green; some of these men undoubtedly used boats. The earliest known by name was William Ashley, a famous figure in the American fur trade, whose party lost two boats in Red Canyon. Another probable boatman, precise identity unknown, was D. Julien, whose inscription on a rock in Cataract Canyon bears the date 1836. A prospector named White actually claimed to have been carried down through Cataract, Marble, and Grand canyons on a raft in 1867. But his fantastic stories were thoroughly discredited by both Dellenbaugh and Stanton.

So, until one man had the courage, the will, and the scientific curiosity to organize an expedition to explore the unknown portions of the Colorado, it remained a river of mystery and terror. The fear of the canyons grew until it amounted almost to superstition. Tales were told around pioneer campfires of gigantic whirlpools, waterfalls greater than ten Niagaras, and

163

yawning gulfs into which the river disappeared to run underground for several hundred miles.

The Indians, who knew the country better than did the white intruders, had woven myths about the river, predicting dire retribution to those who might have the temerity to probe its secrets. They insisted that the great canyons had been made long ago by the Indian god, Ta-vwoats, to permit a wise and good chief to join his dead wife in a better land. Then Ta-vwoats turned a mad, raging river into the gorge so that none should follow. All men, red and white, who had seen the river wondered, many speculated about it, some—abhorring a vacuum— invented stories, but no man knew for certain what might lie in those nineteen mighty canyons until Powell and his venturous crew dispelled the mysteries of the Colorado River of the West in 1869.

It is not given to small spirits to risk the perilous unknown in order to solve a riddle which has baffled men for three hundred and fifty years. But Major John Wesley Powell was much more than an adventurous explorer. He had science to fortify him and a confidence in his ability to overcome any obstacle which the river might put in his way. Even before his nationwide fame as the Colorado River conqueror, Powell's versatile talents had already gained for him a reputation as a geologist, ethnologist, and soldier. At the outbreak of the Civil War he enlisted as a private, quickly rose to sergeant-major, and, as captain of a field artillery battery at Shiloh, he received a wound which necessitated the amputation of his right arm. Mrs. Powell, still a bride, immediately volunteered to substitute for her husband's loss. She formally enlisted and received a pass from General Grant enabling her to follow the army wherever her husband might go. So Powell, with his feminine "right arm," continued in active service, rising to the rank of major at the close of the war.

In 1867-68, Powell, solidly established in geology once more, conducted a series of expeditions to Colorado Territory at his own expense. While exploring the upper canyons of the Grand River he became fired with the desire to have it out with the sphinxlike Colorado. His desire crystallized into action the following winter, and by spring this indomitable scientific go-getter had completely organized an exploring party. Boats were built, personnel obtained, and funds raised. All that remained was to blow the starting whistle and to renounce the world of men indefinitely—perhaps forever.

More remarkable still was the fact that the first Colorado River expedition was Powell's private affair: expenses were defrayed by contributions he had solicited from three Illinois educational institutions, in small amounts from personal friends, and generously from his own pocket. The government did not appropriate one cent for Powell's first expedition, although it authorized the Major to draw rations for himself and his men from Western army posts.

The avowed purposes of the expedition were to make collections in "natural science," conduct a preliminary geological survey, and above all to solve the greatest geographical mystery yet remaining in the United States. It was an ambitious program, but worthy of the man who made it.

THE MAN IN THE BOAT

On the morning of May 24, 1869, at Green River, Wyoming Territory, nine men eyed with some misgivings four boats drawn up on the sandy river. What they saw were trim craft, stanchly built with watertight compartments fore and aft, but seeming pitifully small for the herculean job ahead of them. The lives of the nine men depended on the stoutness and maneuverability of these four boats, which were to take them southward for an unknown distance, an unknown length of time, on a wild, unknown river. Would the boats stand up?

The expedition's one-armed leader seemed to think so. He was competent and assured and seemed to know exactly what he was doing. He inspired the men with growing confidence. So, dismissing the uncertain future from their minds, they set to loading the boats from the mountainous piles of supplies on the beach. There were almost a year's provisions to be stowed away, for no one knew how long they would be gone: complete sets of summer and winter clothing, guns, ammunition, traps, carpenter tools for repairing boats and building cabins, barometers, chronometers, thermometers, compasses, and other instruments.

When the last bulky article had been stuffed into the overloaded boats, and the hatches had been battened down, the heterogeneous population of Green River lined the river bank to watch the expedition depart. Powell raised the little flag on the *Emma Dean,* the boats pushed off one by one, and a swift current quickly carried them downstream out of sight.

The last thread connecting these ten men with the outside world had been cut. The great adventure had begun.

166

That first day the river played with them—taunting them, mocking their efforts. They ran aground on a sand bar. An oar was broken. A boat struck a rock. Two more oars were lost overboard in the confusion but were recovered. The river flowed on swiftly, deceptively smooth, biding its time.

But the overburdened boats performed well; the men gained assurance as they learned to handle them. Three of the boats were built of oak, twenty-one feet long, stout and double ribbed. Powell's flagship, the *Emma Dean*, was of pine, fast and light, five feet shorter than the others. The major had named it the *Emma Dean* after his wife. So, even on the Colorado, he relied in spirit on his feminine "right arm."

For two weeks the expedition drifted down the river without mishap. Some days were given over to exploring the surrounding country, but the usual routine consisted of quiet gliding downstream alternating with exhilarating runs on fast water through ever deepening canyons. There were enough rapids to add spice to the daily run with only one so threatening that portaging the boats was deemed necessary. But each day the river became visibly angrier and roared its menace more loudly to the echoing cliffs.

Sixteen days the river waited, then struck—hard.

On June 8 the party passed between the towering rock portals of the Gate of Ladore into a tremendous canyon with walls three thousand feet high. Rapids followed each other in quick succession, and the boats plunged and reared in a welter of wild water. Several times a boat struck a wave broadside and was instantly flipped over. But always her crew doggedly hung on to the capsized boat until smoother going was reached where they could right it and climb back aboard.

167

The next day, after a morning of running rapids, a particularly ominous-looking place appeared ahead. The *Emma Dean* was landed in the quiet water above the rapid. Powell, stepping ashore, signaled the other boats to come up. As he went forward to reconnoiter he heard a shout above the roaring water. Turning he saw one of the boats, the *No-Name*, shooting down the tongue of the rapid into a channel spiked with dangerous rocks. Halfway down she struck one of these, rebounded from the shock, lurched forward half filled with water, and spun drunkenly on. Two of the crew had their oars wrenched from their hands, leaving the third desperately trying to control the boat. But it was hopeless. Powell watched in helpless fascination as the *No-Name* crashed broadside with terrific force into a second rock and split wide open; her crew instantly disappeared into the surging water. The wrecked boat was seen again with the three men clinging to it as it careened down a channel filled with rocks. What was left of the *No-Name* struck a third time and was dashed to pieces, men and fragments sweeping down the river out of sight.

The crew, however, fought through the rapid and managed to pull themselves ashore on a rocky island below. There they were stranded until the others came up, with a fast current running either side of them, another fall just below. The rescue was a ticklish business. The *Emma Dean* was pushed out into the river as far above the island as possible and, with a skillful handling of the oars, was brought to the island's upper point. The three men jumped aboard and were landed safely on the mainland, where the party shook hands with them as solemnly as if they had returned from an adventurous journey around the world.

168

The loss of the *No-Name* at Disaster Falls crippled the expedition. A quarter of the provisions were gone, and many of the scientific instruments, and a few days later, at the first opportunity, one of the crew of the *No-Name* left the party. After the accident the danger and menace of the river lay like a shadow over the men as each day's run took them deeper into the unknown wilderness. Every man knew at last that running the river was the big job. The other purposes of the expedition had to be secondary.

For weeks they descended the river, threading canyon after canyon, running one rapid after another. One evening their campfire spread into dry willows and brush, exploding into flames so suddenly that the men were able to save themselves only by escaping to the boats with their clothing and hair singed. On the same day, as the crew of the *Maid of the Canyon* were lowering her around a rapid with lines, she broke away, but fortunately the runaway boat was captured in an eddy below. Oars were broken and lost in the frequent skirmishes with the rapids, and boats were upset. On July 11, a mountainous wave bowled over the *Emma Dean*, throwing Powell and two of his shipmates overboard. One of the men would have drowned but for the quick action of the other in reaching out and pulling him to the boat. The next day one of the crew of *Kitty Clyde's Sister* was knocked overboard. His foot caught under the seat, and he was dragged head down through the rapid until in smoother water he could be hauled back into the boat.

And so it went as the weeks strung out into months. On July 17, the expedition reached the junction of the Green and Grand rivers. Immediately ahead lay the greatest mystery of all —the Colorado. At this critical point in the journey a checkup

169

showed that rations were beginning to run low. Because of the loss of the *No-Name*, together with frequent mishaps and spoilage by constant wetting, the party's original ten months' food supply had been reduced to an amount which Powell estimated would last but eight weeks longer. Food for half a year had disappeared in fifty-eight days! At that rate the men would starve long before they were released from the imprisoning walls of the Grand Canyon. But, gloomy as the outlook was, every man wanted to push on.

So, after overhauling equipment, repairing battered boats, and exploring the fantastic land of colorful rock surrounding the river junction, the expedition shoved out into the Colorado on July 21. The three boats were quickly swallowed up in the depths of a great canyon filled with enormous rapids too dangerous to run. The men sweated and strained portaging the boats over the rocks. Dead tired, they tried to run the lesser rapids. But the *Emma Dean* was swamped, throwing the leader into the river, and three more precious oars were lost.

For eight days Powell and his men struggled through this giant gorge, which they named Cataract Canyon. It was similar to those on the Green but with a difference. Since the Colorado was a larger river than the Green, every feature and detail was on a greater scale. The party proceeded cautiously with the constant fear that just ahead lay tremendous falls which could not be avoided. Science could successfully snub superstition in civilized lands, but, after all, the popular stories of heroic-sized Niagaras and yawning gulfs might be true. In Cataract Canyon it began to look as if anything could happen on the Colorado.

But the river was not the only hazard. Powell, himself, had several extracurricular adventures on land. Throughout the journey he investigated side canyons and scaled cliff walls, one, two, three thousand feet, to survey the adjacent country. Sometimes the major had company, more often he was alone. Although Powell was an agile climber, the missing right arm handicapped him to such an extent that his explorer's enthusiasm occasionally got him into precarious positions. Usually he managed to extricate himself alone or with a companion's help, but once in the Grand Canyon he found himself spread-eagled against a vertical cliff four hundred feet above the river. As he could neither advance nor retreat, he shouted for help. The men climbed to the ledge on which their leader was suspended and passed him a line. He was unable to let go with his one hand to grasp it. Eventually he was rescued by means of oars pushed into crevices in the rock, along which he edged his way to safety.

August 13 found the expedition entering the mile-deep gorge of the Grand Canyon—the climax of the Colorado. Portages were impossible, for grim, black granite walls rose sheer from the water's edge. The boats tossed from side to side as towering waves broke over them; two capsized, and men fought for their lives in the tempestuous rapids. But they pulled through, landing beside clear, sparkling Bright Angel Creek—one of Powell's happiest inspirations among the hundreds of names which he bestowed.

The food problem was now acute. The bacon had spoiled and was thrown away, leaving only some dried apples, coffee, and enough moldy flour to last ten days. But, exhausted and undernourished as the men were, they hadn't yet lost their nerve.

For ten days they traveled down the seemingly endless trench of the Grand Canyon. Gigantic, unscalable walls shut them in, reducing the sky to a strip of blue overhead. The roar of the river throbbed incessantly in their ears as they raced with starvation to the Canyon's mouth. And each day the chance of winning appeared slighter.

On August 27, taut nerves finally snapped. That morning the party reached a series of rapids worse than anything they had yet seen. All afternoon Powell and the men scrambled over the cliffs on both sides of the river, scanning the rapids for a possible way of getting the boats safely through. The major picked out a route which he believed could be followed, but it would take every bit of skill and ounce of muscle they had. And they would need plenty of luck, as well. He announced that the party would run the rapid next day.

That evening one of the men argued against proceeding further, advising Powell to abandon the expedition altogether. At any rate, he would go no further with the boats. His brother and one of the other men agreed with him; all three would rather take their chances on reaching the Mormon towns up the cliffs and seventy-five miles across the unknown desert. They wouldn't stay another day in the Canyon and be drowned like starved rats in a well.

Powell sat up that night plotting his course. He concluded that the mouth of the Virgin River could not be more than forty-five miles distant in a straight line. By river perhaps it was double that, but he knew that open country intervened and the party should be out of the Grand Canyon in a few days.

All night the leader paced the sandy shore of the river he had almost conquered, debating whether to give up with victory so near. It was solely his decision. At one time he almost made up his mind to abandon the river and take the chance that they

172

could reach the distant settlements. But then he wrote in his record, "For years I have been contemplating this trip. To leave the exploration unfinished, to say that there is a part of the canyon which I cannot explore, having already almost accomplished it, is more than I am willing to acknowledge, and I determine to go on." At dawn on August 28, the leader had made his decision.

Five men stood by him. But after a solemn breakfast the other three were more determined than ever to leave the river. They begged Powell not to go on, assuring him that it was sheer madness to risk such rapids in leaky boats with fast disappearing rations. It was their last chance of getting out of the Canyon alive. But the five stalwarts stuck to their guns, whatever the consequences. It was a solemn parting; each party thought the other was taking the more dangerous course.

The expedition, now short three men, sorrowfully abandoned the flagship—"my *Emma Dean*," Powell called it affectionately. Without a single upset, they ran the wicked-looking cataract which had appeared so bad the day before and called it, significantly, Separation Rapids.

The three left behind on the shore climbed a rocky point and watched the two boats battle the rapid until they disappeared around a bend. Then the trio turned away from the river and headed up a side canyon. They were never seen again. Their fate was not known until the following year when Jacob Hamblin, Mormon friend of the Indians, learned that the three men had been ambushed and killed by the Utes.

At noon on the day after the separation, the little party in the *Maid of the Canyon* and *Kitty Clyde's Sister* drifted swiftly out of the Grand Canyon into open country. On August 30, ninety-eight days after they had started, they were greeted by Mormon settlers at the mouth of the Virgin River.

Victory at last! The incredible giant had been vanquished. "The relief from danger and the joy of success are great," wrote Powell. "Now the danger is over; now the toil has ceased; now the gloom has disappeared . . . our joy is almost ecstasy."

So the man had conquered the river.

But the circumstances leading to the desertion by three of Major Powell's party at Separation Rapids grew into a first-class mystery story with the major featured as the leading suspect. Robert Brewster Stanton, who followed Powell down the river in 1889, heard various rumors from old-timers and other vocal historians that all had not gone well in the Powell party. It was said by some that friction had existed which touched off an explosion on August 27, resulting in Powell's ordering the three men to leave the party. A further nice touch was that the major had named the Dirty Devil River in southern Utah after one of the trio!

Stanton tried to sift all the evidence. His voluminous material and transcripts of interviews relating to Powell's first expedition were gathered in his book, *Colorado River Controversies*. That seems to be where they, properly, lie buried. Powell, himself, rightly kept any reference to personal cat-and-dog fights out of his report. And no rumors have ever dimmed his reputation as an explorer or man of science.

THE SECOND JOURNEY

The major returned to civilization to learn that he was dead. Lurid stories of tragedy and disaster had appeared in newspapers

174

throughout the country, relating with horrible details the loss of all but one of the party. Few men have an opportunity to discover what the world thinks of them after they are gone, but Powell read his obituaries with considerable satisfaction. He found that he was held in high esteem by the people of the United States.

But the indefatigable geologist-explorer refused to play dead for long. His first expedition had met with so many accidents and losses of essential instruments that Powell was dissatisfied with its scientific accomplishments. He set to work at once to interest Congress in a second Colorado River Expedition. He was successful, as usual. In 1870, an appropriation of ten thousand dollars was voted, followed by a further grant from Congress in the session of 1871-1872 for proceeding with a topographical and geological survey of the country adjacent to the Green and Colorado rivers.

So once again a small group of men assembled at Green River, Wyoming. And on May 22, 1871, the United States Colorado River Expedition, Major John Wesley Powell, leader, was under way. They were much better provided for than the first party: their three boats were superior; the provisions were more varied; each man was equipped with an inflatable rubber life jacket; and on the deck of the *Emma Dean II* an armchair was strapped—probably affording the most luxurious, though top-heavy, descent of the Colorado ever made.

The chronicler of the second expedition was an enthusiastic, teen-age lad of all trades, Frederick S. Dellenbaugh, who wrote, sketched, painted, and mapped his way down the river. Powell, himself, scarcely mentioned the second expedition in his reports. Strangely enough, no credit was ever given to the seven men

175

who accompanied him, although only through their combined efforts was their leader able to complete the job he had set himself. More curious still was the major's reticence in the case of A. H. Thompson, his brother-in-law as well as colleague on the trip, whose geographical work largely contributed to its success. Not even faithful Dellenbaugh, in later years Powell's Colorado River Boswell, could ever explain away his leader's gross slight in ignoring the work of the loyal and gifted men of the second expedition.

The eight of them spent an active five months proceeding down the river, exploring, mapping, photographing, and surveying as they went. Adventures were plentiful, but no serious accident prevented the party from brilliantly achieving the scientific objectives of the trip. The Major's second expedition forced the reluctant river giant to give up its few remaining secrets.

In October the party went into winter camp by the mouth of the Paria River at the crossing now known as Lees Ferry. From this northern Arizona base the men carried on their exploration for the next ten months by land, ranging far back to the cold, high plateaus on both sides of the river. Under Professor Thompson's direction they also completed a triangulation net which formed the basis for the first good map of the Colorado River country. Taking to the boats again, they ran down through Marble and Grand canyons to Kanab Creek, where the voyage officially ended September 10, 1872.

So, after three years and three months of intense effort, Powell had accomplished the great aim of his life—the exploration of the Colorado River of the West.

Major Powell's adventurous exploits rather overshadowed the man and his work. But it was the pursuit of accurate knowl-

176

edge rather than of adventure which directed his actions throughout life. The solution of the Colorado River enigma was but Powell's first contribution to an exact scientific knowledge of the new West of his day. Largely through his efforts the government was persuaded to initiate an exhaustive survey of the entire Western country under the unified control of the Department of the Interior. From the consolidation of the Powell, Wheeler, and Hayden surveys grew one of the most valuable government services ever undertaken, the United States Geological Survey. And Powell was its director from 1881 to 1894. His further contributions to a better knowledge of the West were in the fields of archaeology and ethnology. Until his death in 1902, Major Powell was chief of the Bureau of Ethnology in the Smithsonian Institution at Washington.

But it is his river story which keeps Powell's name alive to new generations who come to delight in the vast, wide-sweeping Canyon Country. His professional achievements hold the admiration of a few specialists, but his courageous ventures stir the imaginations of all. Today, at Sentinel Point on the Grand Canyon's South Rim, stands a stone monument to his memory. Here people from all parts of the world read the name, John Wesley Powell, learn his story, then look down a mile below to a narrow chocolate-colored ribbon of water, the noisy, brawling Colorado, the incredible giant, first conquered by the nerve and will of an incredible man.

AFTER YOU, MAJOR POWELL

The reports and maps of Powell's expeditions were best sellers throughout the country, vying with the latest novels in popularity. Among the thousands of readers none was more fascinated than Mr. Frank M. Brown of Denver, Colorado. As he read, an astounding idea took form in his mind. He would build a railroad from his home state to California through the canyons of the Grand and Colorado rivers. This audacious "water-level route" would carry coal from Rocky Mountain mines to the mushrooming boom towns of southern California. Mr. Brown went into action, interested capital from other hopeful spirits, and organized the Denver, Colorado Canyon and Pacific Railway with himself as president.

In 1889, Brown and Robert Brewster Stanton, his chief engineer in charge of construction, headed an expedition down the Colorado to survey a route for the proposed railroad. For seventeen years no one had attempted to follow in the wake of Powell. Presumably his warnings and graphic accounts of dangers had mellowed with age, for seldom was a party less well prepared for a rugged job than the Brown-Stanton expedition. Their six boats were suited to an afternoon's row in the park; their provisions were grossly inadequate. They were not provided with life preservers, and no consistent plan of organization or procedure had been worked out by the leader. But most fatal of all was the mental unpreparedness of the expedition's sixteen members. They underestimated their adversary, the Colorado—and paid for it.

The Brown-Stanton party never had a chance in their unequal battle with the river. The very first day one of the boats had a hole stove in her side. In fact, all six boats upset or swamped on the least provocation, so that the men were forced to struggle along the rocky shores portaging their frail cockleshells or dragging them forward with lines. Their impromptu raft of

178

zinc boxes, containing most of the provisions, was lost over the first rapid in Cataract Canyon, reducing the party to starvation fare. The boat carrying the cooking outfit was the next sacrifice to the river giant: she struck a rock, broke in pieces, and disappeared. Mishaps and disasters followed each other with sickening regularity until the battered expedition, exhausted and underfed, arrived at Lees Ferry. The party was intact but in a pitiful condition. It was a miracle that they arrived at all.

The order to abandon the river should have been given then. But it wasn't. Despite their desperate experiences both Brown and Stanton were anxious to carry the railroad survey through the Grand Canyon. So new provisions were brought in, and the party bravely set out to tackle Marble Canyon. In Sheerwall Rapid, Brown's boat capsized, throwing him into a whirlpool. He was instantly sucked under water, never to be seen again. Stanton's boat passed the spot a half minute later, but all he saw was a notebook swirling in the angry waters which had so suddenly swallowed up the leader. The party waited all day, sadly watching the river for some sign of Brown's body. But the Colorado roared on down to the sea as if puny men had never existed.

With Brown's death the leadership of the expedition fell to Stanton. Once again the one-sided struggle should have been given up. But apparently no such idea occurred to the new leader. For five more days the discouraged party descended Marble Canyon. Then tragedy struck again. In a rapid above Vasey's Paradise two more men were drowned. This was too much even for a party inured to disasters. At last Stanton gave the order to retreat.

But he was a fighter. By November of the same year he had

179

organized a new expedition to continue surveying the railway line. Stanton still had faith in the Denver, Colorado Canyon and Pacific—a faith which those who have followed him find it difficult to understand. His party of twelve men in three stanch boats started below Cataract Canyon, entered Marble Canyon December 28, and reached tidewater in the Gulf of California four months later.

Stanton's party had their share of Colorado river adventures, but the dogged engineer came out with a completed railroad survey under his arm. He believed implicitly that the project would be carried out, but his data, which had cost three men their lives, gathered dust in some desk pigeonhole, and the echo of locomotive whistles will probably never be heard in Colorado canyons.

The next protagonist was a native of Utah named Nathan Galloway. This redoubtable Mormon trapper and boatman held the stage for many years, making numerous trapping journeys through the canyons of the Green and upper Colorado. In 1896, and again in 1909, Galloway navigated Marble and Grand canyons from Lees Ferry to Needles. On the latter trip, completed in the remarkable time of thirty-eight days, he was head boatman for Julius S. Stone's photographic expedition.

Galloway is generally remembered by rivermen for his improvement in the technique of running rapids. Before his time oarsmen faced upriver, relying for direction on signals or shouts from a shipmate in the stern. Galloway reversed the boat, running it stern foremost. In this way a boatman faces the rapid and can see where he is going and make every stroke of the oars count in pulling against the current. All rivermen have adopted Galloway's method. Nowadays, if an oarsman loses control, so that his bow spins around downstream, he is, in river parlance, "pulling a Powell," and is properly chagrined —providing he is still alive.

The Kolb brothers—Ellsworth and Emery—residents of the South Rim of the Grand Canyon, took the first motion pictures of the Colorado on their trip down the river in 1911. Emery Kolb made a second descent as a boatman for the United States Geological Survey party in 1923. This party, which completed quadrangle and damsite surveys of the area in 1923, was under the direction of Claude H. Birdseye. Frank Dodge, another veteran of the Colorado, accompanied the expedition as rodman. At Diamond Creek a boat upset, spilling supplies into the river. Fortunately the water was shallow enough at that point so that most of the canned goods were recovered after several strenuous hours of rescue work. But the cans came up minus their paper labels. This made meals for the next week somewhat a sporting proposition: breakfast might consist of pea soup and sauerkraut, while a dinner of Hawaiian pineapple with evaporated milk would be ravenously consumed.

In 1927, Clyde Eddy, journalist, traveler, and lecturer, advertised in newspapers and outdoor magazines for young explorers to run the Colorado. Out of more than one hundred applicants he picked a crew of twelve college men to man his three boats. The Eddy youngsters, with a dog and a bear to add to their troubles, ran the distance from Greenriver, Utah, to Needles in six weeks. The leader's rather harrowing story is thrillingly told in his book, *Down the World's Most Dangerous River*. His experiences demonstrate that it takes more than youth to acquire the steadiness and calm endurance that make a good whitewater boatman.

Eddy's book is no exception. Colorado River literature generally is pretty grim stuff, with strong men crying like babies, wrecked boats, dissensions, desertions, and sudden death. The canyon walls are lined with broken oars, moldering boats, even bleaching bones—mute evidence of those who didn't make it. Even the successful expeditions rarely come through unscathed.

But perhaps the most pathetic story yet told of the river is that of the Bride and Groom. Mr. and Mrs. Glen Hyde of Idaho decided on an exciting and unusual honeymoon—a trip down the Colorado. They came to Greenriver, Utah, in the summer of 1927, built a Salmon River type scow weighing almost a ton, and launched it for their wedding journey late in the fall. Glen Hyde had had considerable whitewater experience on Idaho's husky Snake and Salmon, while both he and his wife were old hands at camping in the wilderness. They had a difficult and backbreaking trip with innumerable portages and lining jobs to Bright Angel Creek, which they reached in November.

From Phantom Ranch the Hydes climbed to the South Rim to see Emery Kolb. He presented them with a copy of his brother's book, *Through the Grand Canyon from Wyoming to Mexico,* and urged them to take his life preservers for the remainder of the trip. But both Hydes, being strong swimmers, declined his offer and started confidently on the last half of their journey.

Three weeks later, when the couple were long overdue, Idaho's Senator Borah sent an army plane to search the Canyon. Emery Kolb, as observer, spotted the Hyde's scow eleven miles below Diamond Creek. With Ellsworth Kolb and the Chief Ranger from Grand Canyon, he got a boat down the rough road from Peach Springs. The next day the honeymoon craft was found, riding easily in a small rapid, its stern line caught in the rocks. Kolb's book was lying open on the seat as if unhurriedly placed there.

The Hydes were never found. Some believe the girl was pulled into the river by the tug of the scow she was holding against the current while her husband went downstream to inspect the rapid. Both she and Glen Hyde, when he attempted to rescue her, might have been hampered by silt filling their clothes. If that is what happened, even powerful swimmers like the Hydes would have little chance of surviving the rapid.

It is possible, of course, that their boat got away from them, leaving the pair stranded on a strip of shore. They may have tried to escape by climbing the cliffs. But even if they had been successful, they might have been no better off than before. The country above the Canyon is barren, without water, without food, without hope of life.

Seven years passed before another party tackled the river. But from 1934 to 1938 traffic reached a peak; five expeditions successfully navigated Marble and Grand canyons during that period. In 1937, Buzz Holstrom built his own boat in which he made the trip alone. The following year a new chapter in Colorado River history began when Norman Nevills brought two lady botanists from the University of Minnesota safely through all the rapids of the nineteen canyons from Green River, Wyoming, to Lake Mead. Nevills ran the river again in 1940, 1941, and 1942—the first man to lead four Colorado River expeditions. Since the war two more Nevills' Colorado River jaunts have put the roaring rapids and grim canyons in

183

the category of a tourist trip. Thus, in the last seventy-seven years, barely a split second in the geological life of the Colorado, the river has felt the impress of man. Not much of an impression, to be sure, but enough to give some understanding, a little insight, into one of the world's most secret places.

184

CHAPTER EIGHT

RIDING GRAND CANYON RAPIDS

By Weldon F. Heald

THE EIGHTEENTH EXPEDITION

Norman Nevills lives up on the San Juan River, a tributary of the Colorado, at Mexican Hat, Utah, where he has a private navy of fifteen boats. Boats are Norm's life, rivers his religion. They are in his blood. He has run six thousand rough-water miles on Western rivers with the record of never upsetting a boat.

But Norm's great love is the Colorado. No man knows it better. He has studied the river for twenty years, read, countless times, all that has been written about it, and shot every one of the thousand man-eating rapids of the Green and Colorado from Wyoming to Lake Mead in high water and low.

I first met Norm Nevills by chance in the spring of 1941 under the towering stone arch of Rainbow Bridge. Our party had packed in over the trail from Arizona while Norm had hiked up from the Colorado with some people he was piloting down to Lees Ferry. We talked for ten minutes, exchanged addresses, and went our ways. But I plodded up the trail nursing secret ambitions. Norm's river talk is infectious.

A month later I received a characteristic telegram from him.

"Decided to shoot the Colorado a third time," it read. "Want another member to fill out crew and share expenses. This is definitely not a 'dude' trip, but to get pictures and work a kayak through for the first time. Will be a grand trip. How about it?"

I wired to Mexican Hat, "Can't row, but when do we start?"

So two months later we pushed off from Lees Ferry on our 350-mile journey to Hoover Dam. There were six in the party. Norm, with Agnes Albert of San Mateo, California, and William J. Schukraft from Chicago, led in the flagship, *Wen*. Dell Reed, Norm's neighbor from Bluff, Utah, and I followed in the *Mexican Hat II*. Our third boat, the kayak *Escalante*, was piloted by Alexander E. Grant from Dedham, Massachusetts. "W. E. N." were Norm's father's initials, but the "II" attached to our boat looked ominous. I never dared ask what happened to the *Mexican Hat I*.

According to the skipper's log, Nevills' 1941 expedition, the eighteenth successful party to make the passage of Marble and Grand canyons, departed from Lees Ferry at 12:15 P.M., July 15. He wrote:

These embarkations are awfully nervewracking, and it is with relief that I finally give the signal to shove off. The two fifteen-foot cataract boats are quickly readied for the start, but the kayak needs a lot of tinkering. As I look at the frail foldboat, I, like the others, have serious misgivings as to any possibility of its surviving the heavy water of Grand and Marble canyons. At any rate we will be able to pull Zee out even if we can't save the foldboat. So I'm hoping for the best.

We all were. Zee Grant's fragile entry in the Colorado River steeplechase was a sleek, cloth-covered craft, seventeen feet long, weighing but sixty pounds. The interior, with the excep-

188

tion of the cockpit, carried a varied assortment of inflated beach balls while sponsons made of huge inner tubes from Fifth Avenue bus tires were strung along each side to give steadiness. Zee carried a tire pump, for there are no service stations along the Colorado.

The rest of us were very kind to Zee before the start. We regarded him as a brave young man who had picked on the wrong river. However, Zee was no novice in rough water. He had won most of the foldboat championships in America. But the kayak's first test would come at Badger Creek, eight miles below Lees Ferry. Would Zee make it? We thought we knew the answer. Says Norm:

1:35 P.M.-3:50 P.M. BADGER CREEK RAPID. We pull in on the left and under the very slim shade of a great boulder have lunch. As soon as possible I go down to look over the rapid. My first hunch is confirmed; it can be run! This is a great satisfaction as in '38 I lined and last year there was a mighty tough and rocky channel. Now it is a straight shot through, guarded by two holes where the water plunges over submerged rocks. But there is a well-defined tongue. As it is hard to see from above I have Dell signal me for position so I won't miss the tongue. All is set. I slide through with the *Wen*, soon followed by the *Mexican Hat II*. I leave Dell below the rapid to bail and be ready to push out in case of an accident to the foldboat, and go up to signal Zee. He starts. Too far left. I signal him over. Now he's too far right! I signal him over. Still too far to the right. I signal him again. This time he whirls his boat about with a few heavy paddles—and he's 'way too far left. I yell and signal frantically. Zee raises up in the boat and sees his predicament, turns the foldboat around, paddles like a madman—but is swept on into the worst hole in Badger. As I start to run for the *Wen*, some two hundred yards downstream, I watch the river. The foldboat almost immediately sticks its nose

189

through the big wave at the lower edge of the hole—upside down! No sign of Zee. The boat goes on through maybe a couple of hundred feet when I spot Zee bobbing up ahead of the *Escalante*! He holds himself back and grabs the boat. Dell has by now made it out into the river. We start to take off, but as I see that Dell has got Zee okay I pull back to shore. Later Zee explains that his air inflated life preserver went to pieces in the heavy water and all that saved him was an emergency gas bottle preserver! From the time I shoved off in the *Wen* until Zee got to shore downstream a ways, only twenty-five minutes elapsed. But it seemed hours. I feel a great relief that the *Escalante* can get into such tough water and come through in such good shape. Zee never let loose his paddle during all the underwater maneuvers.

4:15-4:30 P.M. Here at Mile 8½ is where Zee landed on left side. We all assemble here to talk it over.

Zee described being sucked down, mauled, and rolled over and over, traveling twenty-five miles an hour under water. "I felt like a handkerchief in a washing machine," he said.

5:05-6:00 P.M. SOAP CREEK RAPIDS. We land on right, and a glance suffices to show that it is easily run. Although it is getting late we all want to take a crack at it. I think it's good psychology for Zee to take it on. I slip through, riding the big waves. They are *big* fellows. Good twenty feet high. I say to myself in the middle of them, "Why, they're just like mountains." Grand ride. Dell slips off to the right and misses the fun. Zee comes through riding the big ones high, wide, and handsome! The boy can really take it! My respect for the foldboat is rapidly mounting, though I do know that fast-hitting side waves or breaking waves will flip him. No good spot to camp so we go on.

6:15 P.M.-8:25 A.M. CAMP. Nice place. Left-hand side just below Canyon at Mile 12½. Eleven and a half mile run today.

190

This is the most we've made the first day out. We're all dog tired, but spirits are high.

JULY 16. EMBARK at 8:25 A.M. We are all eager to be on our way. I cook breakfast; the dishes are done by Dell.

8:50 A.M. SHEERWALL RAPID. Lots of fun. Agnes gets splashed.

Poor Brown. His dreams of railroad building ended here.

9:15-9:40 A.M. HOUSE ROCK RAPID. I have an idea this may be a tough baby, but upon drifting down upon it I see that one can easily slip off on the right side of the tongue to miss a few of the rather heavy waves in the main channel. I go ahead, signal, and Agnes and I run on through, followed by the *Escalante*. Zee does not back paddle enough and goes right on into the heavy water. About the third wave proves his nemesis, and over he goes! He climbs right back on the upside-down boat and paddles to shore without assistance. The *Mexican Hat II* comes through okay, and Zee's boat is soon ready to take off again. An upset a day! Oh me, what is this going to mean before we get to Lake Mead!

10:25-10:55 A.M. NORTH CANYON RAPIDS. I run through with the *Wen,* taking most of the big water. Zee takes the big water all the way—a very beautiful run. Dell slides off and misses the big fellows.

11:05-11:10 A.M. TWENTY-ONE MILE RAPIDS. We get a real ride, though it's not hard to run.

11:45 A.M.-12:30 P.M. MILE TWENTY-FOUR AND A HALF RAPID. *Wen, MH2, Kayak,* all through in fine shape. This is a bearcat in real low water.

191

12:40-2:15 P.M. LUNCH. Left. Good shade just above CAVE SPRING RAPIDS. In the cove here, stuck in a crevice, is an old handleless pick.

2:45 P.M. MILE THIRTY RAPID. This little rapid has a lot of whirl-pools at the bottom, and we are much amused to see the *Escalante* spun around three times in short order.

4:00 P.M.-8:50 A.M. VASEY'S PARADISE. CAMP. Hard to land at this stage of water with very poor anchorage. We finally contrive to moor the boats, then all indulge in the luxury of the fresh, cold water from the waterfall and springs which are running more water than I've seen on the other two trips.

JULY 17. EMBARK, 8:50 A.M. This morning I am taking over the foldboat for a try at it, while Bill and Zee are going to manage the *Wen.* At MILE 34 I run a little rapid in the *Escalante* and get through fine, though I find turning the foldboat much harder than the big boats. The trick seems to be to quarter the kayak away from what you want to miss, then paddle like the dickens. I take Agnes aboard with me! We arouse some consternation when I an-nounce that she and I are going to run the next rapid together in the foldboat. We do so and come through with no more than a ducking. Then I turn the *Escalante* over to Agnes and get back aboard the *Wen.*

10:05 A.M. Arrive MILE 36½. I pull in left, followed by *MH2.* Agnes comes along drifting well out to midstream. I yell at her to make for shore as there is a heavy current into this rapid. Her efforts are not enough, and just by a miracle she gets the *Escalante* close enough to shore at the very brink of the rapid to get hung up on a rock. Dell takes me out past the rock in the *MH2.* I dive over to Agnes and get a firm grip on the foldboat while Dell goes on down over the rapid. A rope from shore is thrown us and we soon get landed.

192

10:25-10:55 A.M. I shove off in the kayak and run my first snorter in it. Make it fine, riding the big eddy right back to near the top, then run it again! All in all I run this one three times! Dell brings Zee through in the *Wen*, but she seems to feel a stranger at the oars as it nearly capsizes with Dell and he gets it full of water. Zee looks much perturbed.

12:02-2:30 P.M. We land on the right in the shelter of the upper of the ROYAL ARCHES. Good spot for lunch. It's windy on the river. Everybody sleeps as if we have nothing to do.

2:55 P.M. PRESIDENT HARDING RAPID. We arrive in a high, disagreeable wind. The rapid, as usual in high water, has quite a zip to it. We run on the left without stopping, though Zee lands for a second to get a better view.

3:40 P.M. Oh me! Wind and rain!

5:00 P.M. NANKOWEAP CREEK. CAMP. 20-mile run. After dinner tonight we light a great pile of driftwood that lights up the whole canyon. It sends a glow to the three-thousand-foot rim above and a great ways up and down the canyon. All in all it's a great camp. Wind has died down, and the weather looks pretty good.

JULY 18. We stay in camp today as we are ahead of schedule. This morning is devoted to a climb up to some Indian cliff ruins five hundred feet above the river and some others at the mouth of Nankoweap creek. Get back at 1:00 P.M., and the rest of the day is spent just lazying around talking about the big rapids that got away, etc. Yesterday Bill got quite a thrill out of a little rapid above MILE 36. He was much perturbed but came through grinning from ear to ear.

Just for fun I have put two X's on the foldboat to indicate the two upsets so far. Zee joins in with the idea gleefully.

Funny. After breakfast today we all took salt tablets, and Bill and I were positively sick. We almost lost our breakfast.

Tonight we have another big fire that is terribly spectacular and sit around talking until midnight. How time flies! We have lots of fun working ourselves into a lather over Hance, Sockdolager, and Grapevine—the three biggest rapids. I really believe that my psychology will work as usual in painting such an awful picture that the reality will seem much lesser.

JULY 19. We get up at 6:45 A.M. after a night of wind and sand blowing. Everyone seems happy and rarin' to go. Sky is overcast and maybe holds a storm for this afternoon.

SHOVE OFF 8:30 A.M. The NANKOWEAP RAPIDS are just fun.

9:25-9:35 A.M. Foot of KWAGUNT RAPID. Splashy and fun. No need to look over. *Wen* and *Escalante* come through without shipping water, but *MH2* gets a ducking. We stop to let Bill dry his movie camera.

10:15 A.M. Lots of fun and nice going. Here we enter Grand Canyon.

10:35 A.M. LITTLE COLORADO RIVER. Small flow in little Colorado Canyon, and I win a milkshake. We go right on as this is an uninviting spot.

11:25 A.M. LAVA CANYON RAPID. Nice and splashy. Have trouble through here in keeping bearings, as at different stages of water the rapids come and go, while the topography is confusing.

LUNCH. We go a few hundred feet over to Tanner's old camp at foot of disused trail for lunch. Left side. After lunch we elect to

194

explore the old workings. At the mine entrance the exploring party dwindles down to Agnes and me. We go way back to every tunnel end and have much fun making spooky noises in the dark. There are several hundred feet of workings, in spots caving quite badly. In one place I go across an old plank that spans a water-filled shaft. It's quite a thrill. Upon returning to the mouth of the mine we all sit around awhile and talk. Return to Tanner's Camp, pack up the lunch equipment, and take off.

3:05 P.M.-7:50 A.M. MILE 68½ CAMP. Left. 16½ mile run. We have the same camp as in '38, even using the same fireplace. We go over to sand flat to build a big woodpile for a signal fire for watchers at Desert View on the South Rim. Get in for some heavy work! After dinner we go over to burn the pile. It makes a beautiful blaze, and we watch anxiously for answering lights, but we see none. Next year will arrange to have a rocket set off as a signal that we are observed. I later found that we were seen coming into camp this afternoon. We entertain ourselves with gruesome stories of the horrors awaiting us tomorrow at Hance, Sockdolager, and Grapevine.

DANGER CAN BE FUN

There is a tingling feeling of suspense about running big rapids—half anticipation, half dread—which was intensified that first morning in the Grand Canyon by Norm's hair-raising stories of what was ahead. He keyed us up as a football coach does his team before the big game. Norm's method is pretty strong medicine. It even works on himself. But I suspect this watch-spring tension is the ideal attitude with which to run the Colorado. With it—danger can be fun.

JULY 20. Up at 6:00 A.M. Everyone in fine fettle and anxious for the thrill promised in today's run to Bright Angel Creek.

195

SHOVE OFF 7:50 A.M. TANNER RAPIDS 7:56 A.M. Lots of fun.

8:35 A.M. UNKAR CREEK RAPID. Land right. Mile 72½. We look it over and find it will be fun, but must use a bit of care. Away we go and have a marvelous ride.

Unkar Creek Rapid can be seen from Cape Royal on the North Rim, looking from five thousand feet above like a little riffle in a brook.

9:30-9:35 A.M. SEVENTY-FIVE MILE RAPID. A glance and away we go. Only trick to it is that you have to pull hard right at the bottom, and I don't get over far enough. We land in a hole, and what a ducking! Weldon out front swallows a ton of water. I have taken him over in my boat with Agnes, ready for the big fellows. This will leave Dell with only Bill.

To enliven things further I have a new song:
(Tune—A Man Comes To Our House)
Grapenuts in the morning,
Grapevine for lunch,
But I have a feeling, in fact it's quite a hunch:
When old man Hance sees us walking on the beach,
He is a mighty lesson, to us a'going to teach.

9:50-11:05 A.M. HANCE RAPID. Mile 76½ left. This is a whizzer. We look it over until 10:15, at which time I shove off in the *Wen*, running toward the left from the middle. I go through three holes in succession and fill up to the seat. What a ride! Pull in some ways below, bail, then signal Dell through. Comes through fine, then *Escalante* runs it, playing the left bank. This rapid is a number one toughy at any stage of water.

SOCKDOLAGER! 11:27-11:40 A.M. At top looking it over. 12:07 P.M. all safe at bottom. Well, this is a honey! After my big build-up I'm even surprised myself. In '38 this looked like a pretty for-

196

midable piece of water—but this year—oh me! The tongue drives hard to the right wall, bad holes on both sides, making a tricky problem to get through. We had a real thrill taking off. Made it fine. Foldboat and *MH2* come through beautifully.

GRAPEVINE RAPIDS. Mile 81½. 12:35-12:45 P.M. looks over. 1:00 P.M. all safe at bottom. After Sockdolager and the sight and ride it presented I didn't seem to feel quite so impressed with this fellow, although it has a mean channel. I took off with Agnes and Weldon, drifted down on the tongue, saw we were going too far right, so pulled hard left, and almost pulled us into some really tough holes. I pulled back hard to the right—and we had it made. For a minute, though, I thought church was really going to let out! We had promised ourselves not to eat lunch until Grapevine was under our belt, so we are looking for a lunch spot.

1:15-3:15 P.M. LUNCH. Left. Mouth of Boulder Canyon. Putting the toughies safely behind goes to our heads, and the first thing I know the whole caboodle of us are talking at the top of our voices at once!

3:35 P.M. EIGHTY-THREE MILE RAPID. It's nice running, though the waves are high and sharp. This is grand going from here on in, and we're riding them high, wide, and handsome. We go out of our way in the *Wen* to get a ducking—and get it! I get off my bearings a bit and keep thinking each rapid we come to is MILE EIGHTY-THREE. There is some comment.

Just above Bright Angel we are horseplaying. Agnes falls off the stern deck on top of me. I lose my balance and collapse on Weldon in the bow! What a day, and what a grand bunch. This is truly the merriest and happiest outfit that ever tackled the Colorado. This crowd bears out my theory that one or two gripers or whisperers can spoil a whole party.

197

We have fortified ourselves for a gala reception at Bright Angel Trail. We feel sure there will be a clamoring multitude to welcome us.

4:15 P.M. BRIGHT ANGEL CREEK. Mile 87½. Woe is me! I really thought we would have at least some kind of a reception committee. But not a soul! Not a solitary person is in sight as we come majestically in, holding perfect formation for the photographers.

"HIGH, WIDE, AND HANDSOME"

Phantom Ranch lies at the bottom of the Grand Canyon close by clear, sparkling Bright Angel Creek. We spent two days there making the most of our one contact with civilization. The six of us reveled in the sybaritic pleasures of soft beds, cold drinks, showers, and a swimming pool.

At Phantom, Norm's wife, Doris, met us with mountainous stacks of provisions packed down the trail on mules from the South Rim.

"You can't run the Colorado on hardtack and beans," says Norm. And so we enjoyed such rare delicacies as fresh bread and eggs throughout the trip. Several hours were required to pack all the food and stow it away in the watertight hatches of the cataract boats. They were groggy from weight when we pushed off from the beach at Phantom Ranch on July 23.

Somehow it seemed as if the trip really began after leaving Bright Angel Creek. For ten days we would be isolated at the bottom of one of the world's great gorges with no way out except by shooting a hundred roaring rapids. But the six of us were finally a working unit ready for anything the Canyon might offer.

198

And we found, soon enough, that the Canyon meant business. At Hermit Falls, six miles below Phantom Ranch, we had our first lining job. There the river drops too fast even for spunky cataract boats to dare the twenty-five-foot waves. Lining is an arduous task, sometimes taking three hours before the last boat is through. But to us it was a new experience spiced with a different kind of danger.

In lining, everything movable in the boats must be unloaded and portaged to the foot of the rapid. Then, with every man pushing and pulling with all his strength, the six-hundred-pound boats are eased down over the boulders and cascades through the narrow channels close to the shore. As the boats haltingly progress they are snubbed, first with the bow line, then the stern line, to prevent them from being whisked away by the current or smashed against a rock.

Lining is slow work, but exciting. The channels are deep and swift, while the footing is slippery, and glasslike rock protrudes from the water at all angles. Fortunately for our aching muscles Lava Falls, a hundred miles below, was the only other rapid we were forced to line.

We were dead tired the first night out from Phantom Ranch. We had run Granite Falls and Horn Creek Rapid as well as lining Hermit. But a sandstorm came up, making our dreams restless affairs in which we continued to fight the river all night.

JULY 24. 8:10 A.M. SHOVE OFF. Run BOUCHER RAPID right off the reel. Wonderful fast going. Surprisingly enough it's about the fastest water we've had so far on the trip. We made a good twenty miles an hour.

199

8:50 A.M. MILE 99½. This stretch through here is real sport and goes like the dickens over these small rapids. Hardly a place in the canyon more fun to run than these.

9:30 A.M. MILE 104½. RUBY CANYON RAPIDS. Run all these just looking over from the boat. River a bit red this morning but doesn't seem to be any higher. In '40 we had quite a bit of grief through here with rocks, but this high water is a cinch and is perfect going. We get a few drops of rain.

10:05-10:15 A.M. Well! This rapid has definitely changed! In '38 the channel *was* a sort of serpentine affair, staying mostly to the right. But this time the takeoff is near the left and switches over to the right a bit, then drops on through. It's beginning to rain.

11:00 A.M.-1:14 P.M. SHINUMO CREEK. LUNCH. We are glad to pull in here, though it's just stopped raining. We are cold so the boys build a fire. Funny weather. We stop here quite a while and take naps. We are finally disturbed by the hot sun driving down on us!

Running rapids, loading, bailing, and landing boats are damp occupations. But being constantly wet had its practical side. A merciless summer sun beats down into the barren canyons, sending the midday temperatures skyrocketing to 110°-115°F. But as we were air-cooled by evaporation all day long none of us suffered with the heat. In fact, when the sun disappeared behind high-piled thunderclouds, which gathered on the Canyon rims each afternoon, we actually became cold.

1:35-2:00 P.M. Left under overhanging ledge. We pull in here, driven to shelter by a terrific upstream driving rain! We are thrilled by the sight of many waterfalls forming from the literal cloudburst.

200

Across the canyon rocks are falling from the cliffs. One on our side, as big as an army tank, plunges into the river close to us.

WALTHENBURG RAPIDS. Arrive 2:25 P.M. *Wen* off 3:00 P.M. All at bottom 3:25 P.M. Leave 3:45 P.M. Another surprise! A flood has overtaken us, and this rapid has strong lashing waves in the center of the main drag. I decide to run the main channel. This is tough water. The waves have an awfully hard lash to them. The *Escalante* sneaks on the right and plays the filth, hits two rocks, and in crossing gets some hard going over by heavy water.

4:35 P.M.-8:50 A.M. ELVES CHASM. CAMP. Mile 116½. 20-mile run today. Difficult landing but we anchor on left. The creek is running red-colored water. Creek is on left, then a hundred and fifty feet of sand offers a good camping place. The boats are tied up and I have just put out the camping equipment when I see figures madly dashing around. I join the rush and find that another fork of the creek has discharged a flood that is coming clear across the sand bank. We gather up all equipment in the nick of time and lose nothing. But most of the sand is washed away, leaving ledges. It's quite a thrill and novel experience. This second water is a dirty brown. Although the flood passes over the boat anchorage it holds fast. The flood hit at 6:15 P.M. Little sand left, but a grand night's sleep nevertheless.

JULY 25. SHOVE OFF 8:50 A.M. Well, well, well! In taking off I bang into a rock, bounce off, and hit another!

The river rose three feet. I almost forgot: yesterday, in climbing from his foldboat at Walthenburg Rapids, Zee went up the cliff some fifteen feet, lost his grip, and came tumbling down into the river. What luck that no rocks were lurking under the surface! This stream at Elves Chasm is known as Arch Creek. We leave a register up in the cave for future parties to sign. I am going to get the names of past parties gradually filled into it.

It's clouded up again this morning. Looks as if rain would overtake us once more.

10:00 A.M. MILE 121½ RAPID. The bow-heavy *Wen* really got us slugged in this one! Going to have to shift my load. The foul red water is unpleasant stuff to get socked with.

10:40 A.M. FOSSIL RAPIDS. Fun to run. Starting to rain and is getting cold.

11:15 A.M.-1:35 P.M. LUNCH. Build a fire here where we've pulled in on the right. See a king snake. It's banded black and white, 18 inches long. Finally stops raining.

BEDROCK RAPID. Arrive 2:35 P.M. At bottom 3:10 P.M. On again 3:25 P.M. A real kick and a dangerous piece of water. We have a bit of a time getting Zee to a vantage point to look it over. Weldon goes overland to lighten Dell's boat and meets us at bottom. It's a hard one to climb around, he finds. Agnes and I shove off in *Wen*. Near bottom get a good ducking. Dell and Zee come through fine. Bill rides with Dell.

DEUBENDORFF RAPID. Arrive 3:45 P.M. *Wen* off 4:00 P.M. All at bottom 4:25 P.M. On again 4:35 P.M. This is a honey! I go through, get socked in a hole, blinded by muddy water. Dell right in my tracks. Zee plays the right bank and keeps out of the big water. Good thing, as the power in these waves would have thrown him over like lightning.

5:05-5:15 P.M. TAPEATS CREEK. Land on right looking for a camp spot, but this is definitely no good. No anchorage, a flood down Tapeats Creek would catch us, and there's quicksand here! Therefore we decide to drop down a ways.

5:20 P.M.-8:55 A.M. CAMP. MILE 133½. 17½ miles today. We are now camped on the big bar just below Tapeats Creek. It's like

202

ice water, but most of the gang take baths. Looks stormy a bit, but don't think it will rain. Nice camp. The sunset lights back on the Powell Plateau are gorgeous.

JULY 26. Up this morning with just a few clouds. River up six inches to a foot.

8:55 A.M. SHOVE OFF. Fine going this morning.

9·30-9:50 A.M. DEER CREEK FALLS. Water over falls half again as big as in '40. Brrr! The air and water are cold!

10:05 A.M. Indian cliff ruins. See some new ones this trip just upstream. Don't stop though.

10:12 A.M. MILE 138. This is the famous rapid where I dumped Doris and John in '40.

10:29 A.M. FISHTAIL CANYON. Small rapid here.

11:15-11:20 A.M. KANAB RAPIDS. Glance over from right. Marvelous riding, and we hate to see them end.

12:05-2:20 P.M. Left under ledge. LUNCH. MILE 148½. We are just eating when a heavy rain comes up. We are really pleased as it has caught us in a grand sheltered spot. After a bit of rain some beautiful waterfalls begin to come over the cliff walls, and we are treated to a rare sight. The high, ribbon-like falls come down from around 1,600 feet. Sky clears and we have blue sky for take-off.

Just before we get to UPSET RAPIDS I shove the *Wen* under a big waterfall and try to get Agnes and Bill wet. Waterfalls everywhere pouring over the cliffs.

203

UPSET RAPIDS. 2:40-2:50 P.M. All at bottom 2:55 P.M. This would be a tough nut to walk around in this high water, and anyway we're all spoiling for a good ride. Off we go! Boy, oh boy! One big wave passed us up going like a freight engine. I swear if it had hit us we'd have stayed hit!

4:25-5:00 P.M. HAVASU CANYON. MILE 156⅔. This is a disappointment. Here I've extolled the beauties of the sky-blue water, and we find the rains have made a red stream instead. We row right up through the narrows to the first waterfall. We try for a camping spot, but although it's late we decide to look for a more favorable place. Remembering the high walls through this section I have qualms about picking a camp site this side of MILE 164 CANYON.

6:30 P.M.-10:00 A.M. Right MILE 164 CANYON. 30½ miles today. We came rolling in anxious to make camp. Into MILE 164 RAPID we went. It was rough. Current drives hard to the left wall, and there are some ugly waves. We were barely through when Dell and Weldon ploughed in. Dell later reported that they came very near to upsetting when a hard lashing wave struck them. But Zee—over he went! He climbed back in, found he was facing wrong, and turned around! We all landed laughing, completely exhilarated by our experience. Zee made it right on in under his own power. Nice camp here, and we like it. As we are ahead of schedule we plan to fiddle around in the morning, taking our time.

THE LAST HUNDRED MILES

Easy days are few on the Colorado, but the twenty-seventh was one which gave us a rare opportunity to relax and enjoy the river. The rapids were just big enough to be interesting without the sense of strain which we had been under for the

204

past five days. So we shouted companionably from boat to boat or took our ease on the decks, marveling at the ever changing procession of rock towers and pinnacles outlined against the blue Arizona sky.

A small excitement was logged at lunch:

We go into the mouth of a canyon a ways and find shade under a tree. Partly through lunch I glance up and see a bull snake resting in a branch above Dell's head. This evokes a mad scramble. We shortly move on and take off again.

Animal life was surprisingly scarce. Each day we scanned the cliffs for mountain sheep. Signs were plentiful, and at one place we came across a fine skull with huge curving horns, but we never caught sight of those famous hoofed rock climbers. Of rattlesnakes, centipedes, and scorpions we saw no trace, although we kept our eyes open in stony and brushy places.

On the afternoon of July 27 we had our second lining job:

LAVA FALLS. Arrive 2:40 P.M. Same tough setup as in '38. We obviously have to line. Start lining: *Wen* 3:05, finish 4:10 P.M.; *MH2* 4:30, finish 5:00 P.M. Zee lines *Escalante* alone.

July 28 was another leisurely day, as we were well ahead of schedule. The skipper recorded, "It's fun to have no place to go and lots of time to get there." So we camped in the middle of the morning.

10:50 A.M.-8:45 A.M. CAMP. Right. Nice willow tree and a dandy place to lay over. Mile 192½. After lunch Agnes and I take on a sixty-foot basalt cliff back of camp. I take one ten-foot spill and never do get anywhere. We all join in a good laugh as I'm supposed to be giving climbing lessons! Nothing daunted, Agnes and I set out to climb a peak that rises about a thousand feet. We

205

take no water and reach the summit dry. Grand view. See signs
of mountain sheep. Going down Agnes gets some cactus thorns!
We land in camp *dry*! Some grapefruit juice really hits the spot.
After dinner we keep awake for some time swapping yarns, singing, etc. We are anxious to get some fresh water as this river water
is a bit flat. First quarter moon is overhead.

The next morning we saw the first signs of human life since
leaving Phantom Ranch six days before.

10:05-10:35 A.M. PARASHONT WASH. Mile 198½. As we are
going by I look toward a ledge at right of canyon. See something
suspended by a wire. Possibly a camp. We land to investigate. It
proves to be a trapper's camp. A coyote trap is sprung close by.
A stack of dishes under an oil can. Around the corner more evi-
dences of recent camping. Nobody around though.

Sixteen days from our start at Lees Ferry we came to our
last camp at Diamond Creek. Hoover Dam was still over a hundred miles away, but for most of the distance we would be
towed down the blue waters of Lake Mead.

We lay over another day at our final river camp, spending
most of the time enjoying a busman's holiday immersed in a
Diamond Creek pool christened "Lake Zee" in honor of its
chief engineer.

At Diamond Creek civilization was just around the corner.
Our river days of unbroken companionship, unfailing good
humor, and perfect co-operation were soon to end. We all re-
gretted it. We had grown to believe it was the natural order
of things for the six of us to be shooting the Colorado together;
what was abnormal was the world to which we were returning.
Agnes best expressed the feelings of the entire party when, after saying her last good night, she called back to us above the

206

roar of the river, "I'd turn around tomorrow and do it all over again."

At noon, August 1, the three boats slid down Bridge Canyon Rapid into the quiet water of Lake Mead.

Three days later Norm wrote his last entry in the log for the Eighteenth Expedition:

> Around 9:00 A.M. we approach the BOULDER CITY LANDING. Met by big boats. Pictures taken, and Zee is sensation of the hour— and justifiably so as he turned in a swell job of bringing his fold-boat through. Well, anyway we made it!

As we tied up to the landing a lady ran up to Norm. "Oh, Mr. Nevills," she said, "was there any time when you were really frightened?"

"Only once," Norm assured her.

"When was that?" she asked.

"From the time we shoved off until we reached Lake Mead."

CHAPTER NINE

THE CANYON WILDERNESS

By *Weldon F. Heald*

Over the hill from Flagstaff lies another world. There, amid the vast horizons of northern Arizona, is an ageless land far away in space and time from the America we know. It is the Indian Country—our very last frontier.

The introduction to this homeland of the Navajo and Hopi is as sudden as it is unexpected. Going north from Flagstaff on Route 89 your car climbs gently through a sunny open forest of ponderosa pines. On the left you catch glimpses of the snowy San Francisco Peaks between the trees. Ahead, rising over green meadows, are the ruddy cinder slopes of Sunset Crater. You are in a mountain country with a northern feel to it. Even the occasional ranch houses of logs or unpainted clapboards are the homes of hill people. They might be in Canada or the high mountain valleys of Colorado.

Your car tops the hill. The pines stand aside. Before you the road leads straight down through scattered piñons and junipers into a treeless land of glowing color stretching a hundred miles to meet the sky. You are upon the Coconino Divide, a boundary between two contrasting climates, two distinct civilizations, two eras of time. With the first view of the region you feel its detachment from the everyday concerns of human existence. It seems to stand apart, silent, changeless, impersonal.

The thin line of the road fading into the desert below is the sole reminder of man. Everything else belongs to the realm of geology. But the soft blending of brilliant colors robs this land of emptiness or desolation. To the east the rose pinks and orange of the Painted Desert glow as if from an inner light; long lines of vermilion and ocher cliffs break away into violet-shadowed canyons; distant buttes and mesas are outlined in deep blue on the northern horizon.

Color and space are the two characteristics which give to the Southwest Country its peculiar flavor and atmosphere. If you are sensitive to changing color-tone combinations I imagine you may experience a particularly grand Southwest symphony atop the hill on Route 89 looking north to the Indian Country. And, as with great music, this color-space symphony has the power to break down restricting human barriers, permitting you to perceive dimly that there are further dimensions of existence.

One afternoon in June, Randall Henderson and I turned north from Flagstaff, drove up through the pines to the Divide, then coasted down the long straight road into the desert. We were bound for Mexican Hat, Utah, the starting point of a long-deferred boat trip down the San Juan River. Both of us had been absent from the Southwest for three years, but once again we felt our pulses quicken with a feeling of discovery, of coming into a stimulating new land. It is that feeling which puts a faraway look in a man's eyes, makes cowpunchers out of

212

high-school boys, and transforms insurance salesmen with large families into dusty desert rats.

Randall is the editor of *Desert Magazine*. He spends his life roaming the Southwest and describing what he sees in vigorous Western prose. Wherever he goes thousands enjoy the trip, for Randall is the proxy for desert lovers all over the country. You will run across friends of his in lonely out-of-the-way places from northern Nevada to the Mexican line and from Santa Fe to San Diego.

A few miles down the highway from the Divide a dirt road wanders five miles east across the desert to Wupatki National Monument. There, strung along a ridge, is a series of Pueblo ruins inhabited in the eleventh and twelfth centuries by ancestors of the Hopi.

At the bottom of the long hill from Coconino Divide is Cameron, situated on the edge of a cliff by the Little Colorado River. We had dropped four thousand feet in thirty-five miles and were now in the Navajo Reservation. Cameron, at the junction of Route 89 with the South Rim road to the Grand Canyon, is an Indian trading post gone tourist, the last outpost of our hotel, coffee-shop civilization.

As the late afternoon sun cast long shadows over the Painted Desert, Randall and I pulled into Cameron. Friends were there, and soft beds still had their charm. It would be many nights before we had more than the stars to pull up over our heads.

It was evening rush hour at this Navajo shopping center. Indians were steadily filing in and out of the store. Others were standing like dark statues along the wall outside enjoying a touch of city life. Two braves stood face to face while one solemnly felt the other's arms, chest, and shoulders—a sign of

213

Navajo friendship. Over by the coffee shop young Hopi girls giggled together in shy amusement as they waited for their evening shift behind the counter. Horsemen mounted Indian ponies, trotting out across the desert in a direct line to distant hogans. They carried food for the week in white men's tin cans. Tourists watched the native silver craftsmen bending over their intricate tasks, exclaimed over the high prices of Navajo rugs, or discussed in loud voices how many hundreds of miles they had driven that day with practically no gas at all.

Cameron is a meeting place of the white race and the red. But the distinction between the two remains sharp—very little blending occurs in this border country. The Indians use the white man's machine-made devices, from oil cans to automobile trucks; the whites buy Indian handicrafts; but neither race can see much of value in the other's civilization. To most of us the red man is incomprehensible but on the picturesque side. The Indian stoically endures us in his country, even finding our customs mildly amusing. Perhaps the Indian's attitude is the more understanding of the two.

But the great reservations of the West are a historic anomaly, an artificial last frontier. They are the result of an Indian policy which has kept America's aboriginal inhabitants wards of the government, marooned in prehistoric cultural islands. Although this policy was one of pure expediency, it has had at least one fortunate result: without it, the surging, irresistible, imported civilization of the Anglo-American would have swept away every vestige of Indian culture into museums and history books.

The red man was notoriously nonassimilable; he is still so today. But Indian tribes artificially sequestered in semi-isolated

214

reservations, living at an economic level far below that of the white man, increasingly present a minority race problem. The ultimate solution seems to lie in the direction of the Indians' eventual absorption into the surrounding civilization as citizens of the United States. They are not ready for such radical change as yet. The transition may take generations. But it is hoped that in the blending of cultures we may benefit as well as they, for there is much of value in the Indians' way of life.

INDIAN COUNTRY

Dust was blowing along the dry bed of the Little Colorado next morning as Randall and I drove across the suspension bridge. Ten more miles of paved highway, then we turned east into the narrow dirt road which is the Broadway of the Indian Country.

A few miles beyond the turn dinosaur tracks wander across the bare red sandstone. They seem a fitting welcome to this unique land. The fact that this three-toed monster went about his business a hundred million years ago causes no surprise. What is time under the Arizona sky?

J. B. Priestley has written about the American Southwest and its people with greater understanding than any other author I know. Perhaps it takes a sympathetic, philosophical Englishman really to understand us. Like most of our countrymen, we haven't the time for it. But again and again Priestley emphasizes the newness of the Southwest, its untouched freshness, the lack of historic background. To him it seems that empty, widespread areas as big as English counties lie waiting to be filled with the minutiae of human affairs.

215

For a man with the remarkable time sense of Priestley it is surprising that he does not feel the overpowering age of this land. Compared to it, his own misty, green, overpopulated island, with its few thousand years of human history, is a callow upstart in the race for venerability. A veneer of man's culture on the earth's surface reduces us to human clocks and human horizons. But on the deserts and over the Canyon Country of the Southwest, man's hours, days, and years can no longer be used as a yardstick with which to measure events. Here geologic time still inexorably rules the deep, winding canyons, soaring buttes, and wide mesas. The Indian, perhaps, but not yet the white man, has become a part of it.

Priestley's writing, however, does suggest that physical sensations are only a part of one's experiences in the discovery of a strange, unfamiliar country. I heartily recommend his *Midnight on the Desert* as a guidebook to the possibilities in mental exploration of the American Southwest.

Our road followed a wide valley between Moenkopi and Kaibito plateaus. Above green fields, cottonwoods shimmered against the pink cliffs of the valley walls. The white summits of the San Francisco Peaks, fifty miles away, glowed softly against the southern sky. Groups of Navajo hogans clustered in little communities near the road, their doorways always facing east. Women were performing their morning household tasks in summer arbors built of poles, surrounded by an indiscriminate confusion of children, dogs, and goats.

The hogan—circular, dome-roofed home of the seminomadic, sheep-herding Navajo—is usually built of logs covered with sod or mud. Their owners abandon them when moving on to

216

greener pastures or burn them whenever there is a death in the family. The present hogans are conspicuously humble, but the Navajo tell that their homes are patterned after a magnificent prototype built of sandstone adorned with white shells, turquoise, obsidian, and jet. Such a lordly hogan must have graced one of the Seven Cities of Cibola, those fabulous Indian metropolises which the Spaniards failed to find.

We climbed out of the valley, rounded a corner, and suddenly were in the center of Tuba City. This onetime headquarters for the Western Navajo Reservation was once a Mormon settlement. It was laid out in 1878 and named for a Hopi chief, but the ambitious appendage, "city," must have been due to pioneer enthusiasm rather than to reality. Tuba City is listed as having "Pop. 150." However, as it consists today solely of a trading post, Indian school, and hospital, it probably reaches that congested condition only when the last two institutions are filled to overflowing with red-skinned inmates.

The government buildings are typically depressing. The alumni of Indian schools must have difficulty in feeling any attachment toward their alma maters. Grim, featureless, barrack-like buildings they are, with the odor of regimentation about them. If we really hope that Indians will absorb some of the better aspects of our culture, let us make their schools light, comfortable, and attractive—as attractive, say, as the pueblo-style buildings of the University of New Mexico at Albuquerque.

Below, in the valley from Tuba City, is Moenkopi, the most westerly of the eleven Hopi villages. Moenkopi, like most Indian pueblos, looks as if it were a part of the landscape; its cluster of flat-roofed houses merge imperceptibly into dun-colored sandstone ledges.

217

The Hopi, "Peaceful People," numbering about twenty-five hundred, occupy a reservation completely surrounded by that of the Navajo. Unlike the latter, the Hopi live in eleven permanent villages picturesquely perched on mesa tops. The two tribes come from different stock, speak dissimilar languages, and have no customs or ceremonies in common. Compared to the Navajo, the Hopi are old-timers in the country. Descended from the prehistoric cliff dwellers, they have carried on their communal pueblo life for untold centuries. The Hopi are agriculturists: corn, beans, and squash form their chief sustenance. Since the coming of the white man they have added peach orchards and small irrigated fields of onions, chili peppers, and other delicacies so terraced that not a drop of water is wasted. The Hopi have many arts, the most distinctive of which are the complicated sand paintings and *kachina* dolls representing masked gods who bring rain and other blessings.

But these Indians are best known for their religious ceremonies performed with magical rites and symbolical dancing. Each village holds annual dances intended to produce rain, ward off illness, or promote well-being. The most famous are the Snake Dances during which the performers hold live rattlesnakes between their teeth. Neither the Indians nor the snakes appear to mind this unconventional collaboration, and no Hopi that I know of has ever been bitten. All these dances are well worth seeing for their primitive mystical quality. They reflect the stark, unyielding land in which the Hopi people have lived and of which they have become an integral part.

Randall and I passed the road to the Hopi villages and turned northeast into the heart of Navajo-land. Of all the In-

218

dian tribes in the United States the Navajo is the largest. Numbering today about fifty-six thousand, they inhabit a reservation that is larger than New England. Their land, comprising parts of Arizona, Utah, and New Mexico, extends from desert washes, across high arid plateaus of sagebrush, greasewood, and yucca, to mountains banded by piñon and juniper and carrying on their broad summits large areas of pine, spruce, and fir. There is evidence that this region, now streaked with ribbons of wind-blown sand, once supported a population as dense as that of our Midwestern farmlands of today. Throughout the Southwest increasing dryness has caused the abandonment of cliff dwellings and pueblos and forced the migration of peoples to unknown areas.

Beyond Red Lake we left the main road, hoping to make the headquarters at Navajo National Monument for lunch. We had heard that Katherine and Bill Wilson were there holding down the job of custodians while Jimmy Brewer, ranger-in-charge, was overseas. We hadn't seen the Wilsons for several years so it wouldn't have been neighborly to pass within twenty miles of their doorstep without dropping in for a call.

Turning off main roads in the Indian Country is an awesome affair not to be undertaken lightly. You figuratively take a deep breath and hold it until you reach your destination—providing you do eventually arrive there. The odds are stacked against anything with wheels on Indian Country side roads. The obstacles of a steeplechase are honest and aboveboard compared to the crafty pitfalls lying in wait for innocent drivers.

The United States Indian Service has not permitted paved or oiled roads in this section of the Navajo Reservation. Such roads are of no particular benefit to the Indians, who ride

219

horseback or drive rickety, wobble-wheeled carts. And boulevards would only tend to bring in hordes of tourists. The main roads are graded, although I have been hopelessly bogged down in sand on one of them within twenty feet of a trading-post front door.

But the side roads are called such simply because we have no word in the English language diabolical enough to describe them. They usually consist of a pair of sandy tracks winding aimlessly uphill and down until they eventually arrive where it was promised they would. Even these tracks often give up entirely in washes, necessitating scouting expeditions forward, while across bare, rocky ledges the route is ducked or marked with paint in the manner of a foot trail. In wet weather my advice is to stay where you are and read a good book; wherever it is you want to go, you won't get there.

Of all hazards, by far the most treacherous are the numerous washes. They vary in size from small gullies to wide valleys. The greater part of the year Arizona washes are "upside-down" streams; the water seeps underground beneath a dry surface of sand, gravel, and boulders. But when the least trace of dampness shows—watch out! There may be quicksand, and if rain is falling in the hills there is the possibility of flash floods, which roar down these channels with the suddenness of a lightning flash.

Several years ago a doctor friend of mine, his wife, and their nine-year-old son started out one bright July morning from Dinnehotso trading post up near Monument Valley. They intended to drive direct to Canyon de Chelly through the wildest part of the Northern Navajo Indian Reservation.

"You'd better go 'round by Tuba City," an old-timer advised as he squinted up at the brilliant sky.

"But that's more than a hundred miles out of the way," protested the doctor. The old-timer spat expertly at the hitching post.

"You want to get there, don't you?" he asked mildly.

The doctor laughed at the tobacco-chewing alarmist. "Oh, we'll make it all right. I've been on these roads before," he said.

Their car was soon swallowed up in the dust on the direct route to Canyon de Chelly. The old-timer resumed his nap in the shade. And a little white cloud no bigger than a lady's handkerchief suddenly materialized over the Carrizo Mountains.

By noon the doctor and his family had bumped, slewed, and vibrated half the distance. The road had been a shade better than taking the car cross country, the doctor thought, but he would have respected the opinion of anyone holding otherwise. The point would not have been worth an argument. They had a picnic lunch and a siesta before tackling the second part of their journey.

When they took to the road again, high-piled thunder clouds were building up into the sky, trailing gray-blue curtains of rain across the hills. After a few miles it began to sprinkle. Big juicy drops which resembled miniature bombs hit the dust. The doctor eased the car into a wash, dropping into low gear to negotiate a ten-foot creek at the bottom. It was ten feet too much. The rear wheels bit into wet sand, burrowing deeper with each frantic spurt of the accelerator.

The doctor and his family were through going places for the

time being. At best it would take two to three hours of expert mud-engineering to get the car out, if at all. The doctor looked the situation over. The rain fell harder.

Behind him he heard a roar. It sounded as if a Santa Fe streamliner were speeding down the canyon toward them. His wife screamed and pointed. Over his shoulder the doctor saw a wall of water from bank to bank. It wasn't far above them, and it was coming fast. There was no time to reach the bank. The doctor scrambled onto the roof of the car, helped his wife up, then pulled the boy out through the rear-door window. Within two minutes a muddy torrent swept around the car. The water continued to rise rapidly.

Some of their gear was in the back seat, tied with stout rope. They managed to haul this up through the window. Unfastening the rope, the doctor tied one end to the door post of the car. Then he let himself down into the water, which was running waist deep with a powerful current. By keeping a tight hold on the rope he reached the bank, where he tied the other end to an old juniper. With the help of the taut rope the mother and son joined the doctor on the bank.

Once again they were just in time. The three of them, wet, cold, and exhausted watched the coffee-colored flood sweep higher around the car minute by minute and finally engulf it entirely.

The doctor and his family spent a damp, miserable night without food, blankets, or fire. At sunup they started walking. The flood had subsided during the night, but their car was nearly buried in sand and gravel. Around noon they came to a settlement of Navajo hogans. The Indians gave them food and lent them horses as far as Rough Rock. The next day the trader

222

there drove the doctor and his family by truck to Dinnehotso, from where they hitchhiked from one trading post to the next until they reached Flagstaff and a train home.

The old-timer's remarks upon the doctor's ignominious return are not a matter of record. He probably said nothing. But it is good common sense to listen to old-timers in the Indian Country when they squint at the sky, spit reflectively at hitching posts, and mildly give us dudes advice.

Even in dry weather it is wise not to plan on reaching a given point at any definite hour. It is an accomplishment if you arrive the same day. Beyond Shanto trading post the track leads steeply for a mile up over bare rock ledges hugging the face of a cliff. It required almost an hour for Randall and me to surmount this obstacle. The procedure was: *crawl five hundred feet in low, gasp, vapor lock, stop, wait ten minutes; proceed six hundred feet, cough, vapor lock, stop, sit fifteen minutes. Repeat until top is reached.* This is an excellent way to get to know the country intimately, but it is exceedingly low-grade transportation.

A few miles from the Monument we began to buck drifted sand. We slewed through two miniature dunes, but the third got us. The rear wheels spun in the loose sand up to the hub caps, but the car wouldn't budge. Randall, being a desert-wise motorist, carries everything needful for any eventuality in the capacious rear deck of his car. So we rummaged among sleeping bags, food cartons, gasoline and water cans, even candy for the Indians, until we found a shovel and two steel running boards from a discarded Model-T Ford. We dug holes in the sand around the rear wheels, then ran the car along the Ford's run-

223

ning boards. Four times we did this before we were free of the drift. Another hour gone!

But by noon we were winding up through the piñons and junipers to the Navajo National Monument headquarters. This Monument was created in 1909 to protect three large cliff dwellings inhabited in the thirteenth century by Pueblo Indians. The superb trio are known as Keet Seel, Betatakin, and Inscription House. Perfectly preserved by their protecting caves and the dry Arizona atmosphere, they look as if they had been abandoned yesterday, although their inhabitants mysteriously disappeared six hundred and fifty years ago—and no one knows why or where they went.

The Monument headquarters is atop a mesa almost eight thousand feet in elevation. It seems to float in the sky, its dooryard a hundred miles of Arizona canyons, cliffs, deserts, forests, and mountains in every direction. The custodian's house is built of warm red native sandstone. It is as much a part of the country as a Navajo hogan, but as modern and comfortable as a new suburban home.

Katherine and Bill Wilson welcomed us with true Indian Country hospitality. Out here life retains the uncomplicated, open aspect of the frontier. The land still belongs to the Indian. The only white people in the region are licensed traders, government rangers, Indian Service employees, and their families— a few hundred so thinly scattered over a huge area that each looks upon a family ninety miles distant as his neighbors. Thus they form a community, and are interested in each other's doings.

Human beings originally hived together in communities for mutual protection and benefit. We have existed in swarms for so many centuries that today's average citizen has come to regard living and working among crowds of his fellow humans as the normal and desirable way to spend his three score years and ten. And the trend is increasingly centripetal; human progress is counted in terms of annihilating distance to bring us all closer together. We feel that the hermit, the frontiersman, the explorer are interesting fellows, but slightly pathological. They are the escapists, we crowded urbanites the well-balanced realists.

However, the centripetal social system is not paying the dividends in human understanding that were so rosily promised. We have almost succeeded in bringing the human race into a world community, but with the physical obstacles all but overcome we are faced with the unpalatable fact that living together in this new shrunken world of ours is the most difficult problem before us today. It is discouragingly significant that the greatest strides recently made in transportation are for the purpose of dropping super bombs on our newly reached neighbors.

In other words, perhaps we can no longer see the world for the people. Out on the mesa tops, in the mountains and deserts, people are important, too—very much so—but the importance of the nonhuman environment orients viewpoints outward, away from oneself. And after all it is easy to get along with neighbors eleven miles distant.

In Southwestern homes, more than any other place I know, there are books on people's living-room tables about birds, trees, animals, wildflowers, rocks, and even snakes. They are volumes well-thumbed from much use. Rarely does a conversation go on for long without reference to the surroundings in which a family lives. The discussion may turn to chipmunks, a newly discovered cactus, a hummingbird, or a near-by bed of geodes. Such people cannot help having a genuine, healthy interest in their nonhuman environment which tends to make them adjusted to a fuller and happier life.

Their attitude is summed up in an answer I heard an Arizonan give to a lady visitor. She looked from the native's porch out over a slice of emptiness as big as Rhode Island.

"Why do you want to live so far away?" she asked.

He looked at her in surprise. "Far away from what?" he said.

After lunch Bill Wilson saddled a couple of horses. He wanted me to see his prize exhibit—Betatakin. It was only a mile out across the mesa, and I wanted to stretch my legs, but to a Westerner it is inconceivable that anyone should use his own two legs when four others are available.

We rode in the brilliant sunshine among scattered piñons and junipers, the only sound the horses' hoofs clop-clopping over the rocky ledges. Growing sparsely out of the red soil were dwarf cactus, scrub oak, and the curious little joint fir or Mormon tea. This jointed, leafless shrub, rarely more than three feet high, is no relation to the true firs nor even to the pines, but has a small family all to itself, blessed with the tongue-twisting name of *gnetaceae*. The "medicinal" powers of the joint fir in certain social directions were well known to the livelier element among the earlier settlers.

If I were to choose one picture to symbolize the Southwest, it would be of an Indian squatting on his heels at the edge of a cliff beneath a stunted piñon—or perhaps a juniper. The brave would be gazing out over the canyon wilderness of his homeland, with the gnarled, storm-whitened branches of the tree

226

reaching out into the blue sky over his head. The Indian and the tree share equal honors in my imaginary picture, for they are both typical of the Southwest Country.

The partnership between the piñon and the juniper is one of the most constant associations found among trees. It is also one of the most distinctive. Together they dominate hundreds of square miles in the seven Southwestern States. Nowhere in the world can you find duplicates of these semiarid woodlands between the deserts and the mountain forests of pines, firs, and spruces. Above six thousand feet, the piñon-juniper woodlands spread as far as the eye can see, uphill, across valleys, and over mountaintops, looking like huge blue-black blankets torn where cliffs and canyons break the surface.

The piñon is a true pine, a stocky, tough member of the family. But throughout its range aridity and rapid evaporation have stunted and hardened it into a veritable son of the desert—thrifty, resourceful, and saving. The same is true of the juniper. Rarely do these two trees grow over fifteen feet high, and they form an open, sunny, pygmy forest that is strange, silent, and appealing.

In a quarter of an hour we rode out of the woodland onto a bare rocky point where a canyon had taken a giant bite out of the mesa. Tying the horses, Bill Wilson led us over to the edge of the canyon cliff. Three hundred feet below us, recessed under a great natural arch in the opposite wall, was Betatakin. The effect of this remote, dead city of the wilderness was theatrical, unreal. It was difficult to reach back through time seven hundred years to visualize these abandoned rooms, ceremonial kivas, courts, and patios occupied by living human beings; to bring to life men, women, and children busy about their daily tasks.

But it wasn't hard to see that those prehistoric people had imagination and resourcefulness. They picked a veritable pocket-sized paradise in which to live. Along the canyon bottom a clear, spring-fed stream glints between white-boled aspens. Oaks, huge Douglas firs, and ponderosa pines climb the shady gulches in the canyon walls. Game must have been plentiful, while berries and piñon nuts were theirs for the picking. It could only be stark catastrophe which forced these people to leave for an unknown destination. And I imagine that there was longing for many a year within their breasts for Betatakin, their beloved home.

SPACE WITHOUT TIME

With regret we left the Wilsons'. We would have liked to stay the summer on their crystal-clear mesa top. But if Randall and I spent summers, and winters, too, at each delectable spot, we would have to have all the days of Noah's nine hundred and fifty years. Not having them, we slid down off the mesa back to the main road, then through rocky Marsh Pass to Kayenta.

For many years Kayenta was the home of John Wetherill, trader, guide, geology student, and friend of the Indians, one of the best-known and best-loved characters the Indian Country ever had. His recent death, followed closely by that of Mrs. Wetherill, was a personal loss to hundreds of their friends throughout the Southwest, both red and white. No one knew the country better than John Wetherill or the Indians more intimately than his wife. She was known to the Navajo far and wide as *Shimah Yazzi*, "my little mother." Although John

Wetherill's most famous discovery was Rainbow Bridge in 1909, a discovery made possible by Mrs. Wetherill's friendship with Ute Indians who had seen the bridge, he brought to public attention scores of other natural wonders and hidden cliff dwellings.

From Kayenta the road turns due north, climbing up over a divide into Monument Valley. The gateway is as unbelievably fantastic as is the valley itself. To the right the ash-gray volcanic spire of Agathla Peak soars 1,255 feet above its sloping base; on the left is Owl Butte.

Before I first saw it I had never heard of Owl Butte. No one had prepared me, and I still don't believe it. Agathla Peak is aspiring gothic; Owl Butte is unashamed baroque. At the tip end of a long, even-topped yellow cliff rises a salmon-pink sandstone monolith two to three hundred feet high. Narrow at the base, it bulges at the center into two great overhanging stone wings, tipped by a small owl-like head. Presumably for thousands of years this huge, silly pink bird has sat perilously perched on the edge of its cliff for no reason at all. Owl Butte is nature with a sense of humor.

The sun was far down in the west when Randall and I drove up to Harry Goulding's trading post in Monument Valley. We had been looking forward to an evening with the Gouldings, but the post was deserted, every door tightly padlocked.

An old Navajo materialized out of nowhere. With silent interest he watched our baffled investigations around the post.

"Where Gouldings?" we asked.

The Indian slowly came to life. He held out his hand, laboriously counting his fingers. "One-two-three-four-five-six-seven," he solemnly intoned, then majestically swept his arm toward the west. "Gone!" he announced in the manner of a revelation. The Indian enjoyed the recital, for he repeated it several times. But his information was more picturesque than accurate; later we found that he had been going through this identical routine for all visitors for the previous ten days.

When we tried to get into one of the stone cabins for a night's lodging the Navajo counted on his fingers up to three. We guessed correctly that three dollars was his price, for he took the bills, smiled, and then disappeared into the emptiness whence he had come.

Visitors to the Indian Country can rarely tell whether a Navajo can't or won't speak English, for they are not talkative with whites. A Navajo caller will often sit in a trader's living room an entire evening without saying a word.

Several years ago a Navajo called on me when I was camped near Rainbow Bridge. I will repeat our conversation verbatim; it is not a strain on my memory.

"Cigarette?" I asked as the Indian squatted on his heels beside the fire.

"Huh," he said, reaching for the proffered pack. ("Huh" means "Yes" in Navajo.) Five minutes passed as we smoked. Then I pointed to the overcast sky.

"Rain?" I said.

"Huh," he answered, shrugging slightly. ("Huh" means "Maybe.") We smoked some more.

"Where you live?" I asked conversationally.

"Huh," said the Indian. ("Huh" means "None of your business.") Finally he threw the end of his cigarette in the fire, then rose.

230

"Good-by," I said.

"Huh," he said, and disappeared over the hill. ("Huh" means "So long" in Navajo.)

Evening was coming on as Randall and I peacefully settled ourselves for a smoke before the cabin. The sun had already set behind the red sandstone cliff at our backs but was still sending golden shafts out across the valley. Each upstanding butte, tower, and spire glowed vermilion against blue-black shadows. The dying sunlight, too, caught the snows of the Abajo Mountains far to the north and slanted across the twisted canyons and mesas of the southern Utah wilderness in a complicated pattern of light and shade. As the last warm glow lingered on the highest tower, the stillness was broken by the running notes of the canyon wren cascading down the cliff behind us. Then silence—the complete silence of emptiness.

In Monument Valley maroon buttes, pillars, and pinnacles tower almost a thousand feet above the desert. They are scattered like the ruins of a mammoth dead city in which have survived only the tombs of giants and obelisks commemorating forgotten gods.

There are many fascinating things to be found in Monument Valley. Even life is there, unobtrusively, and water if you look for it. In summer Indians tend sheep and their women weave rugs in the shadow of the great stone totem poles. But to me Monument Valley is too fantastically unbelievable to be real. Except for the colors of rock and sky and distant mountains it might be on the moon—a dead landscape of utter loneliness wrapped in a tangible silence almost like a physical ache.

231

Darkness came down over the desert as we sat in front of our cabin. The valley filled with shapeless black forms in the night. Above us stars winked out like tiny searchlights or gathered in luminous clouds in the velvet sky. The powerful batteries of silence were turned full upon us.

In cities we know always that we belong to humanity; on a mountaintop we merge with the earth around us; but at night in the desert we seem a part of the universe. Time ceases to exist. We look backward through the ages, forward to the dim future, upward to the constellations. Time and space are blended into one enveloping unity. Another dimension opens up before us.

But we are humans after all. We cannot escape except for brief moments from ourselves or the demands of our bodies which are part of us. So we suddenly return to our little human compartments, laugh, yawn, light a final cigarette. Then we turn in for a refreshing, dreamless, desert sleep. As a friend of mine remarked while polishing off the last of a Thanksgiving dinner, "Let's not labor the point; there's a lot to be said for the physical pleasures."

FAST WATER IN THE DESERT

Twenty-four miles north of Monument Valley is Mexican Hat, Utah. This settlement is probably further from a railroad than any other place in the United States. Named for a near-by red shale formation shaped like a sombrero, Mexican Hat sits baldly on a treeless bluff above the San Juan River surrounded on all sides by the southern Utah-northern Arizona wilderness. "The Hat," as the handful of residents call it, is a name on the

232

map rather than a town. However, its history records stirring times in the past: a gold rush in the nineties petered out only to blossom into a short-lived oil boom in 1911. There is still yellow gold in the hills and black gold underground, but not many seem to care. Today Mexican Hat dispenses scenery to visitors. It is a base for exploring trips to natural bridges and cliff dwellings and headquarters for Nevills' San Juan River expeditions.

Rising in the southern Colorado Rockies, the San Juan cuts through the northwest corner of New Mexico, then flows west to its junction with the Colorado ten miles north of the Arizona line. For a distance of a hundred miles in Utah the San Juan has excavated a series of canyons one to two thousand feet deep through some of the most colorful rock scenery in the world. No towns, settlements, or even ranches are seen on this stretch of the river; the only signs that men have been there are occasional abandoned mine workings, crude Indian pictographs, and long-deserted cliff ruins on side canyon walls.

Norman Nevills and the San Juan River are not exactly synonymous, but you can't mention one without bringing up the other. Since the day that Norm settled beside the San Juan at Mexican Hat almost twenty years ago he has made the river his own personal concern. As near as he can remember he has run the San Juan by boat forty times.

For several years before the war Norm piloted parties from Mexican Hat to Lees Ferry. These expeditions covered the distance of 191 miles—114 on the San Juan, 77 in Glen Canyon on the Colorado—in six or seven days. The Nevills have built a fleet of flat-bottomed, square-ended boats especially designed to ride the sand waves and rapids of the San Juan. The Indians

233

say Norm's "water ponies all time plenty buck." That is a fairly accurate description, for during the spring floods from the melting snows of the Rockies the San Juan makes a fast, exhilarating run. At that time the four worst rapids—Government, Paiute, Syncline, and Thirteen Foot—are respectable imitations in miniature of Granite and Lava Falls on the Colorado.

Mexican Hat was a mobilization point that June morning when Randall and I drove down from Monument Valley. We were the advance guard of eleven enthusiasts who had mutually promised themselves a San Juan outing. Every one of us had been forced to forego the trip for three years, but we were now converging upon Norm and Doris Nevills from all parts of the West with the speed of escaped convicts. Three years' postponement had stored up a fanatical energy rarely let loose upon Mexican Hat.

The settlement, roughly awakened from its peaceful sleep beside the river, relived another brief moment of feverish activity. Cars, with and without loaded trailers, dashed about on apparently important missions. Boats, bottoms up, were being readied for the trip. Navigating gear and camping equipment were collected and checked. Doris supervised the assembling and packing of supplies; a chain of helpers tossed canned goods from the cellar to a waiting truck bound for the river landing. Each hour or so another car arrived bringing additional adventurers from Denver or San Francisco.

In the afternoon a young bride and groom from Boston drove up. They were on their way to the Pacific Coast, but their eyes lighted when they understood the reasons for Mexican Hat's unusual liveliness. It was plain to see that Los Angeles via the

234

San Juan was the way they wanted to go. A council of eleven was held, but the decision was known at the start. Another boat was pulled out of the shed. It was immediately christened the *Honeymoon Special*. The party was now thirteen.

San Juan River launchings are spirited affairs, made more so by a tough little rapid which sweeps by the Mexican Hat sand bar. Norm and Wayne McConkie, old hands at this game, skillfully piloted the *Music Temple* and *Hidden Passage* down through the fast water. It looked easy the way they did it. But, when it came our turn with the *Rainbow Trail*, we suddenly found that there were several more things to do than we seemed to have time for. The result was that the rapid took over as complete boss of the situation.

Meanwhile the dreamy casualness of the groom's launching caught the *Honeymoon Special* in midrapid with no one at the oars. So our two boats fluttered downstream, pitching and whirling with the abandon of autumn leaves in a millrace. Just after we had narrowly missed a collision between the *Rainbow Trail* and the *Honeymoon Special*, the bride, gamely gulping spray, was heard to say, "George, dear, is it all going to be like this?"

It wasn't—fortunately for us. Below the rapid we straightened out, following the leaders with as much dignity as strenuous bailing would allow. But our seamanship remained at a level which gave the San Juan a sporting chance to win in every engagement.

A few miles below "The Hat" we entered the Goosenecks. Here in a narrow, gray-walled gorge, twelve hundred feet deep, the river loops in a series of horseshoe bends around which the boats traveled six miles to gain one. The center loop is a three-mile detour, but the dividing ridge at its narrowest point is only three hundred feet across.

There is nothing in the character of the rocks through which the river has cut to explain its erratic behavior. The Goose-necks are a supreme example of an entrenched meander. According to geologists, the San Juan several million years ago wound sluggishly over the surface of a level plain. A slow regional uplift forced the ever quickening stream to cut into the plain with the inherited pattern of its original meanders. Once entrenched the river could not change its course.

The full impressiveness of the Goosenecks is lost from a boat because only a small part can be seen at one time. But from a vantage point on the north rim the entire sweep of the river is in view as it makes three gigantic loops, separated by narrow, precipitous dividing ridges.

The San Juan was running high and swift. We ticked off the miles between soaring rock walls of ever changing colors. Very little rowing was required except to guide the boats away from whitewater foaming over submerged rocks or to pull out of eddies and whirlpools. We soon became acquainted with sand waves, learning to buck them in time with a fair show of non-chalance.

Because of the heavy load of sediment, sand waves are particularly prevalent on the San Juan. Caused by temporary concentrations of silt in the rapid current, they rise suddenly from any part of the river. In fact, they had a disconcerting habit of forming directly under our boat. For a few minutes they hump up in parallel series resembling the wake of a stern wheeler, often five to six feet from trough to crest. Then as quickly the waves subside, only to reappear somewhere else. A boat caught in

236

a series of sand waves imitates a bucking bronco in slow motion.

Eventually we all adopted modified versions of Norm's unique method of meeting sand waves. He would set the *Music Temple* broadside on, then, as the boat tipped sharply abeam on the first wave, he, Randall, the historian, and the photographer threw themselves against the upper gunwale shouting in unison, "Yogi!" This strange rite was repeated until the waves flattened out. The canyons of the San Juan echoed with wild calls of "Yogi!" as each of the four boats took on a series of sand waves.

Norm visualizes his supernatural yogi as a sort of protector who skims along in front of the boat, black robe flowing, white beard streaming in the wind, as with outstretched arms he calms the waters before him. Norm's success as a boatman may be due to his impassioned calls upon his yogi, but it is noticeable that he quietly and efficiently works out his own salvation in bad stretches of water.

Twice during the afternoon the naturalist spotted Rocky Mountain sheep far up on the cliffs. They seemed interested in the boats, stopping to look down curiously as we floated by. Then, turning, they raced upward with easy, graceful bounds. At one point a mother bighorn led her lamb across a steep, broken talus slope. The baby hopped from rock to rock with little more effort than its stout-legged, sure-footed parent.

The ornithologist, too, was busy making discoveries. He pointed out from the deck of the *Hidden Passage* a blue heron, a circling vulture, and the huge shaggy nest of a golden eagle perched in a niche in the canyon wall. The eagle family was apparently not at home, but we were awed by the size of their living quarters. They compared to the average bird's nest much as the Waldorf-Astoria does with a five-room bungalow.

237

One more hurdle remained before the artless boatmen in the *Rainbow Trail* and the *Honeymoon Special* were allowed to rest their aching muscles. Government Rapids stood between us and supper. One of the "Big Four," this rapid has had an evil reputation since a United States Geological Survey party lost a boat on the rocks there in 1921. After looking over the fast churning water we were frankly relieved when Norm and Wayne McConkie took over the job of running the four boats through. With no responsibility except to hang on I had a glorious, rough, wet ride flattened on the fore deck of the *Music Temple*.

We camped on a rocky ledge where Slickhorn Gulch runs into the main canyon. Twelve hungry people rustled wood, peeled potatoes, opened cans, or stood hopefully beside the fire encouraging Wayne, who efficiently stirred the steaming pots and pans. Wayne McConkie is a genial, blond, two-hundred-pounder from Moab, Utah, who teaches biology and manual arts at the high school there during the winter. Summer vacations he spends on the river as one of Norm's best boatmen. That first evening we learned that cooking was another of Wayne's accomplishments.

Later, around the campfire, Norm told us stories of gold prospecting in the San Juan country and of the search for oil which brought his father into the region in the twenties. All around us at Slickhorn Gulch were remains of oil-drilling equipment precariously packed down a rocky track from the plateau above. But not a drop of oil ever went up the trail in the opposite direction. Lost mines and fabulous bonanza sand bars figure in San Juan gold legends as they do throughout the West. But here the river gives a new twist to some of the stories.

238

Perhaps the best-known tale in which the river plays the part of villain is that of James Douglas, who discovered a rich gold-bearing sand bar while prospecting the San Juan during the extreme low water of 1909. The river rose, the sand bar disappeared. For twenty years Douglas waited patiently, always hoping that low water would once more uncover his bonanza. Finally, in 1929, the old man, despairing of the fortune which the river kept from him, jumped off the San Juan Bridge at Mexican Hat. Five years later the river went dry.

The fire died down to embers. One by one the party disappeared into the darkness to individual camps on ledge or sand bar. Tired after a long day, we stretched out luxuriously in our sleeping bags under the stars. We slept. The river, inky black, roared on unheard.

INNOCENTS AFLOAT

Perhaps one of the most unusual events that has occurred on the banks of the San Juan since the days of the Spaniards took place next morning. Time turned back in this timeless land. Once again, after a hundred and seventy years, high mass was held for travelers in a remote canyon in the Utah wilderness. One of our shipmates in the *Rainbow Trail* was a high Episcopal priest, missionary to the Navajo. In the early Sunday morning twilight he said mass in full white vestments with cross of gold before a rock altar, the sandstone and limestone walls of his natural cathedral towering hundreds of feet above him. At the close of the service, with benediction, the first rays of sunlight tipped the highest rim of the mighty cliff across the San Juan.

239

But the priest became neophyte again when we pushed out into the river for the second day's run. With the engineer at the oars the padre and I became "back-seat rowers." A conference preceded every maneuver. What is that ahead?

"It's a sand wave," said the engineer, pulling to port.

"Looks like a riffle. Keep straight on," was the padre's contribution.

"It's a submerged rock. Better pull to starboard," I said. "Look out!"

Too late. The boat was sucked into the fast water. It lurched over the rock into the hole, where it spun up on its beam, nearly upsetting. The engineer and I in the cockpit were thrown but managed to hang on. The padre, however, was instantly swept off the forward deck into the river. He disappeared. The water was swift, and the rocks looked bad, but in a few moments the padre came to the surface. We hauled him in. That was that. But another lesson had been learned the hard way: when something looks like a submerged rock, it probably is.

The groom's method of navigation differed markedly from ours. It consisted of spending as little time at the oars as possible. The *Honeymoon Special* drifted unattended for hours through riffles, down rough channels, past foam-fringed rocks, while its captain and his attractive first mate tinkered with amazingly complicated motion-picture equipment. It seemed as if some specially appointed super-yogi were taking care of the newlyweds.

Even he occasionally found the assignment too tough to handle. At one point we rounded a bend traveling fast on rough water to find the *Honeymoon Special* tilted sharply against a great boulder in midstream—stuck fast. The bride and groom

240

clung to the upper gunwale with spray breaking over them as if from the prow of a speeding motor boat. We could do nothing as we shot by but shout useless advice which they couldn't hear. But the yogi got them off somehow without capsizing the boat, for down they came in a few minutes through a particularly evil-looking channel we had all taken pains to avoid.

But if there is one characteristic which the San Juan possesses above any other it is variety. In the afternoon we came out of the canyons into a broad expanse called Paiute Farms. Here, on the fertile bottomlands south of the river, the Indians raise corn, squash, and melons. Scattered over the green meadows were primitive ramadas built of poles covered with brush, but we saw no more signs of life here than in the deepest canyons.

The river widens out at Paiute Farms to a mile from bank to bank. The muddy water braids into myriads of channels from a few inches to a foot deep. Among the innumerable choices there may be one which will float a boat, but we couldn't find it. So, when the boats rasped on the sandy bottom, stopping with a jerk, over the side we went to push and haul until the current caught them again. At one time all four boats were being escorted down river by their passengers, splashing through ankle-deep water. Altogether about an hour and a half were devoted to "push-boating" on the San Juan.

One of the most effective color contrasts on this colorful river is the constant green fringe of tamarisk against the brown, red, gray, buff, pink, lavender, and yellow of the canyon cliffs. The water level of the San Juan varies too greatly for native cottonwoods and willows to become established on its banks. But the sandy shores and bars are crowded with a thick growth of feathery green tamarisk from five to ten feet high. Yet these thrifty,

241

flood-resistant thickets are newcomers to the Southwest. The tamarisk, Tamarix gallica, is a native of the Near East, stretching along desert waterways from eastern Europe to India. But after its introduction to southern California it spread with the rapidity of rabbits in Australia, a thousand miles up the Colorado and its tributaries.

The second day we threaded the heart of a wilderness too barren, apparently, even for animals. With the exception of mountain sheep and a few birds we saw no life whatever. Fish there may have been, although Norm, strangely enough, has no fish story in his repertoire. All old-timers, however, insist that eight kinds of fish, two of them good eating, live dark, secluded lives in the muddy Colorado and its tributaries. The catfish, so they say, is similar to its cousins in Middle Western streams, but the "minnow," a species of whitefish, sometimes attains a weight of thirty pounds.

But this land is not wholly a lifeless waste of rock and sand. In the late afternoon we stopped at Nevills Canyon to take on fresh water. Here a miniature fall drops over a cliff into a pool banked with ferns and shaded by willow, box elder, and redbud. In every canyon are found these cool, sequestered oases—green islands of life amidst an ocean of aridity.

During the complicated landing operations at Nevills Canyon the groom and the padre got involuntary duckings. By this time, however, we were all becoming amphibious, often diving over the side and swimming by the boats when the sun beat down upon us too enthusiastically.

At the Great Bend the San Juan makes a nine-mile loop, returning to within a half mile of its starting point. From the

242

western apex of the loop the Colorado River is but six miles distant, but the San Juan twists and turns for thirty-four miles before the two streams meet.

Just beyond the Great Bend we camped the second night beside a sandstone rock which had fallen from the canyon wall. We were not the first who found this a good campsite. Ancient Indian petroglyphs decorated one side of the rock; mountain sheep, several men, and a large six-fingered hand were clearly outlined. One could almost see the red-skinned artist stand back and grunt in admiration of his own genius. His comment was undoubtedly, "Huh!" ("Huh" meant "Good.") Whether he counted the fingers we cannot tell, but six must have been an unusual number on any one hand even in those far-off times.

The third day we reached the Colorado. But the San Juan had a last fling at us in Paiute, Syncline, and Thirteen Foot rapids. Although these compare to the roaring cataracts of the Grand Canyon as house tabbies do to lions, they are rough and tricky pieces of bad water, requiring constant alertness. This I know personally, for I took the *Music Temple* through Paiute. The navigation was mediocre; halfway down I had a split second of thankfulness that the stout boat would undoubtedly arrive at the bottom intact even if I threw the oars away. But the most remarkable feature of the run, the passengers said afterward, was the kaleidoscopic change of expression on the strained face of their floundering pilot.

In the early afternoon the four boats floated out of the San Juan's narrow canyon into the broad brown flood of the Colorado. The two rivers join in an almost inaccessible region of bare red sandstone sculptured into domes and bosses by the action of wind and water. A labyrinth of sheer-walled canyons

243

has been cut into the rock, making land travel so difficult that perhaps only a few hundred white people have ever seen this important Southwestern river junction.

We were now in Glen Canyon. Although it is one of the nineteen gorges of the Colorado, Glen Canyon is a placid interim in the rough-and-tumble life of the river. Roaring out of notorious Cataract Canyon in central Utah, the Colorado settles down to a quiet rest for one hundred and fifty miles—almost as if it were preparing for the final supreme ordeal of Marble and Grand canyons.

We traversed the lower half of Glen Canyon from the mouth of the San Juan to Lees Ferry. The river, often a mile wide, flows serenely between vertical red sandstone cliffs rising several hundred feet from the water's edge. The upper parts of the cliffs overhang giant arches and alcoves cut into the smooth rock faces. Where the canyon walls break down or draw back from the river, shale and limestone buttes and pinnacles rise in the distance against the western sky; to the southeast the blue snow-streaked dome of Navajo Mountain swells above radiating white limestone buttresses. Glen Canyon is big, spacious, almost panoramic after the narrow gorge of the San Juan. We liked it.

A few miles downstream we unrolled our sleeping bags on a series of ledges which shelved down to the river. After dark Norm and the coed lighted a huge pile of driftwood, then rowed around the cove in the firelight. Our camp had the holiday spirit of a carnival in Venice. It lacked only the guitar and "O Sole Mio." The naturalist and the historian held a philosophical discussion until midnight, while the groom discoursed on science to as many as would listen. We expanded under the influence of Glen Canyon in our various ways—then slept.

EXPLORING MYSTERY CANYONS

Glen Canyon cuts through the last remaining region in the United States where geographical discoveries are still being made. As late as 1940, a Nevills party exploring a tributary of the Escalante River discovered a natural arch larger than Rainbow Bridge. In 1944 Harry Aleson, the unconventional "Up-Colorado" adventurer, turned up two more from the remote canyons of southern Utah. Scores of cliff ruins still await the coming of the first white man; miles of twisting canyons hold secrets seen only by Indians and occasional prospectors.

Exploring the adjacent country is a fascinating sideline of a trip down Glen Canyon. With climbing rope, and pitons if you really want to be tough, you can go where no one has been before, then return to the boats by exhilarating rope rappels over the clean faces of the canyon walls.

We all woke up with "explorer's fever" that first morning in Glen Canyon just as Powell had seventy-six years before us. For the next three days we pushed up tributary canyons and trekked across sandy plateaus one side of the river then the other.

Our first venture was Hidden Passage, just below camp. Behind a well-camouflaged entrance a narrow, twisting corridor between vertical walls leads back into a maze of cliffs, domes and knobs. We followed the winding passage for a quarter of a mile until we were stopped by a waterfall. This was surmounted by the use of a rope. Then we scaled a high ledge which overlooked the entire lower basin of the Canyon. Within the enclosing walls was an utter confusion of smooth barren rocks with pre-

245

cipitous sides dropping into unseen depths. I could think of nothing it resembled on earth or elsewhere unless it might be a corral full of pink, hairless monsters of Gargantuan proportions.

But what I will always remember about Hidden Passage is the upper waterfall at the head of the Canyon. There the corridor widens out into a vaulted hall at the head of which a slender thread of water falls into a clear pool. From the twilit room we looked up to the overhanging walls far above us, enclosing a narrow slit of sky between. There in the deep blue midday sky shone one brilliant star.

On the eastern bank, almost directly across the river from Hidden Passage is Music Temple. This was one of Powell's favorite spots. He camped two days there in 1869 and stopped again on his second expedition. We hiked up the wooded gorge into a dome-roofed cavern five hundred feet long and more than two hundred feet high. At the farther end is a pool under a skylight in the roof made by the stream which comes down through a thousand feet of rock. One wall is a mass of maidenhair ferns, columbines, and moss. Every cough and whisper resounds throughout this great stone shell. Powell wrote, "When 'Old Shady' sings us a song at night, we are pleased to find that this hollow in the rock is filled with sweet sounds. It was doubtless made for an academy of music by its storm-born architect; so we name it Music Temple."

Names of members of Powell's first and second expeditions are still plainly visible carved on the walls. But more recent visitors use a can for a register of their names.

Near the entrance to the gorge Wayne found an old-fashioned box trunk half hidden beneath a scrub oak. Its lock and hinges fell apart at a touch, revealing the carefully packed

246

effects of an unknown traveler. We examined the contents for some clue as to his identity. First to come out were a black broadcloth coat and trousers. Then followed high black button shoes with heavy socks, ankle-length woolen underwear of itchy thickness, unused medicinal soap in original paper wrappers, sewing kit, novels of the late nineties, and a Tacoma newspaper clipping, telling of a shipwreck in Puget Sound, dated February, 1896. For fifty years this trunk had lain undisturbed, every article perfectly preserved in the dry desert air.

We carefully replaced the contents of the trunk and left, speculating about its owner. Did he come by boat? Why did he bring a trunk to this wilderness? What would be his reason for caching it? Where did he go? And most interesting of all— who was he? A nice little problem in detective work awaits anyone who follows up the single clue—the newspaper clipping. Or perhaps it isn't detection at all, but history—another paragraph in the human story of the incredible river giant.

A few miles downstream from Music Temple we edged the boats into the narrow entrance of Mystery Canyon. For a quarter of a mile we rowed up a quiet winding inlet, the splash of the oars echoing from overhanging rock walls within arm's length of the boats on either side. A hike up the canyon above the inlet brought us to a domed room where we lunched beside a pool on a bank of ferns and columbines.

Several years ago Norm discovered foot- and handholds chipped out of the rock in the canyon wall. They lead to the only ledge which gives access to the upper part of the canyon. Halfway up the cliff the holds have almost crumbled away, so Norm has been baffled so far in his attempts to reach the ledge. He believes these precarious steps were made by Indians to

247

reach cliff dwellings above. Someday Norm intends to bring tools to enlarge the steps, but until he does we can let our imagination picture another "Lost World" above these ancient steps in Mystery Canyon.

Mystery Canyon is Norm's by right of discovery, but we felt we had a proprietary interest in the next one two and a half miles below. Our party named it. The Board of Geographic Names may still be in ignorance of our canyon's existence, but we have already seen its name boldly printed on a map—TWI-LIGHT CANYON.

This gorge is the most unusual of the many we explored. A steep, intermittent cloudburst stream has carved a corkscrew gash out of solid rock, at each loop undercutting deep, cave-like recesses. A weird semi-twilight pervades this sunless defile. It is silent, without life or movement except on those rare occasions when floods thunder down its tortuous course. Twilight Canyon is the unfinished excavation for a world that is still building—for what, we wonder? Man himself seems to be just a piddling incident in the vast plans going on about him.

Early in the evening we rowed into a backwater at the entrance to Forbidden Canyon and called it a day—one of the fullest we had ever put in. We camped on a ledge above the inlet, our kitchen and dining room walled by an ancient cliff ruin. A swim in the inlet, a fire fall pushed over the edge of our cliff by Norm and the photographer, a meteor lighting the night with the brilliance of a lightning flash brought an end to the day's extravaganza. But we turned in early with the knowledge that next day the curtain would rise on the greatest drama of all.

Four and a half miles up Forbidden Canyon, Bridge Canyon branches off. Spanning Bridge Canyon a mile and a half

248

above the junction is Rainbow Bridge, perhaps the greatest single natural wonder in America.

We were up early and on the trail before the sun had reached down to us. The rough track followed the little stream in the canyon floor, crossing and recrossing it as we ascended. Along the creek diminutive waterfalls alternated with deep clear pools banked with ferns and overhung with willows and oaks. These natural rock basins were so tempting on our return under the hot afternoon sun that we indulged in more swimming than walking. The coed held the record with seven swims on her way back to camp.

A mile up Bridge Canyon we turned a corner. Ahead of us, framed in a V-shaped notch formed by the upper canyon walls, hung a bow of stone against the sky. It appeared to float there, impossibly high, unreal. A few hundred yards farther the cliffs retreated, revealing Rainbow Bridge spanning the canyon, a perfectly proportioned arch of salmon-pink sandstone.

The wonder of Rainbow Bridge as we stood looking up at it has little to do with its size; the wonder is that it is there at all. The fact that the national Capitol could be placed under the great stone arch with room to spare leaves us a little cold. The impact upon our imaginations cannot be measured by such tangible quantities as length, breadth, and thickness.

The real wonder of Rainbow Bridge is that of water carving stone; of the billions of storms which brought the water, of the stone itself, laid down ages ago as drifting sand dunes on a Jurassic desert. The wonder is the sun, the wind, the clouds, vegetation, chemical action, the forces within the earth—all working together for millions of years to produce this perfect masterpiece. And Rainbow Bridge, too, will pass as all things

249

do, for nature produces no finished products. So far as we know she works in a universal chain of processes which has no ending.

But, as we have observed before, man soon returns to his own horizons; we lunched heartily on such things as beans and sausages in the shadow of the arch 309 feet above our heads.

After lunch Randall, the photographer, and I took the climbing rope and scaled the canyon wall to reach the top of the bridge. To gain the arch itself we roped down sixty feet from the south buttress onto the rounded sandstone runway which we followed to the top of the span. On the return we speedily reached the canyon floor by rappelling over the cliffs up which we had so laboriously climbed. The thermometer was ninety-four degrees Fahrenheit on the bridge, one of the highest readings of the trip. Never was canned grapefruit more welcome than was that we found left for us in the creek.

We took a last look at Rainbow Bridge framing the blue bulk of Navajo Mountain, then hurried down the canyon to our chain of swims back to camp. The great stone arch in the wilderness exerts a spell on all who see it. In the brassy sun of midday, in moonlight, in storm, distantly from the summit of Navajo Mountain, or from a plane flying above it—the wonder of Rainbow Bridge is that it is there.

Two more days the four boats floated lazily down the broad river through Glen Canyon. We landed at Kane Creek and climbed the bluffs to the steps cut by Father Silvestre Vélez de Escalante and his Franciscan brothers when they crossed the Colorado on their way back to Santa Fe after an unsuccessful attempt to find a route to California. These steps, still plainly visible, were made to enable the fathers to get their animals down the steep sandstone side of Padre Creek. We waited as once again a padre descended the route of the fathers, stopping in their enduring footsteps to pay tribute to those sturdy churchmen who overcame the obstacles of a strange, savage land over one hundred and sixty years ago.

The last night we slept in front of the wide arch of Outlaw Cave just over the Arizona line. Here an alleged horse thief named Neal Johnson had his hideout for several months while a sheriff's posse searched the country for him. But later justice —or injustice—caught up with Mr. Johnson over in Nevada. He was hanged.

The next noon we lunched with Frank Dodge, the veteran riverman, in his shady ramada beside the Paria River. Then the four boats shot through the last riffle down to Lees Ferry. The trip was over; we were landlubbers once more. But each of us had gained from our experiences on fast water in the desert—we were richer for having memories of the wonderland through which it flows.

Our cars had been shuttled the two hundred miles from Mexican Hat, so Randall and I were soon speeding down Route 89 toward Flagstaff and the all-night drive to the Coast.

As we were having dinner at Cameron the bride and groom arrived. They sat down beside us.

"You know," said the groom, "we got almost here when we found our brakes wouldn't work. We didn't know it but we drove seventy miles an hour the whole way without any brakes at all."

The Hopi waitress brought our check. In a few minutes we were ready to leave.

"We'll be seeing you in California," said Randall. "What point are you making for first?"

251

"The top of Mount Whitney," said the groom.

We knew then that Norm had lost his yogi. The white-haired, black-robed protector had found where he was really needed. He had just skimmed down from Lees Ferry guiding a brakeless car and was now bound for the summit of the highest peak in the United States.

CHAPTER TEN

ON FOOT AND IN THE SADDLE
By Edwin D. McKee

The canyons of semiarid regions are hostile, desolate places. More than any other, the Grand Canyon is hostile and desolate. Such was the opinion of James O. Pattie, who, with his father, was the first American to see this canyon, for he spoke of its walls as "those horrid mountains that forever onward go." Similar thoughts were expressed by Lieutenant J. C. Ives while making a notable exploration of the region in 1857 and 1858, three decades after the Pattie trip, for he wrote in his diary about this "profitless locality" and made the prophecy that "the Colorado River, along her lonely and majestic way, shall be forever unvisited and undisturbed." Even Clarence Dutton, eminent geologist and masterful describer of scenery, tacitly admits that according to usual standards of beauty the Grand Canyon has for the newcomer forms that seem grotesque, magnitudes that appear coarse, and color esteemed unrefined, immodest, and glaring.

In spite of the overwhelming aspect of the Grand Canyon and the difficulties of climbing except on the approved trails, there surges up in one the same strong urge to climb and to explore that great mountains invoke in all real lovers of the out-of-doors. True, it differs from mountain climbing in many respects and is, in a physical sense, the reverse. But it holds as reward that same satisfying feeling of conquest. Proof is found in the degree of pride attained by the person who has descended the depths and returned, whether on muleback or by foot. He has accomplished something that cannot be achieved except by one who is willing to undergo certain physical discomforts and to exert himself beyond the norm of everyday life.

It is obvious that other factors enter into consideration as reasons for impelling the "out-of-doors" person to descend this canyon. High in importance among these is the desire to experience personally the great changes that are encountered in climate, in vegetation, in animal life, and in scenery. The contrasts are amazing, and simply to be told about them by some individual who went before is no substitute for experiencing them oneself. It is essentially the difference between reading about Europe in a geography book and visiting Europe.

Nor are contrasts of the Canyon to be fully appreciated merely by being alternately on the Canyon rim and at the bottom. If this were true, one might ride serenely down in a tram car and avoid all the bother and annoying experiences, not to mention occasional real hardships, experienced in hiking or riding the trails. But de luxe methods and time-saving devices are not substitutes. It is the little things of nature and of scenery all along the trail that go to make up the experience that is lasting. Actually tram cars have been built and used in connection with construction projects in lower portions of Grand Canyon, but, fortunately, the trams were later removed by government order, for they were not intended to be and never could be substitutes for the experiences of trail trips into the depths.

256

PROBLEMS OF THE TRAIL

Canyon climbing, at its best, entails difficulties. Among these is the fact that the uphill portion, the most strenuous part, comes last instead of first as in mountain climbing. Frequently, therefore, the hiker has to start the ascent when already weary. This, of course, applies primarily to those attempting a round trip to the river and back in a single day. Such individuals are also handicapped by reaching the high altitudes, with accompanying rare atmosphere, near the trip's end when fatigue is already in evidence.

A second and equally significant factor in causing Grand Canyon climbing to be difficult, at least in the summer season, is the heat. This affects the mule-rider as well as the hiker. Quite normally, in the Canyon bottom, the thermometer reaches a daily maximum well above one hundred degrees Fahrenheit in the shade during most of late June, July, and August. Although a dry heat and, therefore, not oppressive as it would be under moisture conditions, nevertheless it taxes one's strength and causes much trouble for those not properly equipped and outfitted. The factor of thirst—for there is little or no water along most trails—is also an important consideration, and, even where it is plentiful, water must be used sparingly and with discretion. Sunburn may likewise cause much discomfort, for at high altitudes the sun burns deeply, and in the Canyon bottom it has added potency through reflection from the rock surfaces.

The conditions encountered in traveling a desert canyon like Grand Canyon, whether on foot or by horse, and in camping in it, are so different from those along mountain trails of better-

257

watered regions that the beginner should consider them with care when equipping. I have known of experienced explorers who suffered greatly because of poor calculations in this connection. One biologist, fresh from a month of climbing in the High Sierra, took with him on a hard canyon trip the type of food used in the mountains, and suffered in consequence. Many articles were too dry for him to eat after strenuous climbing in the heat. There was another case of a famous arctic explorer who carried several cans of peanut butter with him on a week's trip in Grand Canyon only to find the sight of this once cherished luxury becoming more and more distasteful after each day of hiking in the hot sun.

Camping in the semidesert canyons of the Southwest has both advantages and disadvantages over camping in most mountain areas. Among the definite assets is an almost complete absence of mosquitoes and of fog or dew. Furthermore, the rainfall is of such a character that it is possible to sleep out under the stars for long periods without using any tent or other shelter, and, even during the time of summer cloudbursts, which come with violence nearly every afternoon, the evaporation is such that much of the ground surface dries off within a few hours.

On the debit side of canyon camping are several factors which one must expect and get used to or else one will derive little pleasure from such trips. These include the dust, which may become very troublesome if the wind blows, the heat of summer, and the flies, which may be bad in local areas. One must, of course, learn to watch out for the cactus, yucca, and other plants that stick, as well as for a few animals such as the scorpion and the rattlesnake. Most persons learn quickly through a few experiences. Fortunately, there are no animals whose poison is apt to be really dangerous. Old-timers in the Arizona deserts like to advise, "Everything that moves can bite or sting; everything that doesn't move sticks or pricks."

Most persons visit the canyons of the Southwest during the summer season. The reason is that most people take their vacations at that time, partly because schools are out, partly because it is the "normal" vacation period, but it does not follow that this is the best season to explore the canyons. On the contrary, the early summer, especially June, is usually the hottest, driest time of the entire year, and late summer is the time of daily cloudbursts. In the writer's opinion, the autumn is the ideal time for planning trips in this area. In the winter it is likely to be cold and stormy, even in the low altitudes of the canyon bottoms, and at higher levels there is almost always snow. The late spring months may be very pleasant in the canyon, but the weather is normally rather uncertain and subject to fluctuation. In October and November, on the other hand, it is usually cool, dry, and delightfully pleasant, and I say this despite the fact that on a recent ten-day pack trip made in October my party encountered rain nearly every day.

How best to equip for trail trips and for camping in the Canyon Country is a subject that may have an unlimited number of answers. The many ramifications of the problem include various situations dependent on the length of trip, the method of travel, the time of year, and the type of trail. Then, too, the human element always enters in the matter of difference of opinion. Despite all of the variable factors it is, nevertheless, possible to make certain broad generalizations and some detailed suggestions that are applicable under most conditions.

259

TIPS FOR CAMP AND TRAIL

All sorts of people wear all sorts of shoes. Some suffer discomfort, some don't. The shoe is perhaps the most important single item of clothing to be considered for canyon trips, yet even among experienced hikers there is far from general agreement as to what is most suitable. Personally, I like shoes that are ankle high. Boots add far too much extra weight, confine the legs unnecessarily, and above all are too hot for comfort in summer weather. Advantages usually ascribed to boots, such as protection from snakes or from dense brush and assistance in wading shallow streams, may be largely discounted in this region because of the general lack of such features. On the other hand, low shoes and sneakers are not desirable except as camp slippers, both because they fail to support the ankles and because they allow easy access of dust, dirt, and small stones. Hobnails are good for travel on the trails but poor for rock work and, considering the usual dry character of the region, are perhaps less desirable than good composition soles.

Insofar as the remainder of one's wardrobe is concerned, the principal governing factor is the season. During much of the year, a broad-brimmed hat is not only desirable but a virtual necessity for sun protection. In this connection one may be reminded of the slogan, "When in Rome, do as the Romans do." The local cowboys and Indians demonstrate a wide variety of styles in hats, all suitable to the conditions, although it might be added that a pith helmet of the type usually ascribed to African big-game hunters, or a Mexican sombrero, will serve equally well.

260

In the rainy season a raincoat or slicker should be carried by those traveling on horse or mule. For hikers, however, the extra weight and the additional heat when the coat is worn make this impractical. Most persons will agree that it is better to take one's chances when hiking. Usually a rock shelter in the canyon can be found for the duration of a typical short but violent cloudburst. On the other hand, if one does get caught in an August rain, it is apt to feel cool and refreshing, and the rate of evaporation is such that clothes dry off very quickly afterward.

For traveling and camping in late fall and winter, it is well to remember that the weather may be quite cold even in the depths of Grand Canyon—and this applies especially to the nights. Furthermore, not only is the *actual* length of the nights considerable at this season but the *apparent* length is still greater because of the few hours each day during which sunlight can penetrate the lower portions of narrow canyons. With this in mind it may not be amiss to suggest gloves and, for sleeping purposes, an extra pair of wool stockings and wool underwear. One experienced camper I know always carries a small chemical heating pad, which, upon addition of a few spoonfuls of water, generates enough heat to warm feet all night.

The problem of sunburn should never be considered lightly at the high altitudes found in the Canyon Country. In addition to the broad-brimmed hat already recommended, one does well to carry some protective grease and a tube of lipstick (this applies to men as well as women, and colorless varieties of lipstick are on the market especially for the former). Dark glasses are helpful for many people and may save considerable eyestrain.

As for general equipment for a canyon trip, selection depends

261

largely on the amount that can readily be carried by the method of travel used. If one is hiking and must depend entirely on one's own back, naturally the story is very different from when pack animals are used. A few items which have proved of great value on canyon trips but which, for the most part, can be taken only when horses or mules are employed for packing are a short-handled shovel, a canvas water bag, a collapsible canvas bucket, a carbide "miner's" lamp, an air mattress, and a light-weight but sturdy grill. Also tweezers, for pulling out stickers and thorns, and adhesive tape for blisters, often prove very valuable.

Certain of the items listed above may seem superfluous to anyone uninitiated in ways of desert camping, but they have all proved their worth under various conditions. The short-handled shovel, for instance, is not merely a convenience used in setting up camp but may be a necessity in repairing or building trail on a trip off the main path. Also, it is sometimes needed in digging out a water hole in a dry stream bed or wash. The canvas water bag is desirable because it allows some evaporation and therefore keeps water much cooler than does the ordinary canteen. Air mattresses usually improve one's spirits by allowing a good sleep and are especially useful in some parts of any canyon where the rockiness of the terrain makes it difficult to find or dig a really smooth surface to lie on. One geologist I worked with liked his mattress especially because it gave him an extra five minutes each morning to lie on it while waiting for deflation to be complete! A light grill is recommended as a convenience because in many localities wood is scarce, and the usual type of rod for holding pots is difficult to rig.

Water is the big problem of the desert, and the Arizona-Utah canyons are in a general desert region. It is always advisable to carry some water, whether the trip be long or short. It is also desirable to learn the location and character of springs and water holes before starting, wherever this is possible. Many springs and streams in the region contain salt or alkali in sufficient quantity to make the water unpalatable. As the local people say, "The water is wet only on one side," or "The water is so thick with alkali that you must cut it with a knife." Such waters must, of course, be carefully avoided even if one is very thirsty. I once had the unpleasant experience of being very dry and without drinking water while actually following for many hours and frequently wading a shallow stream of this kind in a narrow Utah canyon. At the bottom of Grand Canyon the Colorado River, muddy though it is, furnishes good water for all uses. The sediment which is ever present in this stream is carried principally in suspension and will readily settle when the water is quiet. Good camp practice, therefore, is to fill all available receptacles as soon as camp is started, and within an hour or slightly more clear water will be available for use.

In planning food for the dry Canyon Country, especially during warm weather, two important needs should be kept in mind. One of these is the furnishing of sufficient liquid material and the other is the replacement in the human system of salt lost through perspiration. For the former purpose canned tomatoes, canned fruit, and juices are very good and should constitute an important part of any larder. For supplying salt to the body, bouillon cubes are especially effective and at the same time form a very easily prepared and pleasant drink. Some hikers like the commercial concentrated salt tablets that are made for desert use. While climbing, in order to keep away thirst and

263

avoid dryness, it is often desirable to suck lemons or to chew on strips of dried meat known as "jerky," which is sold in some stores of the region. Application of a few of these little "tricks of the trail" may go a long way toward making the difference between a pleasant and a disagreeable trip.

THE ELEMENTS HAVE THEIR SAY

The elements have always constituted a favorite subject of conversation, partly because of their influence on man's enterprises, partly also because of their unpredictable whims. They are constantly changing. Sometimes they play pranks, other times they are even and steady. Always they serve as outer garments that tend to change the very nature and complexion of the features that they clothe. Even as a woman takes on new appearance with change from sports attire to evening gown and from dinner dress to lounging frock, so the scenery varies with each change in the weather.

In the Canyon Country of the Southwest the elements often find expression in extremes. Violent cloudbursts, powerful wind storms, snow, and shimmering heat transform the scenery with suddenness and completeness. It is little wonder that human attempts to reproduce the canyons—especially Grand Canyon —on canvas usually seem inadequate and the results inaccurate. Even the best pictures can hope only to show a single mood, the view of a specific place at a specific time, whereas the scene is constantly changing and will never twice be the same. By skillful use of words, a few great writers have given some suggestion of the constant change and the extremes of scenic grandeur brought about by the elements, but these must be rather vague

264

and generalized, for they cannot attempt to cover all of the variety to be found. Little wonder is it that persons who come back time and time again always find the scenery of the Canyon Country different and intriguing.

One of the really great spectacles to be witnessed in the arid Southwest is a canyon storm. Such storms occur almost daily during late July and August. The day begins clear and cloudless; gradually billowy clouds float in on a constant southwest wind; by noon many parts of the blue sky are hidden, and soon after, here and there, yet seldom for long in one place, the rain pours down with violence, the thunder roars, and the lightning flashes. The evening brings dispersal of the clouds, the stars come forth, and the landscape appears fresh and clean—and then the entire procedure is duplicated in form if not in detail the following day.

From a canyon trail the experience of a summer cloudburst is both awesome and wonderful. The suddenness of arrival, the concentrated power of the rain, and the floods that follow are marvelous to behold. A storm may rage for twenty minutes, then lift as rapidly as it arrived. Every side canyon in the area and every depression near by will contain a stream of liquid mud, where shortly before was only bare rock or dry alluvium. In this land of sparse vegetation a single torrential shower often does more destruction than a season's rainfall on the densely covered slopes of a humid region. And should the sun's rays appear at this time, hundreds of streamlets heading toward the canyon bottoms laden with upland mud will appear silvery.

In most canyons of the Southwest numerous beautiful, though short-lived, waterfalls develop over the sides of cliffs following every heavy downpour. Few of these flow for more

265

than two or three hours following a torrential thunderstorm, but many have a considerable drop. In Zion Canyon, where exceptionally high cliffs have been formed in rocks of uniform hardness, waterfalls making a clear leap of over seven hundred feet develop, and "sliding falls" of two thousand feet form in several places. At Grand Canyon the vertical Redwall cliff, which averages about five hundred feet, and the Coconino cliff, of three hundred feet, are responsible for many large waterfalls during every hard storm. As many as fifty such temporary falls—active at the same time—have been reported from within sight of the floor of Zion Canyon, and similar records of large numbers come from nearly all of the high-walled canyons of the region. In addition to size and number, color is an interesting feature of these canyon waterfalls. Few of them have the foamy white color commonly associated with swift currents. They are heavily charged with sand, mud, and other debris, and so appear red, brown, yellow, and various other colors.

While on the trails or camping in the canyons there is not, for the most part, despite the rather terrifying character of these storms, any great danger from cloudbursts, provided normal precautions are taken. The imprudent person, however, may find them very serious, for they represent the unleashing of tremendous power. A never-to-be-forgotten experience of the writer occurred partway down the Grand Canyon where he climbed under a large overhanging cliff for protection from rain only to find to his dismay that a great waterfall soon developed in front of that particular spot. The water landed with a terrific splash but a few feet away, bringing with it mud, then pebbles, and finally boulders, and even though these missiles bounced harmlessly outward, their nearness gave a most un-

266

pleasant feeling. The real dangers thus lie both in the rush of swollen streams and in the sliding and rolling of rock debris. At times of storm the hiker should stay out of canyon bottoms and stream courses and avoid possible areas of moving rocks among the cliffs.

The effects of cloudbursts are experienced not alone within the canyons. Every year people report having been witness to spectacular "walls of water" moving rapidly down and filling dry stream beds or arroyos, blocking or destroying roadways, and even wrecking automobiles that are unfortunate enough to be in the way. But it is in the canyons, where gradients are mostly greater, and where enclosing walls are more confining, that such actions reach a peak. In August of 1938 a great flood that came down Bright Angel Canyon in the bottom of Grand Canyon was determined to be twenty feet high and rolled boulders up to six feet in diameter along the Canyon floor for half a mile. Such storms are relatively scarce, but nonetheless impressive.

An interesting feature of some desert storms is that in their wake certain areas that are normally dry and desert-like may become alive with toads. These creatures apparently aestivate for long periods in the dry ground and then miraculously come forth with the rain. Little wonder that people speak of "raining frogs"!

Rockfalls and landslides resulting from work of the elements are spectacular features that are occasionally witnessed by travelers of the trail. These slides come not only at times of torrential downpour but also frequently when the snow is melting. Most of them occur where weathering has undermined a cliff to such an extent that a portion of its face suddenly breaks loose

267

and falls forward with the pull of gravity. One sunny February day following a night of snowfall, the writer heard the roars of sixteen sizable slides in the jagged cliffs of Iceberg Canyon near the Arizona-Nevada line. Again one may go for months without noting any. In the Grand Canyon, because of the large range of vision, rockfalls are witnessed not uncommonly, and there the roar of a large one may be heard as far as ten miles away, while the dust is seen rising above the Canyon rim like the ejecta of a volcano.

The winter season is one in which remarkable and rather weird scenic effects are produced in the Canyon Country as a result of snow and misty clouds. As nearly the entire region is formed of essentially horizontal or flat-lying rock strata, little covered with vegetation or debris and weathered into alternations of cliff and slope, snow accentuates the banded character. Slopes are covered with white; the cliffs, which naturally remain bare, are mostly red; the result is a series of red and white bands. Although this bizarre color pattern is developed more or less throughout the region when snows are heavy, it is especially striking as seen in the walls of Grand Canyon.

Winter clouds are also remarkable for the effect that they have on canyon scenery. Often they are misty and travel low. They may appear as little wisps or floating islands; again they may accumulate until they fill an entire canyon, blotting out all features beyond the foreground. Many a visitor to Grand Canyon has been immeasurably disappointed upon arriving on the rim to find the view completely obliterated, but when after a few hours, as is normally the case, clouds begin to move apart, giving vistas of gorgeous scenery and brilliant colors ten or twelve miles away, he obtains one of the greatest thrills imaginable. Corresponding experiences are often obtained along the trails at this season and add much to the richness of one's memories.

Clear atmosphere extends the range of vision over vast distances in the Canyon Region. Much of the area is characterized by intense quiet and solitude during large parts of the year, yet one of the elements is always on the move. It is the wind. Streams of air are constantly twisting and swirling in and about the canyons. Above the Plateau a remarkably regular southwest wind is present at all seasons, but down in the gorges air currents are different. Warm drafts move upward; cascades of cool air go down, constantly fluctuating with time and place. Aviators passing over the rim of Grand Canyon at one thousand feet sometimes find their planes steadily elevated, and clouds may be seen to rise after a storm. Cool air settles toward the Canyon floor until lightened by warmth and expansion, then it rises. Camping along the Colorado River one often is impressed by the regularity and power of the air currents that develop each day at about sunrise and again at sunset, frequently blowing sand along the shore. On the trails, and also on the rims, one frequently encounters "pockets" or drafts of definite warm or cold air.

The "dust devil" or whirlwind is a manifestation of the eccentricities of air currents commonly displayed in the Canyon Country wherever quantities of loose sand or dust have accumulated. These "sand geysers" are caused by wind swirling around and upward with a spiral motion into a funnel-shaped column; they are moving atmospheric vortexes which lift sediment high in the air as spouts or fountains. The Navajo Indians of northern Arizona believe that an evil spirit is within

269

each dust devil and will take pains to avoid or appease these spirits whenever possible. White men will avoid them, too, if they realize the sting that comes with the swirling sand!

NATURAL HISTORY OF THE TRAILSIDE

There are in this world many who would "improve" on nature at every turn. I once knew a rancher who, while among the wonders and beauty of Kanab Canyon, could talk of little but how that region might be blocked off into a magnificent pasture for Brahma steers. I have met engineers who practically dreamed of the great "contribution" they could make to civilization by building a road into Grand Canyon. I have seen the forester who scorned the desert because good forests would not grow there. An amazingly widespread notion is entertained by civilized man that it is his duty to remodel and rearrange all things in nature and to tame all that which is wild.

One of the real pleasures of traveling through most of the canyons in the Southwest is that so little evidence of man's endeavors is found within them. Much of their charm is due to the fact that rocks and plants and animals are still where nature placed them. Each form of life seems perfectly adapted to its environment—the result of ages of trial-and-error experiment in the game of life. On every side are demonstrated ingenious stratagems, contrived in the never-ending struggle for existence. There are reptiles that match the rocks, plants that survive drought because of small leaf surface or large water-storage space, mammals developed to walk easily on loose sand, others that can eke out a livelihood from plants despite spines and thorns. These and many other forms of life meet the special

270

requirements of their local communities and therefore add interest and appeal to the trailside.

With knowledge comes appreciation. A visitor to the Grand Canyon once told me that he found it easier and more entertaining as he climbed the trail to count his steps in terms of geologic formations rather than of miles. He realized that he was literally passing through the ages as he progressed and that his trip took him through strata representing many millions of years in the earth's history. Such thoughts doubtless would have been even more intriguing had he been aware of the many ancient plants and animals buried in the rocks about him and of the stories they had to tell concerning climates and landscapes of the past.

In similar manner the botanist or ecologist obtains a certain feeling of satisfaction as he recognizes his approximate elevation through the appearance of certain plants or groups of plants along the way. He knows, for instance, that the catclaw or Acacia greggii seldom grows above four thousand feet in this latitude, that the lower level of the ponderosa or yellow pine is at about seven thousand feet, and that each of a host of other species will furnish him with information. Likewise, the bird enthusiast, the mammalogist, the student of reptiles will all find satisfaction in the knowledge that enables them to understand and appreciate various features along the trail. But one does not need to be a specialist to derive such pleasures. The amateur natural-history student who observes with care and enthusiasm will find an abundance of drama being enacted all about him on any of the canyon trails.

Glance about that portion of trail located at high elevation—say eight thousand or nine thousand feet—as found at Bryce

Canyon or in the Kaibab on the north side of Grand Canyon. Here a person familiar with trails in the mountains of New England or in the lake region of Minnesota will recognize many familiar friends among the plants and animals, but with them will be some new and strange associates. Here one may enjoy the game of trying to recognize the many types of evergreens by their shapes or of testing cross-sections of needles to see whether they are round as in the pine, square as in the spruce, or flat as in the fir. One also may become interested in the groves of quaking aspen, whose white bark suggests from a distance the birch and whose leaves quiver with the slightest breeze, thus justifying the species name of *tremuloides*. If it is early summer these aspens may be causing a local "snow storm" by filling the air and covering the ground with their white, fluffy, cotton-like seeds. If it is autumn, the brilliant golden-yellow leaves may be bringing joy to some color photographer or artist.

In among these trees of higher altitudes are birds and mammals that also bring memories of the northland or of mountain peaks in other regions. The bright red or yellow crossbill, whose name is derived from its peculiar scissor-like beak, adapted to cutting seeds from the spruce cone, is apt to fly past. The noisy Clark's nutcrackers of the jay clan may call attention to their presence by raucous sounds. Red-breasted nuthatches, three-toed woodpeckers, solitaires, and many feathered associates of cool climates bring to mind the fact that these are trails due to be covered deep with snow during a long winter ahead. Here and there a tree trunk chewed by porcupine or the scattered remains of a chipmunk's feast of pine cones are reminders that four-legged forest dwellers also are about, and, if one is lucky, a deer or a spruce squirrel may be seen.

272

Canyon trails at lower levels in this region traverse what are commonly known as the "pygmy forests." These forests are composed of the small nut pines or piñons and the junipers, together with various shrubs such as the cliff rose, serviceberry, and wild currant. Trees grow well apart, and in most places there is little underbrush. Readily apparent is the interesting fact that in this region one goes down, instead of up, to approach timber line, for the lower limit of the pygmy forest is the beginning of the open desert. Of course, there is an upper timber line, too, but at this latitude it is attained only on the highest mountain peaks—above eleven thousand feet.

A majority of the canyons in the Southwest are at least partly within the belt of piñons and junipers. Many of these canyons have a pygmy forest along their rims and upper slopes but extend downward into the desert zone. The trails passing through such forests contain many features of natural history that are unique to the region and for that reason of especial interest to the visitor from afar. It is here that one finds large flocks of garrulous piñon jays, wearing Prussian blue but no crest, and making a terrific noise as they come picnicking through the woods. Here also one normally encounters groups of plump, short-tailed pygmy nuthatches, hanging upside down or in other acrobatic poses, talking continuously in friendly fashion. The more reserved Rocky Mountain nuthatches, the cheery mountain chickadees, and others that call to mind similar forms throughout the United States are also present among the trees.

Where the canyon walls become rocky and rugged, other types of birds appear abundantly. The canyon wren is especially conspicuous because of its weird song that starts high and comes tripping down the chromatic scale with a great display of ex-

273

uberance. Frequently, even when the wren itself is too far away to be clearly seen with the unaided eye, its rich, vibrant song carries back and forth among the rocks. Another equally typical sound of the deep, narrow canyons is the coarse croak of the raven. This call echoes between canyon walls where the large, black birds, looking like overgrown crows, fly about singly or in pairs from cliff to cliff. Then there is the startling sound, like a bullet passing near, made by white-throated swifts as they circle and wheel and dart about with terrific speed among the cliffs. It seems almost unbelievable that any living creature can go so fast and yet keep such perfect control as is demonstrated by these long curving wings that sometimes move, first one and then the other, like a man swimming the crawl. It is a thrilling experience of the Canyon Country to watch and hear these birds zip past one's head and "power dive" into the depths below.

Back among the piñons and junipers again, along the ground, many other creatures of strange habit but of more silent ways come to the attention of the observant hiker. On relatively level stretches, especially along canyon rims, a horny lizard with circular body plan and flattened profile, commonly known as the horned toad, makes his abode. The color scheme of his body blends well with the ground about. Disturb him, and he will puff up as though suddenly inflated and may even emit a hissing sound. He would look as ferocious as any reptile of the ancient Mesozoic were he enlarged a few dozen times, yet for the most part he is a mild-mannered, gentle creature.

Not far away the peculiar home of another catcher-of-insects may attract attention. It is a conical-shaped hole in the sand about an inch deep and half again as wide at the top. Actually it is more than a house—it is a trap used by the wily and cun-

274

ning flesh-eating larva of an innocent adult insect. Down at the bottom of the cone, hidden under loose sand, stays this insect larva—clumsy, covered with spiny hairs, and having mousetrap jaws with which it grabs any hapless ant or similar creature that falls into the pit. Many a fascinating half-hour may be spent in watching the movements of this creature commonly known as the ant lion or doodlebug.

Everywhere along the trail are other fascinating features typical of the pygmy forest area. Usually in spring and summer there are brilliant flowers here and there, varying in type and color with the season. There may be clumps of trumpet-shaped scarlet buglers, and, if there are, hummingbirds are likely to be near by, "treading" the air and whistling shrilly. There may be patches of bluebonnets, the state flower of Texas, or deep blue larkspur, orange mallow, and red or yellow paintbrush scattered about. Later in the season these flowers are largely replaced by others such as the snakeweed and rabbitbrush, and the blues and reds give place to yellows. As in all regions of semiarid climate, the display of trailside flowers varies tremendously with the local rainfall, but under optimum conditions it is almost unbelievably brilliant and beautiful.

So far nothing has been said concerning the main varieties of shrubs that are characteristic of the piñon-juniper belt. There is the cliff rose, which is very common and very beautiful when covered with yellow-centered, cream-colored blossoms, and which, despite a bitter taste that gives it the name of quinine bush, is a favorite food of the deer. It is an evergreen with waxy leaves and, like many other members of the rose family, develops lovely little plumes for transporting its seeds when the wind blows. Even more striking are the larger seed-plumes of

275

a close relative called the Apache plume. Then there is the mountain mahogany of the same family—interesting because the Navajo Indians formerly made a lovely red dye from its roots. Representing the apple family is the serviceberry, very common along many trails and, when in bloom, a mass of white. Its berries are edible. Most beautiful and fragrant of all the wayside shrubs in the area, however, is the syringa or mock orange.

Descending any canyon trail toward the lower limit of the evergreens, one encounters many changes in the plant and animal life. Lizards are found in greater abundance, especially the small-scaled Utas, while some of the larger types, such as the brilliant orange or green collared lizards, make an appearance. The birds are semidesert types, including the rock wren, the black-throated desert sparrow, and the sage thrasher. Mammals are seen less frequently here than in the wooded areas above because most forms are nocturnal, but abundant evidence of their presence usually can be found. Under rock ledges or beneath large cactus plants huge piles of sticks, branches, and various kinds of rubbish testify to the industry of the so-called "pack rat," while on sandy surfaces the tracks of silky-haired, jumping pocket mice or of trim little white-footed mice are common. The mammal most likely to be seen and almost sure to be heard any time any day is the rock squirrel, which rushes about among the crags whistling lustily.

In the zone of dwarfed piñons and junipers and of increased desert conditions, various types of plants peculiarly adapted to the dry environment appear in great abundance. Among these is the century plant or mescal, which forms veritable "forests" in places. This interesting plant grows for many years with only

276

a clump of sharp, saw-toothed leaves above the ground, and then some spring will send up a slender flower-bearing stalk, twelve or fifteen feet high, in a matter of days. After the flowers come the seeds, and then the entire plant dies, leaving only a brown hollow spear to wave and rattle like a ghost for months afterward. The tender shoots of these mescals have long been considered a delicacy by various Indians of the region, and circular rock pits in which the plants have been roasted are visible near many trails.

The yucca—swordlike but friendly—is another conspicuous plant common near the "lower timber line." Its leaves form queer-looking clusters about the base of a stalk as do those of the century plant, but they are narrower and without teeth on the sides, while the stalk normally extends upward but a few feet. Its larger blossoms are creamy-white and at once suggest relationship to the lily family. Of all the many plants in this semidesert region, the yucca has been one of the most useful to aboriginal man. Its pods form a food, its leaves are used for basketry, its fibers for thread, and its roots for soap.

If variety is the spice of life, these canyon trails must have an abundance of spice. A number of them, especially those in Zion and Grand Canyon, extend their lower reaches well down into a true desert environment, and there the features of natural history along the way make a remarkable contrast with those seen at higher elevation. Down where spring comes early and plants grow far apart, the vegetation is of a typical desert type. The little spotted skunk and raccoon-like ring-tailed cat leave tracks in the sand and often examine camp sites at night. Now and then a large scorpion with brown body and yellow legs is found beneath a rock, or a centipede crawls by—reason enough

277

why the camper should shake out his shoe before putting it on in the morning. But by and large there is little to worry about and nothing to fear among the queer denizens of this lower realm, and there is much of beauty and of interest to be found. Large bluish pipe-vine swallowtail butterflies, friendly but noisy ash-throated flycatchers, harmless king snakes with black and white stripes, and a host of other creatures soon convince the observant hiker that this desert is far from desolate and lifeless.

Wherever water comes to the surface, or even near it, in this land of drought, an oasis is formed. Like most oases these are regular paradises for all forms of life, and their beauty is enhanced many times by contrast with surrounding dry areas. The largest of the oases in the canyons of the Southwest are those formed along permanent stream courses. The deep-rooted mesquite and the grabbing catclaw of the desert thrive in these places, but they are secondary in prominence to the large, shade-giving cottonwood, to the box elder, and to thickets of willows and arrowweeds. Down below the trees and larger shrubs, in many places, are clumps of that peculiar jointed plant known as horsetail, whose ancient lineage goes back to the great Coal Age; also there are pretty red or yellow monkey flowers and, in especially sheltered localities, the columbine and maidenhair fern. Trails that follow such water bodies offer many a thrill and surprise for the nature lover, and seldom a dull minute is experienced.

Down among the boulders, wherever permanent streams rush by with white foam and swift current, one is almost sure to encounter the little gray dipper or water ouzel. Continually bobbing up and down on a rock ledge, diving under water and coming into full flight as it reaches the surface, or singing beauti-

278

fully within narrow canyon confines, this little bird seems strangely out of place to those who have always associated him with high mountain regions. But the dipper appears to be just as much at home and to enjoy life as fully in the depths of hot desert canyons, wherever he has rushing water, as in the highest and boldest mountains. One group of geologists working in the depths of Grand Canyon and climbing about with great effort among granite walls noted the ease with which a little water ouzel flew from cliff to cliff and thereupon adopted as a theme song for their expedition, "If I Had the Wings of an Ouzel . . ."

Equally surprising to most people schooled in less arid regions is the discovery that beaver are perfectly at home in many desert canyons of the Southwest. As a matter of fact, the first Americans to visit Grand Canyon—the Patties, father and son—came up the Colorado River in 1826 trapping beaver. Along the permanent streams, wherever the encroachments of man have not forced a retreat, are found trees and logs cut by these busy animals. Occasionally a dam across some stream or a burrow in a mud bank is discovered, though most of these are temporary and difficult to find.

A multitude of other creatures add distinctive flavor to the setting of a desert canyon oasis. There are the ever present red-spotted toads, with low voices, and the canyon tree toads, with shrill, piping calls. The tree toads continually appear in unexpected places, for suction disks on their toes enable them to climb smooth, vertical surfaces. Down in the water are polliwogs, striders, whirligig beetles, and many of the other interesting animals typical of most bodies of fresh water throughout the country, while in the air may be dragonflies, caddis insects, and dam-

279

sel flies. The trail through the oasis is a source of unending surprises.

ROCKS AND FOSSILS ALONG THE TRAILS

With wild life and vegetation any facts observed along one trail at a particular altitude apply almost equally well to any other trail located at the same elevation; in contrast, most geologic features do not reflect a control by altitude but by the age and origin of particular rock formations. Accordingly, generalizations concerning the geology of Grand Canyon may be made for all the various trails in that canyon, as every trail passes through the same sequence of formations in the descent, but such generalizations will not fit other trails in the area. On the other hand, canyons of the Navajo country, including the Painted Desert, and of the Zion portion of Utah, contain different rocks, formed during the age of dinosaurs, and other descriptions are necessary for geologic features along the trails in those areas.

In few other parts of the world is the scenery and topography so closely related to the character and structure of the underlying strata as in the canyon region of northern Arizona and southern Utah. The trails of necessity alternate between very steep and more moderate grades according to the relative resistance of the essentially horizontal strata through which they pass. The very fact that, in ascending or descending, one passes through a series of formations, means that with each change a new set of geologic features is encountered. Thus, at one level may be seen deposits and fossils formed under a sea, while at another are relics of ancient desert dunes or of the floodplain of some long-vanished river.

280

With this in mind we start the descent of Grand Canyon on one of the many trails. Observing closely the rocks at or near the top, we are almost sure to find many sea shells of various types, possibly also some horn corals of conical shape, and other traces of marine life—all petrified yet preserving fine details of ornamentation. On the Kaibab and Bright Angel trails metal labels calling attention to these fossils and their significance have been placed by the National Park Service, but good specimens may be found along nearly all the trails. At some levels, also, great numbers of concretionary spheres of a gray or brown color appear in the limestone, and careful examination shows that these are masses of flint or chert with sponges in the centers. It is a fascinating pastime to see how many varieties of ancient animal remains can be located in this formation and to try to reconstruct in one's mind a picture of the region at that ancient time when the sea washed over its surface.

Farther down in the Grand Canyon one can scarcely avoid noticing the sheer, white sandstone cliff known as the Coconino, for through this formation most of the trails attain maximum steepness. The layers of sandstone within this cliff are seen to slope steeply in several directions and to form great wedges in cross section; these are believed to represent deposits of the lee slopes of ancient dunes, and on them are found, in many places, the tracks left by primitive five-toed reptiles. Here are "footprints on the sands of time." Some were made, apparently, by animals not larger than small lizards, others by creatures having big feet and a stride nearly a yard in length. Some indicate short-limbed, heavy, wide-bodied animals, while others suggest those having long slender limbs and narrow bodies. Many of the tracks are beautifully distinct, and in places they can be traced

281

for considerable distances to where they pass under a covering stratum. These footprints have been found throughout the length of Grand Canyon and along several trails have been uncovered and left exposed in place for visitors to see.

Many another milestone in the record of earth history is encountered as one continues to descend into the depths of Grand Canyon. At the level of the red shales and sandstones are found the impressions of delicate plants, including ferns that look much like modern types, small cone-bearing trees, and queer jointed-stem species, marking a time of great delta accumulation in this area. At a still lower place one encounters the record in limestone of an inland sea—a sea much older than the one represented by the rim rock referred to before. Some portions of it are seen to be composed entirely of the stems of marine animals known as sea lilies or crinoids, and in other places delicate, lacy skeletons of sea mosses are easy to find on the rock surfaces near the trails. It is fascinating to wander along a canyon path and observe, step by step, unfolding pages in the great panorama of earth history. One is finally forced to the realization that one is passing not only through space but also through time. One is traveling back through the ages. Each fifty or one hundred feet that a traveler descends carries him down in the record of earth history some thousands or even millions of years.

Interesting features to be seen at the many different geologic "horizons" in Grand Canyon are almost numberless. In one place may be found ripple marks in sandstone, looking like a washboard; in another place appear the tiny craters of rain drops impressed in what was mud some hundreds of millions of years ago; elsewhere are seen the water-rounded pebbles of an ancient beach. Even where fossils are absent and the original

282

sediments have been completely changed by terrific heat and pressure, as in the rocks of Archean age that form a large part of the bottom of Grand Canyon, there is no less a wealth of interesting features to be seen. Many of these features are difficult to interpret because of the complexity of processes that have brought about their development, but such things as the varied types of minerals, dikes formed of once-molten granite, and examples of rock layers obviously squeezed and tightly folded give the observer at least a faint concept of the great crustal revolutions and mountain-making movements through which these rocks have gone.

In the colorful canyons of southern Utah and of the Navajo country still other and different glimpses into the spectacular history of the earth may be had. Almost everywhere, in this land of little rain and much erosion, the rock surfaces are well exposed, and the record is clear. It is the record of the great "Age of Reptiles," which, although far younger than that of the eras represented in the walls of Grand Canyon, is still unbelievably old when measured by human standards. In Zion, Tsegi, and numerous other canyons, the lowest strata are those of the Painted Desert, soft in character and brilliant in color, containing much petrified wood and many fragments of ancient amphibian or reptilian life. It is fun to travel the gentle slopes and small hills of this marl or limy clay and find teeth or fragments of bony armor plates from some ancient, bizarre creature, or to stumble upon the log of an extinct type of coniferous tree, either with its cell structure still preserved in delicate detail or with the interior beautifully colored with red, yellow, and brown chalcedony.

At somewhat higher levels in the sequence of rocks through

283

which many of the canyons in the plateau area have been carved, there are red mudstones and lagoonal limestones containing the footprints of mighty dinosaurs. The three-toed tracks, some of them over a foot in length, are found in many places in the region, including a small canyon near Kanab, Utah, Zion Canyon, Dinosaur Canyon, and several localities near Rainbow Bridge. These tracks are impressive when well preserved and when exposed so that a series of evenly spaced prints is in view. Unfortunately, in many localities, they have broken up with weathering or have been stolen, and there is a real need for the development of adequate methods of preservation.

Canyon walls above the dinosaur footprint level are in most places formed of a remarkably uniform sandstone, mostly red but locally white, known as the Navajo Sandstone. Aside from the color and great cliff-forming character of this sandstone, probably the most noticeable thing about it is the fantastic pattern of swirls and curves formed by the individual layers that make up the rock—it is known to the geologist as cross-bedding. Nearly every visitor to Zion Canyon remarks about this spectacular feature, and the trails in Zion pass through many areas where it is beautifully exposed. In the walls of the Tsegi Canyons where the great cliff dwellings of Betatakin and Keet Seel are located, in Bridge Creek Canyon containing Rainbow Bridge, in Escalante, and many other places, these amazing structures are beautifully exhibited. They are explained by most geologists as the deposits of ancient sand dunes formed when this region was a great desert.

But the records that represent pages of historical geology are by no means the only geologic features of interest to be seen along the trails. There are many others—features formed

284

long since the rock layers themselves and recent as compared with the fossils in the rocks, yet commanding attention and creating interest. The canyons themselves are the products of erosion that is going on even at this moment, and graphic illustrations of erosive processes on a smaller scale, found at every turn along the trails, belong to this category. There are natural bridges and great stone arches in various stages of development in many of the sandstones, especially the Navajo. There are fantastic pinnacles such as those that make Bryce Canyon justly famous and symmetrical buttes and mesas of the type common in Grand Canyon. Then, too, there are exhibits of huge boulders and rounded pebbles along the Colorado River and other permanent streams—the playthings of the water that have been rolled about but at the moment stand idle; tools that have shared in carving the great gorges.

In many places along the trails mute evidence of great crustal disturbances is clearly visible. Here one sees rock strata bent or folded; at another point testimony that the formations were faulted is given in the form of a clear break through the strata or in rock faces polished smooth or grooved when one surface moved past the other. In the Grand Canyon nearly every trail has been made possible because of great faults that have developed lines of weakness through the strata and ultimately resulted in natural passageways through otherwise sheer cliffs. Their effects on the scenery along the trails and the character of these trails is everywhere striking.

In the visitor's book of a former hotel located on the South Rim of Grand Canyon, a guest of the early 1890's wrote: "God made the Cañon, John Hance the trails; without the other, neither would be complete." The Captain Hance to whom he referred was a famous guide and storyteller of the period when tourists started going to Grand Canyon, and he escorted many parties down the Red Canyon, Old, and Grand View trails. Farther west lived another celebrated trail man, W. W. Bass, whom no less a person than George Wharton James has described as "the only *real* guide." It was Bass who developed and partially built the Mystic Springs Trail and who pioneered the Shinumo route to the North Rim. But today the trails that these Canyon personalities made famous are no longer the ones that the average visitor sees or hears about. The Bright Angel and the Kaibab now are the main arteries of travel and are daily responsible for experiences that are told and retold whenever the name "Grand Canyon" is mentioned.

The main trails of today are a far cry from the routes traveled

The Kaibab Trail, when used in traveling from rim to rim of Grand Canyon, a little over twenty miles by trail, is normally negotiated in two days. Excellent provisions for overnight stops are afforded by the camp known as Phantom Ranch, advertised as "the lowest down ranch in the world," for it is located at the very bottom of the Canyon near the junction of Bright Angel Creek and the Colorado River. This development was started more than thirty years ago under the name of Rust Camp when irrigation was begun and trees were planted. It includes fourteen acres. After ex-President Theodore Roosevelt stayed there in 1913 while going on a hunting trip, it was called Roosevelt Camp, and later in 1925 it was named Phantom Ranch from the canyon of that name near by. Today it is equipped with many modern conveniences and, although still in a primitive setting, may be considered "de luxe" in most respects. While this camp makes a very pleasant stopping place, it is not necessary, of course, to stay here, and those who prefer to remain out under the stars will find a number of fine camp sites along the creek.

The methods used in crossing the turbulent Colorado River at the foot of the Kaibab Trail constitute an interesting history. As far back as 1903, a company of Mormons planned a cable tram, and soon after they accomplished the difficult task of packing the cable down from the North Rim by muleback. To do this the wire was rolled into two coils and each was placed on the back of an animal. One can only imagine the difficulties involved once the mules were fastened together and set in motion on a narrow canyon trail, but despite this only one mule was lost in the enterprise. In 1907 the cable was in operation, supporting a cage capable of holding a mule, and trammed back and forth over the stream. In 1921 the cable tram was replaced

292

associated with the development and history of these trails. These are routes into the wild and remote areas waiting to be "explored" by the experienced hiker or by the old-timer who finds the other sections too crowded for his tastes. More than once I have heard bitter complaints from some nature lover or camping enthusiast to the effect that Grand Canyon is too civilized to suit his desires. Let this same person leave the few miles of paved roadway, the limited "village area" with its hotels and stores, and he can find solitude aplenty.

The trails under discussion can be recommended only to those of good muscle and long endurance, although they are not dangerous under any normal conditions. Most of them should not be attempted by persons who have not had considerable experience in the area unless they are accompanied by a competent guide. They lead into remote, isolated places where a knowledge of the water holes, the suitable camping sites, and the means of taking care of oneself under various unanticipated conditions are essential to an enjoyable trip.

One very interesting though not easy route to follow is that which leads from rim to rim across Grand Canyon in the extreme eastern end. Actually it consists of several trails developed at different times and having different histories. Down from the south side near Cedar Mesa, the section known as the Tanner Trail had been used for centuries by Indians of the region in traveling to the mouth of the Little Colorado River. This route was later developed, sometime prior to 1870, by a Mormon pioneer named Seth B. Tanner, for mining and stock purposes. Many accounts of prospectors who sought the famous John D. Lee gold mines, of horse thieves who hid out in the depths, and of other interesting characters who used this trail still remain as vague stories. There is mute evidence of the activities of these old-timers in the many rock cairns and monument claims found in that seldom-visited portion of Grand Canyon's interior. A cliff dwelling, obviously made by man of post-Columbian times, stands at the isolated junction of the main and Little Colorado rivers, well concealed and well protected from the elements. In it is a small iron plow testifying to the probable intentions of some pioneer to plow the Little Colorado delta. At another remote spot, far up in the canyon of Chuar Creek, an ancient distillery has recently been found at a long-abandoned camp site.

A trail starting near Lipan Point on the south side of Grand Canyon and connecting with the Tanner Trail about fifteen hundred feet down was constructed in 1889 and called the Bunker Trail after one of its makers. Although it zigzags sharply and frequently through the Coconino sandstone, it is an improvement over the other route and has been traveled by pack outfits off and on even in recent years. From where Tanner Trail reaches the Colorado River at the big bend, it is possible to travel north along the east shore of the river some four miles to Lava Canyon, the site of an old mine tunnel at the edge of an ancient flow of basalt and the place where for years the Colorado has been crossed by parties traveling to or from the North Rim. Northward from here a large fault or break in the strata known as the Butte Fault is responsible for a natural passageway into Nankoweap Valley along the west side of a row of huge buttes or mesas. This rough but scenic route has had very little use in recent years but connects with the Nankoweap Trail leading up to the North Rim.

The Nankoweap Trail is a pathway "blazed" by scientists. It

was built by a great geologist and has since been used by a number of other geologists—all intent on reaching a unique series of rocks known as the Chuar group, in which it was believed that fossils representing some of the earliest forms of life might be preserved. Dr. C. D. Walcott, eminent paleontologist, wrote of it as follows:

> During the month of November, 1882, the Director of the Survey had constructed, under his immediate supervision, a horse trail from the brink of a lateral cañon to the bed of Nan-ko-weap valley, 3,000 feet below. Encamped in the snow, often concealed for days in the driving, frozen mist and whirling snow, the party gradually overcame the apparently insurmountable obstacles in the way, and November 24th, camp was formed in the supposed inaccessible depths of the head of the Grand Cañon, a day of reconnaissance and rest. Then the director headed his party of faithful, energetic men and left the writer, who through illness had been unable to share in the building of the trail, with three men and outfit to explore and study the inner cañon valleys between the Kaibab Plateau and the Marble Cañon, and the Grand Cañon as far as could be reached south. Seventy-two days of constant work gave some of the information wished. . . .

Conditions as described by Walcott were in strong contrast to those encountered by the writer in June, 1930, when a blazing sun in a cloudless sky beat down unmercifully, and the vast expanse of bare rocks reflected heat from every part of the Nankoweap, but the geology was still as full of interest and of problems as before.

Three trails that were much used in the 1890's for descending Grand Canyon from the South Rim are the Old, Red Canyon, and Grandview—all located about midway between the Tanner and Kaibab trails or about eight to twelve miles from the Can-

yon's eastern end. The Old Trail has been utilized by Havasupai Indians for untold centuries but was improved by the
famous guide, Captain Hance, who settled near its head. After
this, it was frequently referred to as the Hance Trail and as
early as 1882 was traveled by a Mrs. Edward Ayres, who was
reputed to be the first white woman to go to the bottom of
Grand Canyon. Ropes had to be used to lower people over one
cliff in the lower part. By 1900 the trail was "washed out and
practically inaccessible," according to George Wharton James.
Certainly it is no better today, and, although with difficulty the
route may still be used on foot, virtually no traces of the trail
are left.

The Red Canyon Trail, sometimes known as the New Hance
Trail, is located near Moran Point, a few miles east of Old
Trail, and was built to replace the latter route. Between 1895
and 1898, many tourists coming by stage from Flagstaff descended Red Canyon Trail, and in later years it was used for
packing asbestos out of the Canyon from mines across the river.
Recently an old wooden sign with much-weathered but faintly
discernible words on it, "Toll on Trail, Foot Man $1.00, Saddle
Animal $2.00," was found nailed to a large tree at the trail
head. The name of this trail is very appropriate, for along its
lower portions are rocks of Algonkian age which are the most
brilliant red of any in a canyon noted for its red coloring. Near
the foot of the trail are some of the worst rapids along the entire Colorado River—the Hance and Sockdolager, each of which
accounts for a drop of about twenty feet in a quarter of a mile.
Unfortunate it is that this trail is no longer passable by horse
and is difficult on foot.

The third of the trails commonly used by stage tourists from
300

Flagstaff prior to 1900 was formerly known as the Berry Trail after a pioneer of that name who constructed it in 1892 and 1893. In more recent years it has usually been referred to as the Grandview Trail. It was not built primarily for tourists but to enable the working of copper mines halfway down the Canyon. During much of the time that these were in operation, eight to ten mules with a packer were run over the trail each day. The mines ceased operation in 1907, so the trail was not kept up after that date, but even now it is in fair shape for hiking, although covered in places by slides. Although not a route for visiting the Canyon bottom, it is very interesting for a relatively short trip. In narrow steep portions near the top it is actually built of logs like a staircase or gangplank. Unlike most other trails it follows a ridge rather than a valley much of the way, thus affording splendid views, and it leads to the interesting mining camp, tunnels, and shafts. Near its foot on Horseshoe Mesa is a large solution cave in the limestone.

The name "Hermit," which has been given to numerous objects located in the area about eight miles west of Grand Canyon Village, was originally suggested by the presence in that region of a pioneer named Louie Boucher. What is probably the most seldom traveled and least-known canyon trail today was built by old Louie sometime between 1889 and 1893. The upper part leads to the charming locality known as Dripping Springs, where water drips from the sandstone and maidenhair ferns abound, then enters Hermit basin from the southwest. A continuation of it along the upper west walls of Hermit Canyon descends into Boucher Canyon farther down, and there, among some Cottonwood trees, Louie established what must have been a rather comfortable, if isolated, camp.

301

A second trail was constructed down into Hermit Basin and Hermit Canyon in 1911 and 1912. This trail was built by the Santa Fe Railroad and was for tourist use. It skirted the east side of the Canyon and descended all the way to the river. In 1919 it was turned over to the National Park Service, which maintained it for over twelve years, when it was finally abandoned. Today this trail is still in fair shape although it could not be used by horses without some repair work. The trail is very scenic because of its location on the side of a narrow, deep gorge carved in red rocks, and many natural features along the way have been given picturesque names such as Santa Maria Springs, Cathedral Stairs, and the White Zigzags. About a mile below the top in the White Coconino sandstone is a locality famous for the discovery in it of well-preserved fossil footprints made by primitive reptiles. Many of these tracks, of various sizes and shapes, are found near the trail.

During the past century the main route used in crossing the Grand Canyon was some twenty-two miles west of where Grand Canyon Village is now located. Leading down from the South Rim was the Mystic Springs Trail, used by the Havasupai Indians to reach the Mystic Springs that later vanished, following an earthquake. The trail was improved and continued on down to the Colorado River by the pioneer guide and prospector W. W. Bass, and today it is usually known as the Bass Trail. Leading down from the North Rim, just east of Point Sublime, is the Shinumo Trail, developed in part by a prospector named White. Mining claims are recognized as a cause for this development, but there are indications that the route was commonly used by a band of horse thieves in reaching their rendezvous. In later years Bass developed both copper and asbestos mines in the

302

area and used his trail to the South Rim in packing out these minerals. He also built up a good tourist trade, and in 1900 developed a fine fruit orchard and garden plot near the mouth of Shinumo Creek. It was referred to as Shinumo Gardens. Today the Bass Trail from the South Rim is still passable by horse and is an interesting route, but the upper part of the Shinumo Trail is nearly overgrown with vegetation and therefore nonexistent. The Colorado River was in the early days crossed by a boat at this point, but later a cable tram was constructed. The tram is still to be seen at the crossing but probably is no longer safe.

One other trail that leads into the Canyon bottom within Grand Canyon National Park is known by the romantic name of Thunder River Trail. Actually it consists of two trails that begin some miles apart, in the western section of the North Rim, but join partway down. As the name suggests, the trail leads to a place where a sizable stream of water comes rushing out from rock walls and then cascades spectacularly down below. The trail in its upper portions passes through some fine scenic sections of what is locally referred to as the "sand rocks" or the Esplanade of red sandstone; one curious rock is known as the Crazy Jug. Below the springs, the "river" plunges into Tapeats Creek in a narrow canyon a few miles above the Colorado River. It is possible to reach the river at this point over a rude trail. All of the Thunder River Trail is rough, but a surprisingly large number of parties have traveled it—some on foot and some by horse —within recent years.

All of the trails described thus far from Grand Canyon National Park are ones that descend from the rims into the inner portions of the Canyon. There are, however, some interesting routes for travel, both with and without trails, that follow

303

benches at various levels through the Canyon. One of these is the shelf of green shale known as the Tonto Platform, which is about four thousand feet above sea level, or three thousand feet below the Canyon rims. South of the Colorado River it may be traversed with pack and saddle animals all the way from Bass Trail in the west to Red Canyon Trail in the east, although about two weeks are necessary in order to do this. The air-line distance between those places is not many miles, but the actual travel distance is unbelievably great, for it is necessary to skirt around the heads of innumerable tributary canyons and many branches to each of these. Frequently one sees one's goal a half mile or so ahead but has to travel two or three miles to attain it. Another bench of the same type that forms a natural route for travel is the red Esplanade at about fifteen hundred feet below the upper rim. This platform is narrow in eastern Grand Canyon but from Bass Trail westward makes a good route for travel. An interesting trip along it with pack outfit is from Havasu Canyon east to the end of the Great Thumb, where an Indian trail ascends to the rim.

Travel along intra-Canyon benches makes interesting outings for those who really want to get the spirit of the Canyon, enjoy its solitude and wildness, and forget the ordinary troubles of life. Such trips should never be rush affairs. Portions of them will be over rough and rugged terrain and locally may require some trailmaking to get pack animals through, but, by and large, travel is easy because of trails developed and maintained by wild burros and other animals. Scenery is not so exciting and varied as along the Colorado River, but except very locally no travel is possible along the river except by the very difficult boat method. The really big problem in traveling the intra-Canyon

304

benches is that of water. Without knowledge of the springs and water holes, long trips should never be attempted, and, for that reason, it is normally expedient to have a competent guide. In order to make such a trip pleasant, furthermore, one should pick one's season. The summer is excessively hot; the winter may be cold and stormy even at the lower levels; so the dry fall season or the late spring usually are the best.

TRAILS OF WESTERN GRAND CANYON

Points of outstanding scenic value and trails of unusual interest within Grand Canyon are by no means confined to the National Park portion, which is the eastern half. Although that area is far better known, more accessible, and visited by a vastly greater number of people than any other and, therefore, is commonly thought of as the only part, Grand Canyon is *grand* from beginning to end. The comparatively little-known western portion does not duplicate the scenery farther east but is equally remarkable in its own way. There are brilliant colors, sheer cliffs, and broad expanses enough to impress even the most casual visitor.

Perhaps the most unique "trail" in the entire Grand Canyon is at the foot of Toroweap Valley, where, draining from the north, the valley joins the Grand Canyon near its center. This route is the shortest and doubtless one of the roughest down to the Colorado River. It is located in an area of great volcanism which causes the anomalous situation of making the descent possible, on the one hand, but extremely difficult, on the other. Great flows of black lava have filled up the former mouth of the Toroweap in this section, and later sheets of basalt have

305

come cascading down from above, mostly covering the older lavas and plunging into the stream below. In the colorful words of Major Powell, veteran explorer and scientist of the past century: "What a conflict of water and fire there must have been here! Just imagine a river of molten rock, running down into a river of melted snow. What a seething and boiling of the waters; what clouds of steam rolled into the heavens!"

The Toroweap "trail" starts at the west base of a symmetrical cinder cone known as Vulcan's Throne. This is but one of 169 small volcanoes formed in the immediate area by the piling up of ejected materials around central vents. A similar cone is seen directly across the Canyon perched on the very brink and undermined by erosion in such a way that its "internal anatomy," consisting of a dike extending down into the depths, is partially exposed as in a textbook drawing of a volcano. As one descends into Grand Canyon, part of the time one slides in loose deposits of cinders and ash; at other times the visitor must climb, hand over hand, over firm but rough sheets of basalt, or must pick his way with care among jagged blocks of lava. So fresh do many of these flows appear that it is easy to visualize them as fiery cascades pouring into the abyss. And, by way of contrast, just across the gorge are the horizontal strata of colorful sedimentary rocks that normally dominate Grand Canyon scenery and that form the frame over which these lavas are draped. The trail is spectacular if nothing else. In its lower, steeper portions it follows the break made by a great fault, down into a section where on both sides of the gorge remnants of a great lava dam, five hundred feet high, that once blocked the Colorado River, are plainly visible. At the trail's end is the river of today, still at work cutting downward and roaring terrifically as though resentful at having been temporarily stopped by the lava. Here is Lava Falls—one of the greatest of Colorado River rapids.

Except for the Toroweap, all of the trails from the north side of Grand Canyon leading to the Colorado River are considerably longer than those from the south. This is partly due to the higher elevations attained along the northern rim and partly because most of these trails follow natural passageways formed by canyons, all of which are longer north of the Colorado. The greatest of all the tributary canyons in this area is that of Kanab Creek, which begins in southern Utah and enters Grand Canyon west of the Kaibab Plateau.

Kanab Canyon is the route of scientists. Through its narrow winding passages went several important expeditions in the early days of geological exploration. Major John Wesley Powell ended his second famous boat trip down the turbulent Colorado in 1872 at the mouth of this canyon and through it returned to civilization. Dr. G. K. Gilbert, one of the most eminent of American geologists, also visited here in 1872, and Dr. Charles D. Walcott, former Secretary of the Smithsonian Institution, made studies of its strata in 1879. In all the years since, however, little has been placed on record concerning this vast and beautiful chasm, and only casual sheepherders or local cowboys from the small Mormon towns to the north have broken the solitude of its fastnesses by packing in from above. It is about five days' travel on horse from Kanab, and nearly as much by way of Hacks Canyon to the west, down to the Colorado. It is a trip over wild, rugged country—across the red "sandrocks," around the ends of promontory after promontory of limestone plateau, down a breath-taking trail into an even deeper canyon, and finally along the creek itself in the very bottom, where walls

307

are so close together and so high that one feels lost to the world. Here is an ideal trail for the person who wants to "rough it," to see beautiful scenery, exciting geology, and natural history, and above all to spend a vacation "exploring" with a pack outfit and a good guide.

Farther west in Grand Canyon, between the Uinkaret and Shivwits plateaus and near where the great Hurricane fault cuts into the Canyon from the north, are several large and spectacular canyons down which rough trails have been developed. One of these, known as Whitmore Wash, is used by local sheepherders in descending to the Colorado; another, farther west, is known as Parashant. About halfway down, the latter leads into one of the narrowest sheer-walled canyons of great height to be found anywhere in the region. Cliffs of Redwall limestone are so close together in places that it seems as though a person could almost jump across, and yet the sides are nearly perpendicular for five or six hundred feet.

Approaching western Grand Canyon from the south, the descent is a relatively simple matter, but the scenery is correspondingly less spectacular than in other portions, though by no means poor. Indeed, as one gets near the Canyon bottom and looks up, the brilliant colors and the sheerness of the walls give a very impressive feeling of grandeur, solitude, and natural beauty. This is the land of the Walapai Indians, and a number of trails into the Canyon have been in use by them for a long time. One route—down Peach Springs Draw and the canyon of Diamond Creek—follows such a gentle grade that stages were able to travel it in the early days, and a "rude lumber hotel" was in operation at the creek mouth prior to 1900. In recent years a few cars with good clearance have been able to battle the roughness of the wash and have gone most of the distance to the river during certain seasons.

At Bridge Canyon and at Meriwitica Canyon farther west are fairly good foot trails which start at the level of the Redwall that forms the plateau surface in this area. The descent is not great in either case as compared to that along other Grand Canyon trails. Desert vegetation is especially interesting along these routes, and the scenery is fine, so they are recommended for relatively short but attractive trips.

TRAILS IN ZION AND BRYCE CANYONS

The satisfaction of conducting many groups of visitors through the wonderful Zion-Bryce areas of southern Utah has been the privilege of Mr. Orlo Childs while serving as ranger naturalist for the National Park Service during several summer seasons. In discussing with Mr. Childs the pros and cons of the various trails, so many interesting ideas—attained through his wide experience with parties—were brought out that many of these ideas are here repeated virtually as expressed by him.

One of the "musts" of any introduction to Zion Canyon is the short, easy hike over the often-visited Great Arch Trail. The starting point for this is at the eastern entrance to the mile-long Zion Tunnel, which is reached by travel over the spectacular Mount Carmel Highway—the road that never fails to draw the "Ohs" and "Ahs" of travelers because of odd-shaped red and white rocks along its route. Leaving the parking area near this road, the trail rises quickly twenty or thirty feet above the creek and road bed and then levels off for the balance of its one-half-mile length. It makes its way along a rather constant ledge,

309

now and then dodging back under overhanging "roofs" with enough variety in scenery and diversity in wild flowers to keep interest high. Far below, the bed of Pine Creek is seen to curve through its open cut and then descend from view in stairlike drops, at the same time becoming so narrow and so tortuous that it appears virtually impossible for a man to make his way along the creek bed. Abruptly the trail ends, and to the hiker there opens a magnificent view far down and across the southern end of Zion Canyon. The tiny ribbon of the Mount Carmel Highway emerges from the Zion Tunnels and winds downward to the floor of the Canyon four thousand feet below the distant west wall of Zion. There stands the highest point in the park, West Temple, with the Towers of the Virgin and the Altar of Sacrifice lined up to the north. The striking impression of size and scale gained in this "bird's-eye view" from the rim is of great value to the visitor, for it assists him in retaining true perspective in his succeeding "worm's-eye view," as he goes down into Zion Canyon proper.

The Zion road runs seven miles from the Park entrance upstream along the Virgin River, on the Canyon floor. On both sides the vertical massive walls rise from deep red foundations to creamy white "crests." Gradually those great walls seem to close in at the expense of a constantly restricting valley floor, until the road ends in the Temple of Sinawava. The reason for the end is very obvious—there is simply no more room for both the river and the road. From this point the Narrows Trail takes up and continues upstream for a mile and a half, where it suffers the same fate—not enough room. At the Narrows the river occupies the entire floor of the deep, narrow, red gorge, and, in the distance, as the "V" of the gorge opens at the top, stands the

Zion-Mount Carmel Highway
switchbacks down into Zion
Canyon.

Zion Canyon.

Bald eagle.

Chicadee.

Beaver.

Coyote.

Big-horned mountain sheep.

challenge of a clean, white spire, the "Mountain of Mystery." This is the most-visited trail in the Park, and its easy level course makes available to any visitor the many features of interest along the trailside. Here the deep shade of a narrow gorge makes pleasant walking throughout most of the day. Only for a short period in the middle of the day does the sunlight fill the Canyon.

The climate in Zion Canyon is that of a desert, with midsummer temperatures soaring over one hundred degrees. The hiker soon finds himself taking advantage of any friendly shade. In this dry atmosphere it is often the case that, although the thermometer reaches new heights in the experience of the visitor, there is always relief and comfort in the shade. Possibly this is the reason for the attractive suggestion in the name Refrigerator Canyon, given one of the side gorges. The shade also has its effects on the assemblage of resident plants and animals. An amateur ecologist, who is accustomed to the beltlike zoning of different plants and animals, here finds an interesting confusion. On slopes that catch the sun, cactus and yucca of the Lower Sonoran zone stand side by side with juniper and piñon of the Upper Sonoran. Then within a few yards stand the conifers of the Transition zone, and even Canadian types are identified. Down by the river, mule deer are often seen. There are so many features of biological and geological interest that daily "nature-walks" are sponsored here by the National Park Service in order that all may see and enjoy the Narrows Trail.

One cannot stay long in Zion Canyon without being attracted by the trails that ascend the Canyon walls to the East Rim and to the West Rim. Visitors at Zion Lodge always enjoy looking across at the west wall and watching a hiking party make its way up Zion's most difficult trail to the top of Lady Mountain. A warning sign stands at the foot of the trail to tell the hiker that his shoes must be sturdy, his nerve steady, and his attitude such that he is willing to stay on the trail. The hiker is not far along the trail before he is convinced of the importance of all three suggestions. Upward the trail winds, with countless steps quarried out of the rock and six hundred feet of steel cable strung along over the most difficult rises. It is most reassuring to have one's hand on the cable when there is a fifteen-hundred-foot drop to the river just below. Usually one reminder to stay on the trail is all that is needed. Often the cry is, "Sure, I'll stay on it, but where does it go from here?" At the end of the two-mile climb the adventurer "tops out" on Lady Mountain and looks down twenty-five hundred feet to the river, and to the tiny patch of green lawn in front of Zion Lodge where the even smaller colored dots that are people move slowly here and there, while beetle-like cars follow the curving ribbon of road. From this point Zion Canyon tells its own story of "what happened here." It is easily visualized that a scouring, persistent Virgin River has entrenched itself into a high, flat-topped plateau, and that, while the weathering processes and slope-wash from rains have caused the walls to recede, the very character of those walls has decreed that they maintain their vertical character during the retreat. From here it is seen that what had appeared from the Canyon floor as lofty mountains lined up along both sides of the Canyon course are really just dissected edges of the high extensive plateau into which this deep cut has been made.

All ascents to the rim do not demand such an arduous climb as that of Lady Mountain; the trail to Observation Point on the East Rim and the West Rim trail are carefully graded, and daily horseback trips are made. Yet even this method of climbing

312

is not without its physical discomfort, as many a patron willingly admits, for, along with the traditional effects of an uphill-downhill trip in the saddle, there is always the nagging question, "Will old Dobbin remember to turn when the trail does?" Of course, he always does, but there are many who are not thoroughly convinced by statistics.

For those who hike Zion trails for the grand views they afford, there is always the alternative of exploring such side routes as that of Hidden Canyon, which branches off the East Rim trail and makes its way up beneath the vertical back wall behind the famous Great White Throne. Then, from the West Rim trail, there is the branch out onto the Angels' Landing. This brings one of the greatest thrills of the Canyon, as the trail goes along a knifelike ridge, in one place only three feet wide and a near fifteen-hundred-foot drop off both sides. Yes, there are reassuring one-inch pipes stretched along such places, and many visitors are seen hanging on for dear life. In every group there are those who soon discover the three or four echoes that bounce back and forth down the Canyon as one shouts across the top of Refrigerator Canyon. Angels' Landing at the end proves well worth the detour, as it stands fifteen hundred feet above the river and out in the center of the Canyon, affording an unusual scenic view both upstream and down.

There is one unwritten law governing summer hiking at Zion, and the midseason visitor is usually happy to comply. Hike to the East Rim in the morning, when the Canyon wall is in shade. Take the West Rim trail in the afternoon when it is shaded, and carry your own water. During brief periods in the winter, snow may block the upper portions of these trails, but otherwise all of the Zion trails are usable throughout the year.

313

Altogether there are about twenty-six miles of trails developed for the use of hikers and leading to interesting sections of Zion Canyon not reached by road. These trails are made to fit the interests and capabilities of all types of people, so that any person visiting this canyon should be able to do some hiking. Unfortunate indeed is the visitor who is so rushed or so lacking in ability to "overcome inertia" that he fails to take advantage of any trails. Even though many wonderful views and much that is worth while can be seen from the highways and hotel porches, the spirit of the canyons is to be found along the trails.

To the person accustomed to true canyons, the name "Bryce Canyon" seems a misnomer. Actually it applies to a part of the precipitous eastern edge of a high tableland known as the Paunsaugunt Plateau, and includes thirteen brilliantly colored natural amphitheaters. Each one of this array of alcoves opens eastward with a wide vista beyond. Among the first to be observed by visitors approaching along the highway is one of the largest and most interesting. This particular amphitheater is readily seen to be the dissected headwater area of a stream that flows toward the east, through a small canyon, to the distant valley floor of the Paria River. The canyon was once part of the property of a colorful pioneer settler, Ebenezer Bryce, and, according to local custom, his name was attached to the entire course of the stream from headwater to mouth. From it eventually the National Park took its name.

It is through the great stadium-like headwaters basin of Bryce that the principal trails in this area have been constructed, and, hence, it is here the visitor becomes aware of Bryce Canyon

314

National Park's dual personality. One concept of that personality is gained by those who travel the rim by automobile and are thrilled by the brilliant colors and intricate erosional sculpturing of the plateau edge. Yet an entirely different experience awaits those who take the foot trails and horseback trails down into the maze of colored spires and delicate walls.

Most of the trails into Bryce Canyon are short and easy. The longest of all, the "Peek-a-boo Trail" is but three and one half miles in length and can be walked in forty-five minutes, yet few people care to try for speed records over a course so interesting. Down the Comanche Trail and back by way of the Navajo Trail, starting and ending at Sunset Point, is a most popular trip. Here the predominant reds and pinks seen from the rim are replaced by delicate shades of yellow, white, and lavender. Rock masses that from above are insignificant become statue-like pedestals, standing in defiance of the rainwash and weathering that cause the rim to retreat at a rate of about a foot in fifty years. The return is through "Wall Street," the main street of the "Silent Cry." Then it is that the hiker becomes aware of the reverse of an old axiom, for here "what goes down, must come up." At eight-thousand-foot elevation that is not always as easy as it sounds!

Another trail that catches the imagination—and Bryce Canyon always appeals to those with most active imaginations—is the one that descends to the "Queen's Garden," where "Queen Victoria" surveys her gaily colored, though somewhat inactive, courtyard.

The diminutive, delicate character of the fantastic natural sculpturing in soft colorful rock is the principal feature of Bryce Canyon, down under the rim. One should not miss the oppor-

315

tunity to come to know this dual personality of Bryce Canyon National Park.

The trails of Zion and Bryce canyons that have been discussed are the well-advertised trails, traveled annually by hundreds of visitors. But for the hiker who really wishes to experience something different, there are numerous other areas that can be reached by trails or old roads. Mr. Russell Grater, former park naturalist of Zion and Bryce National Parks, has kindly furnished the following data on trails of the back country not commonly traveled by visitors to this region.

In Zion, the Parunuweap Canyon offers a combination of superlative scenery, heavily vegetated river bottoms, and ancient Indian ruins. Here in this region the early Pueblo Indians once built their homes, and the sites can still be found in many places. The trail leading into this canyon is old and almost lacking in many places. It is possible to go approximately eight miles into the canyon before the terrain becomes too difficult. Drinking water can be found in a number of places, which is a bit unusual for high desert country. The trail is not recommended for the poorly equipped or totally inexperienced hiker.

Another Zion trail seldom traveled by the visitor leads from the end of the West Rim Trail on over the Markagunt Plateau to the Kolob Terrace, thence either down through the broken western edge of the plateau to Cedar City via an old road or on to Cedar Breaks National Monument. The district covered on such a trip takes the hiker through some of the most colorful country in Utah and into elevations exceeding ten thousand feet above sea level, where vast forests of aspen and spruce stretch for miles.

At Bryce Canyon only one trail stands out to challenge the experienced hiker. This trail starts from the Bryce Point region and travels along the base of the brilliantly hued cliffs until it reaches

316

Rainbow Point, where it climbs out on top of the plateau. It is seldom traveled but leads through some of the most picturesque parts of the Park. It can be hiked in one day, but offers excellent opportunities for overnight camps along the way.

OTHER CANYON TRAILS

Canyons in the Plateau Country are legion. Some big, some small, they are like the ranges, peaks, and foothills of a great mountain system in reverse. All of them are accessible in greater or less degree—some by road, some by well-graded trail, others only by the roughest, most difficult type of trail. To attempt a description of all of these is obviously far beyond the scope of this book, but some few representative examples leading to places of outstanding interest merit attention.

Along the southern margin of the Colorado Plateau south and west of Flagstaff, Arizona, a large series of canyons has been cut back from the surrounding low country like scallops in lace. Most of these canyons are several thousand feet deep at their lowest ends and are colorful throughout. Best known among them are Sycamore, Oak Creek, Beaver, West Clear Creek, and Fossil Creek. All of these begin on a lava-covered surface, rapidly descend through horizontal layers of gray limestone and white sandstone, and then expose to view many shades of red and vermilion sandstone in their lower walls.

Beaver Creek, which has branches known as Dry Beaver and Wet Beaver, appears to have been the route used by Pueblo Indians of prehistoric times in traveling between villages on the Plateau and those in the fertile Verde Valley below; it probably also was the passage followed by the Spanish expeditions of

317

Espejo and Farfan to the copper mines of the Verde in the sixteenth century; it has been used by modern Hopi Indians within the memory of the older men of the tribe. Oak Creek, on the other hand, probably was not a main route of travel in early times because of the precipitous walls at its head and the dense vegetation along the stream in its bottom, but today, with the construction of an excellent paved highway down its center, it is by far the best known of the canyons along the southern edge of the Plateau. Oak Creek Canyon is justly famous for its brilliant coloring, its spectacular cliffs, and its beautiful stream, but it is closely rivaled by a less accessible neighbor—Sycamore Canyon.

Some miles to the north of the southern edge of the Plateau is a series of small limestone canyons carved by temporary streams which, when flowing, drain north and east. Illustrative of these are Chevelon, East Clear Creek, and Walnut canyons. All of these are developed in a well-forested portion of the Plateau and, though relatively small, cut through the gray surface limestone into white sandstone below. Compared to other canyons in the region they are lacking in color and impressiveness. Walnut Canyon alone has obtained considerable fame because in its walls are numerous interesting cliff dwellings dating back six or seven centuries. Because of these, the area has been created a National Monument, and an excellent short but steep path has been constructed down one side to the archaeological features.

Northward in the Navajo Country, especially near the Arizona-Utah border, is another family of canyons. These are the

318

wild and rugged desert gorges cut into the brilliant red sandstones of the "Age of Dinosaurs." The region is one in which
mesa and tableland characterize the landscape, where canyons
have vertical walls that are climbed by drifting sand dunes; a
country in which erosion creates fantastic forms in red rocks and
where the Navajo Indian blends perfectly into the desert setting. It is a land that stirs the imagination and that until recent
years has been extremely isolated and inaccessible. Nearly every
stream course, draining toward the Colorado River to the north,
turns into a deep canyon on its way, and even now, with roads
and civilization encroaching ever closer to the borders of the
area, most of it can be traversed only by horse or foot. As in
every desert region, water is a vital problem, and a knowledge
of the springs and water holes is essential to travel in this area.

Outstanding among the many trails of interest in the northern Navajo Country is that which leads to Rainbow Bridge—
one of the largest and most remarkably proportioned natural
bridges in the world. The trail starts at Rainbow Lodge at the
end of a rough dirt road; it circles the west base of a great dome
known as Navajo Mountain, following deep red canyons most
of the way; it traverses an exceptionally narrow and spectacular
divide known as Redbud Pass in going from one canyon to the
next, and at the end of fourteen miles brings one to the great
red sandstone bridge nestled down among some of the wildest
and most scenic country in the United States. The trail is good,
as trails in this region go, for horse or foot, but let no person
attempt the trip if he is unwilling to undergo the little discomforts that are bound to accompany a desert trip over rough terrain. For the more enterprising, on the other hand, the trip

319

may be continued past Rainbow Bridge through the gorgeous scenery of Forbidding Canyon and down to the Colorado River where it rushes through Glen Canyon.

Other trails of the northern Navajo Country that can not be ignored in any description of routes to outstanding features of this area are those that lead to the wonderful cliff dwellings of the Tsegi canyons. The name *Tsegi,* meaning "canyon," is applied to a network of deep gorges of the type found throughout this region and includes branch canyons with such colorful names as Dogoszhi Biko, Betatakin, and Keet Seel, derived from the Navajo language. The latter two names are also applied to cave pueblos of unusual size and interest that are found beneath great overhanging cliffs in these canyons. Keet Seel includes over 250 rooms and fills a cave 350 feet long and 50 feet deep; Betatakin is nearly as large, yet both are dwarfed by the great red canyon walls which surround them. To see these ruins in such a setting is a thrilling experience and can be readily accomplished by those who are willing to "rough it." The National Park Service has developed the area so that a walk of only one mile down into the canyon is now necessary to reach Betatakin from the end of a dirt road on the mesa above. Nine more miles by horse or foot over a rough trail take one to Keet Seel. There are many lesser cave pueblos of interest in this area, and the scenic, geologic, and biologic features are such as to make very attractive to the lover of out-of-doors the "exploration" of all these canyons. Needless to say, this can only be done safely with the assistance and knowledge of a native of the area, but it is nice to know that such extensive untamed and unspoiled areas still remain in this country.

320

North of the Colorado River where it goes through Glen Canyon is another vast area of deep, colorful canyons and seldom-visited plateaus similar to that of the northern Navajo Country. A glance at any road map will show the extensive territory extending from the Colorado to the San Rafael and from Mexican Hat to the Paria that is almost unpenetrated by any road. It is dissected by many canyons and is rough and rugged in the extreme, resembling in many respects the Navajo Country to the south. It is a country ideally suited for extensive pack trips in which fine scenery and interesting experiences, as well as freedom from the ways of a humdrum civilization, are sought. Escalante Canyon, the largest in this area, following the stream course as it winds this way and that between high sandstone walls, is especially delightful to travel through.

The reader of this chapter, if he is familiar with the region, may wonder why no mention is made of certain other beautiful, spectacular, or otherwise notable canyons in the Plateau Province, and the trails within them. There is pretty little Blue Canyon, and its neighbor, Coal Canyon, in the heart of the Navajo Reservation; there are canyons de Chelly and del Muerto, with remarkable cliff dwellings in them; there are the deep Kolob canyons near Zion, the little Colorado and Marble canyons leading up to Grand Canyon, and the Black Dragon of east central Utah. Each person probably has his own particular pet—each canyon certainly has its own features of interest and is remarkable in its own way. The truth of the matter is that there is almost no end to the wonderful canyons of the Colorado Plateau, all of which offer inducements for hiking, riding, camping, and "exploring."

CHAPTER TWELVE

ENVIRONMENT CONTROLS LIFE

By Edwin D. McKee

It was no mere accident that in 1889 the Division of Ornithology and Mammalogy of the Department of Agriculture selected the San Francisco Mountain-Grand Canyon area for initial study in an attempt to comprehend the diversity of climates and of zones of plant and animal life found with change in altitude. The field party, under the leadership of Dr. C. Hart Merriam, realized that few places in the United States offered such contrasts. On one hand was an isolated mountain rising above timber line to an altitude of 12,600 feet; on the other, a desert canyon descending to an elevation of 2,500 feet. In forty miles of horizontal distance, there was a vertical difference of a mile and a half.

Out of the investigation made by Dr. Merriam and his party came an appreciation of the fact that the very apparent zones of plant and animal life, ranging from low to high in canyons and mountains of the Southwest, are in reality counterparts of the great belts of life encountered with change in latitude as one goes northward across the continent. The Life Zone theory emerged. It became a recognized fact that a difference in ele-

325

vation of one thousand feet is roughly equivalent in its effects on plant and animal life to a change of three hundred miles of latitude at sea level.

Advocates of the Life Zone theory generally have recognized on the North American continent seven principal zones, as follows: the Tropical, Lower Sonoran or Lower Austral, Upper Sonoran or Upper Austral, Transition, Canadian, Hudsonian, and Arctic-Alpine. Of these seven, six are represented in the remarkable section between the top of the San Francisco Mountains and the bottom of Grand Canyon; only the tropical is missing. So clearly defined are these zones over the entire Canyon Country that they constitute a very convenient framework for biological comparisons and for making generalizations regarding the climate and the plant and animal life. Obviously these zones do not change abruptly from one to another but blend into one another as the altitude varies; this fact, however, does not invalidate their value or usefulness in classifying the broad floral and faunal associations of the region.

It should be clear to most observers that, since life zones vary with altitude, the chief controlling factors are temperature, which decreases, and precipitation, which increases, with advance upward. Thus, by correlation of natural distribution with climatic factors, a general rule has been formulated which states that the upper limit of a species is determined primarily by temperature and the lower limit by moisture. In brief, each type of plant will extend its range downward only so far as the rainfall will meet its minimum requirements but will be limited upward by the amount of cold that it can survive. Various other factors such as soil depth and acidity, exposure, steepness of slope, and insulation also affect the forest types, but these con-

326

ditions show their influence chiefly on the local plant communities or associations rather than on the broad belts or zones.

Weather records from many stations clearly illustrate contrasts among the various zones throughout the Plateau area. The Fort Valley Forest Experiment Station near Flagstaff, Arizona, has determined temperature and precipitation readings for the San Francisco Mountain area as follows:

Altitude	Mean Annual Temperature	Precipitation Annually
6000 ft.	52.8	16.7
7000 ft.	45.6	22.7
9000 ft.	41.3	34.2
10,500 ft.	35.7	36.4

Similar striking contrasts are found in the Grand Canyon area, where the records indicate annual precipitation on the north side at an elevation of eight thousand feet to be about twenty-six inches, on the south side at seven thousand feet to be approximately eighteen inches, and at twenty-five hundred feet in the Canyon bottom, almost immediately below, only about twelve inches. Furthermore, the temperature of the Canyon bottom averages some twenty degrees warmer than that on the South Rim, and thirty-five degrees warmer than that on the North Rim, throughout most of the year. In desert portions of the Navajo country, even less rainfall occurs than in the bottom of Grand Canyon. H. E. Gregory gives figures from five widely scattered stations at elevations between thirty-five hundred and fifty-five hundred feet above sea level in which mean annual precipitation ranges between five and seven inches. In this country even secondary topographic features exercise a significant control on the climate, so conditions on the floor of a canyon may be quite unlike those on the rim.

A few striking examples may serve to illustrate the extreme differences in climatic conditions that are constantly encountered while going from low to high in the Canyon Country. Snow seldom reaches the bottom of Grand Canyon and, during those rare exceptions, remains on the ground but briefly. In contrast, snow has been recorded on the South Rim (7,000 feet) as late as early June, and in 1933 a snowstorm occurred at Point Imperial on the North Rim (8,800 feet) on July 23. In the Canyon bottom turpentine broom has been found in blossom by February 8, when heavy snows still covered both rims; other spring flowers such as anemone, wild sweet pea, fleabane, and wild carrots were in bloom by mid-February. This is one of the coldest months on top, however, and in 1933 record "lows" of -14 degrees on the South Rim and -25 degrees on the North Rim were officially recorded during February. Another striking contrast is seen in the total snowfall, which, during the winter of 1931-1932 amounted to 210 inches on the North Rim, 97 on the lower South Rim, and none in the Canyon bottom.

Evaporation is a closely related climatic factor which is highly significant in its influence on the belts of plant and animal life, especially in a semidesert or desert region. Measurements made by the Fort Valley Forest Experiment Station indicate that, at the six-thousand-foot elevation on San Francisco Mountain, total evaporation during the summer as determined from a free water surface is about six times as great as the precipitation for that period; at seven thousand feet it is about twice as great, and at nine thousand feet approximately the same as the precipitation. This clearly indicates that, at the lower altitudes, the normal small precipitation available to plant life is further greatly lessened by evaporation. Plants of these zones, there-

328

fore, must be especially equipped in order to obtain and to hold moisture, if they are to survive.

The seven recognized belts or life zones ranging from tropic to arctic, as already described, are controlled by climate but are recognized by certain plants or groups of plants, usually referred to as "indicators." These plants in turn influence the animal life so that each life zone is found to be characterized by a particular assemblage of plants and animals. Of course, there are some plants and many animals that range through, and, therefore, are representative of, more than one zone, but that does not detract from the fundamental concept that definite zones represented by certain restricted species exist throughout the region.

The Lower Sonoran is the desert zone—the lowest, driest, and hottest belt in the region. It derives its name from the state of Sonora in Mexico, where, at the lower elevations, a desert environment is characteristically developed. In the Plateau Country this zone is represented wherever the altitude is less than five thousand feet as in the lower parts of Grand Canyon, the bottom of Zion, most portions of the Painted Desert, and the floors of various canyons farther north. Its vegetation has a distinctive and peculiar character due to the mingling of plants that differ greatly in form, size, habit of growth, and manner of adaptation to the arid climate. Animal life likewise is made up of an ill-sorted group of species that have in common the ability to survive under very adverse climatic conditions. Both plants and animals must make the most of short periods that are very favorable to life in order to endure long periods that are most unfavorable.

Some botanists classify the Lower Sonoran portions of the

329

Plateau province as a part of the "Great Basin Microphyll Desert," in contrast with the "Arizona Succulent Desert" of southern Arizona and the "California Microphyll Desert" farther west, both of which are largely at lower elevations. According to Dr. Forrest Shreve of the Desert Laboratory, Tucson, Arizona, there are only sixteen species of perennials that are abundant throughout this entire portion of the "Microphyll Desert" (east of Grand Canyon), and most of these are semishrubs that are much branched, have soft wood, and bear evergreen leaves. Because soils vary greatly throughout this desert, numerous distinct plant associations have developed within the zone. Principal among these are the species typical of sandy soils, both loose and stabilized, those found on the smooth gravelly surfaces of non-sandy soils, and the crevice plants characteristic of areas of bare rock. Grand Canyon, on the other hand, has in its lower parts a remarkable mixture of desert plants, including not only most of those types found in various parts of the desert to the east but also many of the forms characteristic of the other Arizona deserts. Side by side in this canyon grow plants that have very different life requirements and normally are found only many miles apart.

Plants common in the stabilized, sandy soils of the deserts in northeastern Arizona and southeastern Utah are grasses of the genera Bouteloua and Hilaria or saltbush, prickly-pear cactus, and desert thorn, or Lycium—Mormon tea, rabbitbrush, and narrow-leaf yucca. The last three of these, together with several other genera, are dominant forms in the loose sand environment, while two species of Mormon tea or Ephedra are the chief hummock-forming plants in the sandy plains. In the bare-rock areas, which in places cover many acres, the principal crevice plants are wild buckwheat, serviceberry, single-leaf ash, and a relative of the goldenrod named Aplopappus. In extensive areas where the soil is not sandy, especially on gravel-covered flats, a very woody, small-leaved member of the rose family known as black brush occurs in almost pure stands, giving these areas a very different appearance from adjoining parts of the desert.

In the Grand Canyon and, to a lesser extent, in Zion Canyon, many desert plants common farther west and south make their appearance. Most conspicuous among these are the deep-rooted, thorny trees familiarly known as the mesquite and the catclaw. In the western half of Grand Canyon also are the peculiar ocotillos, looking like bundles of coach-whips, the glutinous-leaved creosote bush which is an outstanding example of a xerophyte, or plant adapted to drought, and the broomlike Canotia or false paloverde (green stick), which is so appropriately named. Then, too, varieties of cactus are more abundant, with the presence of the stiff-spined hedgehog, the large fat barrel cactus, the Opuntia with short spines known as the beavertail, and a great number of others. Extremely pungent plants like the indigo-blossomed turpentine broom are likewise numerous. Altogether, the Lower Sonoran flora of this canyon is remarkable for its many strange types of plants and for its mixture of different elements in close association.

Animal life of the Lower Sonoran zone is composed to a large extent of nocturnal species. In the interior of Grand Canyon, where, on cloudless summer days, a concentrated solar heat is absorbed all day by the surfaces of bare rock, and where the breeze of late afternoon is like a furnace blast, there is relatively little wild-life activity to be seen between early morning

331

and evening. The arid areas to the east and north where sand dunes drift and rock surfaces dominate the landscape are scarcely less oven-like and equally unfavorable to diurnal species. In all of this desert area the fauna is represented by about the same genera, though species vary considerably across the Plateau Province. Some animals found in the dry sandy portions of the Painted Desert do not occur in the Grand Canyon, and, conversely, some forms typical of the stream-course oases and rocky slopes of Grand Canyon are lacking to the east. By and large, however, the Lower Sonoran fauna is similar throughout the region and composed of Mexican desert types that appear to have moved northward wherever the environment was favorable.

Typical mammals of the Lower Sonoran zone are of unusual interest because of their adaptations to desert life. There is the antelope ground squirrel, that scurries from shrub to shrub with white tail aloft, suggesting a diminutive pronghorn antelope waving its "flag." There is the desert wood rat, whose home appears like nothing more than a junk pile with an ample sprinkling of cactus spines on top, but carefully located in the shade of an overhanging ledge or a desert tree. There are pocket mice with silky hair, very long tails, and legs adapted for jumping, and their larger cousins, the kangaroo rats, that are most at home in the sandy stretches. There are many other species, including the ring-tailed cat or Bassariscus, the little spotted skunk, several varieties of cliff mice, the desert harvest mouse, the free-tailed bat, and the smallest of bats in this country, known as the little canyon bat.

Reptiles, because of their habits, are probably the most frequently observed of the Lower Sonoran animals. Lizards, es-

332

pecially, may be seen scampering about at almost any time and place in the desert during the summer season. Some types such as the small earless lizards and the fast-moving leopard lizards are found almost exclusively in the sandy desert areas, while other reptiles, including the large, gray, plant-eating chuckwalla and the Boyle's king snake, identified by black and white rings around its body, are largely confined to the bottom of Grand Canyon and a few other canyons in the western part of the area. Most spectacular of the Lower Sonoran lizards is the colorful collared lizard, in which the males are often a vivid green and the females bright orange, both spotted and with a conspicuous white band around the neck. The western striped racer, having such an extremely slender body and long tail that it is sometimes called whip snake, the thick-bodied, coarsely scaled desert scaly lizard with bright blue sides, and the fast-running, lithe whiptail lizard are all common and characteristic species of this zone.

If the mammals and reptiles of the Lower Sonoran zone are remarkable for peculiar forms and specialized development, they are rivaled in this respect by many of the birds. Among the latter is the roadrunner or chaparral cock, fast-stepping member of the cuckoo family that feeds on spiders, scorpions, large insects, and reptiles. Then there is the glossy, blue-black, crested phainopepla, a silky flycatcher of delicate form, and the Gambel's quail with a queer plume on its head. Aside from these and a few other strange species found largely in the lowest, hottest parts of the region, there are many drab and more normal types of birds that blend into the desert landscape and comprise an important part of its fauna. These include the black-throated

333

desert sparrow, the common rock wren, black phoebe, sage thrasher, and ash-throated flycatcher.

Leaving the hot, dry desert belt and ascending any canyon wall or mesa front in the Plateau Province, one reaches in the course of time the area of piñon and juniper trees constituting the Upper Sonoran zone. The change is not abrupt; far from it. The trees first encountered are dwarfed and sparse. Only junipers usually occur at these lower limits, but as the environment becomes more favorable with increase in altitude the trees are greater in size and number, and presently piñons or nut pines appear also. This forest of piñons and junipers is commonly referred to as the "pygmy forest," for even under most favorable conditions the trees are not large, and they seldom grow close together.

Both piñon pines and junipers, which are considered "indicators" of the Upper Sonoran zone, are represented by more than one species in the canyon country. The Utah juniper, which is the common species from Grand Canyon northward, gives way to the one-seed juniper in many places to the south, and elsewhere, as in the canyons of the Mogollon Rim, to the queer-looking but appropriately named alligator-bark juniper. The two-needle variety of piñon pine found over most of the region is largely replaced by a single-leaf piñon in the northwestern part of the area around Zion Canyon. These small evergreen trees, however, do not constitute the only type of plant-cover within the Upper Sonoran zone. Many extensive open areas throughout the region are covered with sagebrush, while still other places, especially hillsides along the southern margins of the plateau as in Oak Creek and Sycamore canyons, give way to dense thickets of woody shrubs usually referred to

334

as chaparral. These include such plants as the red-stemmed man-zanita, a species of Rhus known as squawbush, Ceanothus or buckbrush, the tough wooded mountain mahogany, and Garrya, commonly known as Silk-tassel Bush because of its delicate creamy flowers. These tough shrubs are so thick in many places that climbing through them is almost impossible. Most of them have leaves that are small, thick, and evergreen.

Mammals, birds, and reptiles of the Upper Sonoran zone are, for the most part, very different from those of the desert belt below. The moderate cold and light snows of winter, together with summer heat that is not excessive, cause this part of the region, between five thousand and seven thousand feet, to be favorable to many species of animals not found in lower areas. Diurnal forms of mammals are more common than below, tree-loving birds are abundant, and reptiles, though less varied and abundant, are numerous both in species and individuals. Among the mammals that are especially typical of this zone are the prairie dog, Mearns coyote, cottontail rabbit, and grasshop-per mouse, all found in the open areas, and the gila chipmunk, gray fox, and several varieties of white-footed mice and wood rats in the wooded areas. The number of common birds is ex-tremely large, but a few of those most frequently seen are the following:

Arkansas kingbird	gray titmouse
piñon jay	common house finch
western gnatcatcher	canyon wren
Say's phoebe	lead-colored bushtit

The most numerous reptiles of the Upper Sonoran zone are two small, thin types of lizard—the swift and Uta—also the

335

well-known horned lizard, commonly called "horned toad," and the large but docile gopher snake.

Above the belt of piñons and junipers comes that of yellow pines known as the Transition zone. Here, as below, there is a characteristic lack of underbrush, and one may travel with ease almost anywhere beneath towering orange-colored trunks that suggest the stately pillars of a cathedral. This tree constitutes an important soft wood of commerce and is lumbered extensively throughout the region. In some portions of the Plateau a variety of white oak known as Gambel's oak is also common in this zone. Except in the southern parts of the Plateau, it seldom grows to any appreciable size, yet by means of a tenuous connecting root system it usually develops into dense clumps or thickets of small trees. The New Mexican locust, which is thorny but in early summer has beautiful purplish-pink flowers, is another common "indicator" of the Transition zone in some canyon walls. In general these trees range from about seven thousand to eight thousand feet in the Plateau country.

Animals of the Transition zone include a large number of common mammal types and many birds that are similar if not identical with forms well known in most parts of the United States. Reptiles, on the other hand, are rather scarce in this zone because of the rigorous climate. Only the horned toad, which literally turns the forest into a huge nursery during the month of August, and the wandering garter snakes that stay around the few water bodies, may be classed as common. Most typical and most unique of the mammals are the tassel-eared squirrels —large gray forms of several species that have red-brown backs, large fluffy tails, and ears that have prominent tufts of hair on them during the winter season. Their associates are the

336

mantled ground squirrels that look like large, over-stuffed chipmunks, the bushy-tailed wood rats, several varieties of pocket gophers, the porcupine, and the Arizona skunk. Many larger varieties of mammals such as the deer and coyote likewise are commonly found among the yellow pines of this zone during certain seasons, but they range through several belts and so can scarcely be called typical of any. A few of the most characteristic birds are the following:

red-backed junco	western wood pewee
western flycatcher	mountain chickadee
pygmy nuthatch	western tanager
long-crested jay	western chipping sparrow
white-breasted woodpecker	Rocky Mountain grosbeak
Mearns woodpecker	chestnut-backed bluebird
mountain bluebird	

At elevations ranging above eighty-five hundred feet in the canyon country, the yellow pines give way to forests of Douglas fir, white fir, blue spruce, and aspen. This is the Canadian zone. It is appropriately named, for most of the birds and mammals that breed here are also familiar forms in the corresponding types of forest in southern Canada, northern New England, and the Adirondacks. There are meadow mice or voles, red spruce squirrels commonly called chickarees, the weasel, and a variety of shrew. Here also one may hear the wild ringing song of the hermit thrush or see the bright plumaged crossbills busily cutting seeds from spruce cones. Three-toed woodpeckers, Rocky Mountain creepers, and ruby-crowned kinglets all lend an air of authenticity to the Canadian zone, and the loud clarion-like call of the olive-sided flycatcher sounds the same as it does in the far North Woods. Then, too, there are some species such

337

as the Townsend's solitaire and the band-tailed pigeon, typical of the western mountains but not found in spruce and fir belts of the East.

Only a few places in the Canyon Country rise above or even to the level of the Canadian zone. One is lofty San Francisco Mountain in Arizona, another the summit of the Kaibab Plateau north of Grand Canyon, and a third the high plateaus of southern Utah as illustrated by the rim of Bryce Canyon. In these favored localities the "indicators" of this zone are well developed at altitudes of eighty-five hundred to ninety-five hundred feet. Elsewhere, in some of the larger canyons like the Tsegi, north-facing walls give day-long shade and coolness that allow a few characteristic "indicators" to survive at much lower elevations.

On San Francisco Mountain the upper portion of the life zone sequence is complete. Above the Canadian zone is the Hudsonian, represented by Englemann spruce and bristle cone or foxtail pine, and above this is the Arctic-Alpine, beginning at timberline, 11,500 to 12,000 feet, and extending to the mountaintop. At Cedar Breaks in southern Utah the Hudsonian zone likewise is well represented, and near by at Brian Head, altitude 11,315 feet, timberline is reached. Even on the Kaibab a few "indicators" of the Hudsonian, including alpine fir and Englemann spruce, are found. Mammals of the Hudsonian are much like those of the Canadian zone in this region, with shrews, meadow mice, spruce squirrels, and porcupines. The birds include such characteristic forms as the goshawk, horned owl, Clark's nutcracker, and evening grosbeak. In the Arctic-Alpine zone, the pipit is perhaps the most typical of the breeding species.

Studies made of the alpine flora of San Francisco Mountain

338

by Dr. E. L. Little show a total of forty-nine species of plants. These occupy about two square miles of surface above the highest wind timber on this isolated volcanic cone and represent two principal plant associations. One is the alpine rock field or lichen association and the other the alpine meadow or Geum turbinatum association. An interesting feature of this flora is that many of the species are arctic-alpine circumpolar forms that are widely distributed in Arctic regions of North America and Eurasia, such as Alaska, Hudson Bay, Greenland, Spitzbergen, and Siberia and extend far south on the crests of such high mountain ranges as the Sierra Nevada, Rockies, Alps, and Himalayas. The generally accepted explanation of this isolated flora is that the plants migrated southward during the last glacial period and later were forced upward on the mountains as temperatures became warmer.

Life zones are so exceptionally well developed and clearly defined in the Plateau Province that even the casual observer is impressed by the marked changes from low to high. The combinations of trees and shrubs that serve as "indicators" of each zone are in many places in such a regular sequence as to suggest that each group is distinct and that boundaries are sharper than actually is the case. As a matter of fact, each individual species has its own particular environmental range with upper and lower limits different from those of every other species. In brief, the "indicators" do not occur as sharply demarcated groups but rather as species with overlapping vertical ranges distributed in shingle fashion. The Utah juniper, for instance, starts lower than the piñon, overlaps it for most of the range, but does not go so high. The Douglas fir, white fir, and blue

339

spruce are all considered "indicators" of the Canadian zone, but they start and end successively higher in the order named. Some plants, on the other hand, such as the true sagebrush, range through two life zones and so are typical of each.

As a final word after describing the orderliness and consistency of life zones over the Plateau Province as a whole, it is desirable to point out "exceptions that prove the rule." As a matter of fact few localities in the world show life zones more distorted and extreme in their variations than do the deep canyons of the Plateau. North-facing slopes with continuous shade cause plants to live at altitudes far below normal for the species; south-facing slopes have the opposite effect. Areas of warm updraft or valleys followed by cold descending air currents change the status locally. "Pockets" in which cold air concentrates or moisture is trapped all tend to upset the usual sequence of zones. The result is that a map giving zone boundaries in the Canyon Country shows an intricate pattern of tongues extending up or down and of isolated patches of vegetation widely separated from other plants of similar kind. It is a characteristic of life distribution in the canyons.

A BARRIER TO ANIMAL LIFE

We stand on the rim of Grand Canyon and gaze at the opposite wall. Only ten or twelve miles away "as the crow flies," and seemingly much nearer in the clear atmosphere of the Canyon Country, is a plateau of similar type but as isolated from us as though separated by an extensive sea or a lofty mountain range. We attempt to go from canyon rim to canyon rim and we become convinced of the magnitude of the barrier before us. By trail, through the chasm, it requires an arduous trip that normally takes a day and a half; by car, traveling around by way of the Painted Desert and over the Marble Platform, the distance is more than two hundred miles. Today these roads are good, but little more than a decade ago they were such as to take two days of travel.

Grand Canyon is a barrier to the movements of man because of the physical factors involved. It is also a barrier to many small animals, but for a different reason—the climatic effect. For these animals the isolation is complete. There is, for instance, a beautiful and, in several respects, unique species of squirrel with fluffy white tail, black belly, and tufted ears on the Northern Rim. On the opposite side is its cousin, similar but with tail partly gray and belly white. These two animals— the Kaibab squirrel on the north and the Abert squirrel on the south—doubtless could descend or scale the cliffs with ease in numerous places and eventually cross from rim to rim if topography were the only barrier. Yet they never make the attempt. They are victims of environment, for they will not leave the neighborhood of the yellow pines that constitute their native habitat even to travel down among the piñons and junipers, much less to brave the desert of Grand Canyon's bottom.

From a biological viewpoint, it seems clear that the similarity between the Kaibab and Abert squirrels is to be explained as the result of common ancestry at a relatively recent time. Apparently these animals became separated and were isolated on the two high plateaus that form the rims of Grand Canyon not in the distant past, when erosion of the canyon was in an early stage, but in comparatively recent years, when the latest major

341

climatic changes brought about a barrier far more effective to them than the physical one.

It probably was at the time of the last glaciation, usually referred to as the Wisconsin stage and dated at about thirty-five thousand years ago, that this story of development began. Temperatures then presumably were appreciably lower and precipitation greater, in this area, than today. For this reason zones of plant and animal life must have extended to much lower altitudes, and very possibly the belt of yellow pines extended continuously across the lower parts of the region. Tassel-eared squirrels then had easy communication from place to place. Later, with amelioration of the climate, causing the glaciers to retreat northward, zones of plant and animal life in Grand Canyon were forced upward. A desert environment took over the Canyon bottom; yellow pine and tassel-eared squirrel moved up with the climate to the Canyon rims. Thus, conditions remained favorable to life, but those animals, highly specialized and adapted to these conditions, were stranded where they gradually developed into distinct species.

Most of the larger animals of the region are, like man, not seriously affected by the climatic barrier of Grand Canyon, since they normally live and travel through a considerable vertical range. Individual deer are known to have traveled from rim to bottom and to have crossed the Colorado River in the course of a day. The same species of bobcat, fox, and mountain sheep are found on both sides of the canyon. But the smaller mammals and the reptiles—wherever their life habits confine them to any particular zone above the desert—show the effects of isolation by the presence of distinct species on opposite rims. The fol-

342

lowing is a partial list of animals that appear to illustrate this effect:

North Rim	South Rim
Utah cliff chipmunk	Gila chipmunk
Kaibab squirrel	Abert squirrel
Colorado pocket gopher	fulvous pocket gopher
yellow-haired porcupine	Arizona porcupine
Rocky Mountain meadow mouse	Mogollon meadow mouse
Colorado bushy-tailed wood rat	Arizona bushy-tailed wood rat
Black Hills cottontail	Rocky Mountain cottontail
Utah gopher snake	Arizona gopher snake
Great Basin rattlesnake	prairie rattlesnake

It has been suggested by various biologists that possibly the Colorado River, with its great size and power, forms an effective barrier at the bottom of Grand Canyon between various species of small mammals and reptiles, but to date no evidence has been obtained to demonstrate this. Along the lower portions of the river, far to the southwest, differences have been detected between pocket gophers and various other types of mammals living on opposite sides of the Colorado, and more detailed studies may prove this to be the case in Grand Canyon. In any event, a large and interesting field for investigation lies ahead of the enterprising biologist who will give his time and effort to a systematic study of animal distribution in the Grand Canyon.

ADAPT—AND SURVIVE

Along Hermit Trail, a thousand feet below the rim of Grand Canyon, I once listened to Dr. David White, eminent paleobotanist, as he explained the significance of some fossil plants

343

just dug from the red shale near by. "These," he said, "grew at a time, many millions of years ago, when the summers were hot and dry as shown by the distinctly xerophytic characters of the flora. Nearly all of the herbaceous plants then had very thick, leathery leaves, many of which were provided with scaly coverings. Plants were dwarfed, and many stems were thickly clothed with scales or spines."

As Dr. White talked, I looked about and realized that desert conditions were here once more. No flood plain near sea level was present as at that earlier time, but the summer was hot and dry, and the modern plants about us were adapted, like those preserved in the rocks, to the necessities of a specialized environment. There were plants with waxy leaf surfaces; there were species protected by spines; there were varieties noted for their long root systems, and all types grew well apart as though spaced with an engineer's instruments.

The struggle for existence is nowhere more intense than in a region of both climatic and topographic extremes, and such extremes are developed by the great desert canyons that dissect the Colorado Plateau. Here are found environments rivaling in harshness those formed during the major "revolutions" of the geologic past—the times that are noteworthy because of rapid evolution and many extinctions. Among plants of this region the methods developed for survival and the results of keen competition for space are many and varied and are deserving of more than a passing mention.

The two most dangerous elements that all plants of the desert canyons must overcome are heat and dryness. These are the principal enemies against which every species has to protect itself. The water situation is acute. In this region there

344

is no appreciable moisture in the air, and in few parts of it is there much water in the ground. Thus, the chief problem in the life of a plant resolves itself into an attempt to keep the hot, dry air from drawing more water through the leaves than is supplied by the roots. Such development of a balance between the water absorbed and the water transpired may be accomplished either by increasing the root system as a means of obtaining more water or by reducing the rate of transpiration through the leaves. Both methods are commonly used.

Illustrations of the remarkable extremes to which certain desert and semidesert plants will go in the matter of root extension are numerous. Some plants send their root systems downward to reach an abnormally deep water table; others spread laterally, close to the surface, thus taking advantage of the slightest rain. Some employ both methods. Probably best known among examples of the deep-rooted species is the mesquite—an acacia-like tree that thrives along the courses of many dry stream beds in very hot areas. Although this tree is usually but twenty to thirty feet high, its roots are said to go down as much as sixty feet. The Opuntia or prickly-pear cactus, on the other hand, has roots that stay near the surface but spread for amazing distances. In one specimen that I examined on the rocky sides of Grand Canyon the roots extended out for five feet eleven inches, although the cactus itself stood only five and a half inches above the ground and was composed of but two main and five secondary joints.

Even in the higher altitudes of the Plateau—above the true deserts—plants show a considerable degree of modification to meet requirements of the semiarid climate. The Gambel's oak, along Grand Canyon's rims, for example, is a great curiosity

345

to the person accustomed to seeing its close relative, the white oak, of better-watered lands. Instead of growing as a tall, thick-trunked individual, this canyon cousin develops a communal life. By means of an elaborate, horizontal, underground root system, it spreads extensively over an area, with shoots arising from runners at various intervals, ultimately to form a colony of thirty or more individuals. Each tree normally will be less than fifteen feet high, and its trunk only a few inches in diameter, but the combined shoots will appear as a miniature grove of oaks with normal leaves and bark.

Modifications in desert plants for the purpose of retaining water that has been absorbed are of many types. Numerous species produce extremely small leaves, thus reducing the amount of surface from which transpiration takes place. Some plants grow thick spongy bark. Others reduce the period of transpiration by shedding leaves early in the summer, while still others "varnish" their leaves with a resinous exudate. Small annuals survive, for the most part, by growing rapidly and maturing during brief favorable seasons—especially after rainy spells—to bring about those remarkable profusions of color that lead to the expression that "the desert blooms."

In many canyons of the Plateau Province the mountain mahogany is seen as an outstanding example of a tree or shrub with leaves perfectly adapted to the requirements of its environment. Instead of having wide and moderately large leaves as in the case of members of this genus native to more humid areas, most of the forms in the desert canyons have extremely small, narrow leaves. Furthermore, the upper surface of each leaf is covered with a waxy coating, while the lower surface, from which the transpiration takes place, is partially protected

346

by a tendency of the leaf margins to curl over it. Nature has provided well for these hardy frontiersmen!

The false paloverde (Canotia), which is common on the western and southern margins of the Plateau, is a true desert plant in which the strange broomlike form results from a rather remarkable type of adaptation. This species is characterized by leaves that are reduced to small deciduous scales. The green trunk which accounts for the common name of paloverde (translated as "green stick") actually helps in the manufacture of chlorophyll. Thus, the problem of water loss has been effectively solved by this unique type of plant.

Probably the most striking example of a plant with leaves protected from excess transpiration by a resinous coating is the common creosote bush (Larrea) that covers vast portions of the Southern and Western deserts. This shrub, which grows with a remarkable spacing of individuals, as though set out by a gardener or planted by a forester, is found in western portions of Grand Canyon and near the mouth of Zion. The function of the "varnish" or coating on its leaves is demonstrated by the fact that this coating is thickest in winter and spring but thins considerably in summer after seasonal growth has been accomplished.

Loss of water in desert plants is not the result of rapid transpiration alone. Both bird and beast, in this land of thirst, are ever ready to take whatever moisture they can get from any plant, and for this reason many types of vegetation are protected by spines or thorns. Examples are too numerous to mention. Other plants avoid enemies because of disagreeable taste, leathery skin, or pungent odor. The hop tree (Ptelea) and the turpentine broom (Thamnosma) are common plants of the

347

desert canyons that are especially noteworthy because of strong, distinctive odors that become especially marked when the leaves are crushed.

Protection from the direct heat of the sun and from the effects of abrupt temperature changes between night and day is also a necessity for desert vegetation. Such extremes of radiation as are encountered would be fatal to most growing plants of ordinary structure, so the desert flora must adapt to survive. Some plants obtain adequate shelter from a thick covering of hairs or, in the case of cactus, from spines. Others insulate themselves with air spaces inside a protective structure. The more one sees of the remarkable mechanisms that have been developed by the desert flora in its struggle for existence, the more fascinating they become.

Probably no group of plants illustrates more varied and effective methods of combating the heat and dryness of a desert climate than does the cactus. Not only do members of this family have exceptionally wide-spreading and, therefore, effective root systems for the catching of moisture, and either no leaves or only small, seasonal leaves to permit minimum loss through transpiration, but, in addition, they have very great water-storage capacity. Stems are green, containing chlorophyll for the manufacture of food material; the centers are fibrous and capable of holding a large supply of water; the armor of spines helps to keep off the sun and, of course, to protect the plant from enemies of the animal kingdom. Many species of cactus have fluted surfaces that allow the plant to expand like an accordion, taking up extra water when available. The barrel cactus, in which the name suggests the shape, is a common type in the desert canyons of the Plateau that illustrates to perfection

348

a water-storage mechanism of this variety. This cactus is sometimes referred to as the "well of the desert" because a drinkable
fluid may be obtained from it by cutting or knocking off the top
and mashing down the fleshy inside. Dr. F. R. Coville, in his
book entitled *Desert Plants as a Source of Drinking Water,*
states that as much as two or three quarts of drinking water may
be obtained from a single cactus in this manner. Specimens that
I have sampled were palatable but scarcely to be recommended
for their taste.

THE BALANCE OF NATURE

Newly formed flower stalks of the century plant were especially abundant along the Kaibab trail in Grand Canyon during June of 1930, and the tall, graceful stems, with spikes of
yellow flowers at their tops, formed a veritable "forest" on
Agave Flats. I remember clearly that as a friend and I hiked
along this trail one day, admiring the spectacle of these flowers
in the canyon setting, we noticed that several large individual
stalks had been chewed off close above the rosette of sharp, saw-
toothed basal leaves a few feet above the ground. What a pity
that such majestic plants should be killed while about to reach
their final glory and before either flowers or seed could be produced!

Nothing was said for a few minutes, and then my friend, who
was a capable biologist, remarked, "It's lucky there are lots of
gray foxes, or all these century plants would have the same
fate." His meaning was not clear. What did foxes have to do
with the destruction of flowers like the century plant? Then he
explained: "One of the few animals that is successful in getting

349

past the sharp basal leaves in order to eat tender shoots of the century plant is the common rock squirrel. With a leap he clears the guardian spikes; then the juicy stalk, resembling a giant asparagus tip, is his for the taking. Little chance do these plants have of surviving where the squirrels abound in exceptional numbers, but, luckily for the century plants, in most parts of the region gray foxes also are common and are energetic hunters of the rock squirrel—eliminate one and the balance is upset, for this is 'the balance of nature.' "

Biological records are replete with interesting cases illustrating the "balance of nature" and the usually unforeseen and unfortunate outcomes of disturbing this balance. The disastrous results of the introduction of new species of plants and animals into lands where these had no natural enemies are well illustrated by the epic stories of the coming of the rabbit and of the prickly-pear cactus to Australia. The histories of local extinctions affecting the growth and spread of other plants and animals in many communities are likewise numerous and interesting, but in few places has a more graphic case, with broad implications regarding the relationship of man to beast, been brought to public attention than in the story of the mule deer on the Kaibab.

This history begins about 1905. Up to that time the Rocky Mountain mule deer, famed for its big ears and its bouncing motion when running through hilly country, lived in moderate numbers in the Kaibab Forest on the north side of Grand Canyon. The normal increase in its population was kept in check largely by the mountain lions or cougars that also abounded in this area, hiding among ledges under the rim rock and hunting with the skill and prowess characteristic of all the big cats. Then came the change. A famous lion hunter named Owen, popularly

350

called "Uncle Jim," arrived in the region with his pack of trained hunting dogs and proceeded to destroy the deer's greatest enemy.

Uncle Jim Owen was remarkably successful as a lion hunter. Trailing with his dogs until he could tree and shoot the great cats, he succeeded in killing six hundred or more in the Kaibab Forest during a twenty-year period. This feat was generally acclaimed one of the great contributions to the cause of wild life— and so it seemed. Deer increased rapidly in the absence of their chief enemy and soon were extremely abundant everywhere in the area. By 1926 and 1927 estimates of their number on the Kaibab ranged between twenty thousand and fifty thousand. A person could drive through the open meadows in the forest at that time and count in one evening upward of one thousand deer quietly feeding in the open. It was a great spectacle.

Then came the "day of reckoning." People began to realize that there were more deer than the range could support, and that these deer would soon face starvation because of their numbers. Already cliff rose and other palatable shrubs at the lower altitudes, where most of the deer ranged during the winter periods of snow, had largely been browsed bare. A "deer line" marked the upper limit of the deer's reach, and the lower limit of green foliage was developed in many parts of the forest. The summer range at higher altitudes was also affected. All undergrowth was stripped bare, young aspens were browsed out of existence, and many other species were eaten as rapidly as they appeared above the ground. Obviously both forest and deer would be destroyed before long if the trend continued.

Something had to be done—and done soon. The alarm spread, and numerous interested organizations, both government and

351

nongovernment, sent representatives to study the problem and to recommend solutions. In one matter all were agreed. The size of the deer herd must be materially reduced if the forest was to be saved. To accomplish this three possibilities presented themselves: first, the cougars or mountain lions might be left alone to help restore a balance of nature; second, the surplus deer might be trapped and shipped away to stock other regions; third, an extended hunting season might be opened in order considerably to reduce the herd. Actually, all three methods were resorted to in solving the problem.

The first of the methods mentioned was one that showed no immediate results, for cougars were too scarce greatly to affect the large total deer population. But cessation of the "war to exterminate cougars" in this area was to be considered part of a long-range program, and its future importance was assured by the fact that at least part of the range under consideration was in a National Park where all species of animals were completely unmolested.

The method of reducing the deer herd by shipping out surplus animals was also on too small a scale to afford a complete solution to the immediate problem of the Kaibab, though it helped. Of especial interest, however, were the results of some of the experiments on the handling of wild life. Early in the program an attempt was made to drive a group of deer from the Kaibab down into Grand Canyon and thence up to the South Rim, where a few of the same species already lived. A large number of mounted men gathered for the purpose and attempted to close in on the selected deer near the head of Nankoweap Trail, but the deer would not be driven. When the men got to the canyon rim, the deer had vanished.

352

Small groups of deer were removed from the Kaibab Plateau by catching young fawns in midsummer through the use of specially trained dogs that would run them down and hold them, uninjured, until a Forest Ranger could reach the spot and prepare them for shipping by truck. One bunch of fawns caught in this manner was transported across Grand Canyon by airplane, thus being responsible for the local witticism that "these probably were the first flying deer." Elsewhere in the forest adult deer were trapped in stockade corral traps, baited with salt and food and equipped with drop doors. These deer also were shipped, but by truck, to various parts of the country.

After trying other methods, it became apparent that the necessary initial and radical reduction in the number of deer in the Kaibab forest must inevitably be brought about through hunting, so this was permitted on a large scale, though carefully controlled, in the National Forest portion of the range. After the first few years of extensive hunting, the deer herd was reduced to more normal proportions and the problem of the Kaibab was no more. Since then the vegetation has come back into its own, and hunting has been placed on a much smaller scale. Still the story of the Kaibab deer remains as one of the classic cases of the results of upsetting the "balance of nature."

USEFUL PLANTS

An official report by Lieutenant John G. Bourke to his commanding officer at Fort Whipple, Arizona Territory, in 1874, includes a passage that reads as follows: "Many species of vegetation whose properties are as yet imperfectly known to us, supply them [Apaches] with resources against starvation when an

353

invading force compels the abandonment of their homes and the destruction of their supplies." Although written about the Apache Indians, this statement might apply equally well to any of the tribes of the Canyon Country. It is a well-established fact that most Indians of this region can feed and clothe themselves and their families in desert areas where a white person would starve to death.

Of all the useful plants in the Plateau Province, my vote is for the piñon. Probaby none other has served man so well or in so many ways. First and foremost is its contribution of food. From the fat cones of this short and scraggly pine of the desert's edge come seeds or "nuts" that have justly obtained fame throughout the country for their tasty flavor. Sold in high-class grocery stores from New York to California, labeled with fancy titles such as Indian nuts and pine nuts, these are the same humble seeds gathered annually from the pygmy forests of Arizona and Utah by Navajo, Hopi, and Havasupai Indians. So important is this food to the local Indian diet that each October there are mass migrations involving entire families and groups of families, traveling by horse, wagon, or truck, to the "hunting grounds" whence scouts have previously reported an abundance of piñon nuts. But if you think the gathering is easy, try it once. My first experience was that of working industriously for several hours, filling a small pail, and then, to my dismay, having a Havasupai woman laugh out loud as she detected with uncanny skill that over half of my "Piñonnes" were only empty, worthless shells.

The professional forester who looks upon trees as a farmer does his crops, and who thinks in terms of potential lumber, finds little to become enthusiastic over in a stand of piñon pines, but not so the native Indian. From its wood the Indian may construct his hut or build his fire, from its pitch he obtains an adhesive or glue. The Havasupai woman uses the gum for waterproofing her basket bottles, and most Indians recognize the value of this gum as an antiseptic. Even for ceremonial purposes the piñon contributes to the lives of many Indians. Little wonder that the piñon has played so important a role in the story of the Southwest!

But the piñon has a rival. Growing alongside it just above the limits of the desert, twisted and gnarled from the struggle for existence, this rival—the juniper—is also a true friend to any man who must live off the land. It produces blue berries that in reality are modified cones, and these constitute a food. It has a peculiar stringy bark, shreds of which are used for tinder in making fires, for making sleeping mats, as stoppers for water bottles, and as torches. Who does not know about the excellence of its red wood, the so-called cedar wood, for the campfire, and who, having used it, can forget the delightful fragrance? Then, too, the relative hardness of the wood makes it desirable for use in building the house known as a *hogan* to the Navajo and a *hawa* to the Havasupai. Both leaves and gum, furthermore, have many medicinal uses—some with real, others with supposed, properties.

Traveling over trails in the Canyon Country, one frequently sees at the lower elevations circular mounds of small broken stones surrounding rocky pits that are five or six feet in diameter and that show the black marks of smoke. These are mescal pits. They are mute evidence of a former important event in the calendar of many Indians of the Southwest. In fact, until quite recent times the Havasupai, the Walapai, the Paiute, and others

355

prepared one of their staple foods—the century plant or mescal —by roasting it in these pits. Whole families or larger groups participated in the gathering of this plant each spring as it matured, bringing in thirty or forty mescals at a time to be cooked by placing on a layer of hot rocks and covering with long grasses, more hot rocks, and dirt. The process normally took from two to three days, but enough mescal, variously described as tasting like candied sweet potatoes and like burnt rhubarb, was prepared at one time to last for a considerable period.

The century plant or mescal is seldom used as a food any more but is still one of the most striking plants in the Canyon Country, where it grows on hot, dry slopes and rocky ledges. Starting as a small cluster of spiked leaves, it grows for perhaps ten to forty years until it becomes a mature plant, large and well armed with long, bayonet-like, jagged, saw-toothed leaves radiating from the compact center. During the many years of its growth, it stores up food in this center, in preparation for the day when it will send up its flower stalk. Finally, one spring, when enough food has been accumulated, a huge flower stalk shoots up from the center and grows rapidly to a height of ten to eighteen feet. It has been known to grow as much as a foot in one day! The upper two-thirds of the straight stalk bears a large number of beautiful yellow, lily-like flowers, each of which later develops a many-seeded capsule. After this supreme effort, the century plant dies, its duty fulfilled and many new plants started on their long life cycle.

Superficially resembling the mescal, but actually very different, is another common and useful plant of the Southwest known as the yucca, Spanish bayonet, or soapweed. This plant is a member of the lily family with stiff, swordlike leaves, commonly spine-tipped and clustered at the base. Some species are broad-leafed; others, narrow-leafed. Most of those in the Canyon Country have leaves that start near the ground, although near the western end of Grand Canyon are the grotesque Joshua trees and other queer, treelike forms. In the yuccas, a stalk usually several feet long projects from the center of leaf clusters, and on it grow large, bell-shaped, creamy-white flowers. These in turn develop into green fruits that hang from the stalk somewhat like fat, stubby bananas and ripen with a peach-pink color.

Uses of the yucca are legion. The common name of "soapweed" suggests a very important one. Yucca roots are dug up, crushed and bruised, and used with hot water to whip up a rich lather employed especially in washing the hair by Indians of various tribes. Even though good commercial soaps are readily obtainable today, the soapweed is preferred by many individuals for this purpose. Indeed, the soft, shiny tresses of many Indian women are a good advertisement for such soap. The roots of soapweed are employed by the Navajos also in washing dirt from wool shorn from their sheep and goats and for scrubbing rugs. The Hopi Indians use the rich lather for many ceremonial purposes.

Any archaeologist who has examined pit houses, cliff dwellings, and other ruins in the Canyon Country is fully aware of the important part played by the yucca in the life of prehistoric man. Dwellings dating back many centuries often contain sandals, mats, baskets, rope, paint brushes, and even cloth made from fibers of yucca leaves. Today a number of these articles are still in use by the Hopi Indians, and, in some instances, the local products are preferred to their imported counterparts.

357

Yucca sandals were replaced by buckskin moccasins with the advent of sheep and goats, yucca twine and rope were discarded, as the course of least resistance, with the coming of cheap string and manila hemp, but potters of the First Mesa villages still employ yucca brushes in making their delicate designs on pottery, and the excellent baskets produced on the Second Mesa are still made of split yucca leaves. Then, too, all of the Indians in this region, today as in the past, welcome the delicious yucca fruits as an addition to their diet. Sometimes these fruits are roasted until the outer skins can be stripped off, when they taste much like a baked apple; other times they are made into a stiff jelly or conserve by boiling and shaping them into pats that are dried in the sun; again, a sweet, liquid-like syrup is obtained from them.

My introduction to the use of ephedra or Mormon tea—a peculiar, jointed shrub that looks very much like a broom upside down—was thorough. While doing geological work in Parashant Canyon, which is in the western part of Grand Canyon, I had a combination packer and cook who made a practice of always gathering and brewing a huge bunch of Mormon tea as soon as each camp was established. This tea proved to be a good beverage, especially when sufficiently sweetened, but in the opinion of my cook, apparently, it was the most essential part of each meal. The Mormon tea has doubtless been used for a drink by Indians of the Canyon Country for countless ages and seems to be much in demand for this purpose in many localities.

Although the older Indians of the region made some use of almost every plant, white man has been slow to learn and has

358

had relatively little need to follow along these lines. In a few instances, however, white man, the newcomer, has profited. Many a hiker over hot canyon trails has learned to cut the dryness in his throat by sucking the sweet, pleasantly acid berries of the Rhus trilobata or squawberry, or, better still, to put these berries in water and make a sort of lemonade. Numerous thirsty climbers have found relief in the delicious, juicy fruit of the prickly pear cactus, easily made palatable by placing on a stick like a lollipop and peeling off the spiny skin with a knife. Most ranchers' wives know the value of the wild currant, the gooseberry, the elderberry, and the manzanita for making jelly, and the thrifty camp cook will take advantage of numerous native "greens," long used by the Indians, for supplementing his menu. The common lamb's-quarters, which taste much like spinach, the beautiful bee plant or Cleome, saltbush, and some mustards are all used in this manner.

CANYONS AFFECT BIRD MIGRATIONS

The topographic extremes represented by the network of deep, narrow canyons in the Plateau Country have marked effects on movements of bird life in and through the region. Some canyons are followed as regular routes of migration; others are quickly passed over as barren wastes to be avoided; still others, because of water in their bottoms, offer temporary havens for the traveling bird. The larger canyons give opportunity for local species to drift up or down with the season and thus to get away quickly from unfavorable weather or to avoid the full effects of sudden storms. Even random observations made by the amateur ornithologist give many suggestions of the abundant, in-

359

teresting problems of bird activity introduced by the presence of these canyons.

Because few real factual data were available, bird enthusiasts of the Canyon Country began about a decade ago to apply scientific methods in a systematic attempt to accumulate knowledge regarding the complex problems of how these canyons affect bird movements. A bird-banding station was organized by the Museum of Northern Arizona in 1932 near the base of the San Francisco Peaks. Another soon followed at Grand Canyon National Park, and, within a few years, active stations for banding birds were in operation at Walnut Canyon, Betatakin Canyon, Zion, and a number of other localities in the Plateau Region. Some thousands of birds, representing several dozen species, were trapped at these stations, marked on the legs with small metal bands containing serial numbers, and then released. The recapture of these "marked" individuals at other times and at other places has, during the course of years, made possible the building up of a considerable file of precise information relative to many aspects of the problem. This bird-banding work in the Canyon Country is but part of the general co-operative program directed and sponsored by the former Bureau of Biological Survey with headquarters in Washington, D.C., but each station in the field, while doing routine banding, has been able to work on its own particular problems.

At Grand Canyon, where more than five thousand individual birds were banded over a seven-year period, a system of ten sub-stations has been used to form a network covering both rims and a few localities down in the Canyon. Thus, it has been possible there to demonstrate many facts concerning the time and direction of seasonal movements, the age, associations, and feeding habits of individuals, and the degree of regularity in local movements. Now and again some bird banded at a faraway point has been captured, as in the case of a Schufeldt's junco banded in British Columbia during the summer of 1934 and caught at Grand Canyon six months later. Also occasionally, a bird banded at Grand Canyon has turned up at some distant locality, as illustrated by a robin marked in March, 1935, and found a year later at Midway, Utah. Such records have interest, but the chief value of the station has been found in the many dozens of records of individuals that moved from one substation to another and the more than a hundred cases of individuals that returned to a substation at some season subsequent to the one in which they were banded. These tell the story of the Canyon's effects on bird life.

Analysis of records from the Grand Canyon substations shows that migrating species such as juncos, and also the so-called residents like nuthatches and chickadees, commonly move east and west along the canyon rim. Between substations only a mile or two apart the movement usually involves a day or two, whereas between substations twenty-five miles apart records of these species show an elapsed time of two to six weeks. Other records indicate that small migrating birds such as sparrows and juncos move down into the canyon bottom from the rims, sometimes taking not over a day or two while "drifting," and then up to the opposite rim. Whether or not any of these species make the trip directly across the ten-mile gap from rim to rim is not known, but there are records suggesting that nuthatches do this.

It seems probable that some types of birds, especially those characteristic of hot, desert environments and those adapted to life along stream courses, travel up and down the interior of the Grand Canyon, following the Colorado River from the west, rather than passing over the high forested plateau to the south. While we were making a boat trip down the Colorado River in the fall of 1936, a large Treganza's heron stayed ahead of our boats for several days and perhaps forty miles, never attempting to rise over our heads or to fly out of the narrow canyon, suggesting that this route along the stream was the most natural one for the bird to use. In the same manner desert species that enter Zion Canyon apparently follow the course of the Virgin River up from the deserts of southern Nevada and western Arizona. Now that Hoover Dam is constructed and a huge lake has developed in this western area, with natural attraction for shore birds and waterfowl, it is interesting to speculate on how many species of such birds new to the area will drift up into the Canyon Country. Already records of several species previously unreported in Zion Canyon and Grand Canyon are probably to be accounted for in this way.

With the operation of bird-banding stations in the Canyon Country, considerable data bearing on the regularity or irregularity in migration of various species of birds have been obtained. Notably consistent are many of the juncos and several varieties of sparrows. Among these, numerous records show returns to a particular substation on the exact day or within a very few days of arrival in the previous year. Some birds of these species returned to Grand Canyon substations at intervals covering four and, in a few cases, five years, indicating a minimum age for the individuals involved.

Special studies of the habits of black-eared nuthatches have been made at Grand Canyon by using combinations of colored celluloid bands, so arranged that individual birds could be identified with field glasses. By this method it was determined that the individuals making up certain flocks stayed together fairly uniformly, and that certain groups were quite regular in the time each day when they visited a particular feeding station. These are but a few of many interesting facts on life history of birds to be found through banding in the Canyon Country.

THE PLANT PARADE

The development of a "plant succession" is by no means unique to the Canyon Country, but it is especially well illustrated there. Every botanist is thoroughly familiar with the manner in which one plant association normally succeeds another within a favorable environment until finally, through the years, a "climax" type is reached. He knows how primitive plants such as lichens serve as pioneers, collecting moisture and making soil; how mosses and then seed plants increase the soil and give some shade; how finally the series is concluded when the typical forest type best adapted to that environment is able to establish and maintain itself.

In canyons of the Plateau Province, where semiarid to arid climate prevails, and topographic extremes are developed, the demonstrations of plant succession are exceptional both for their number and character. Under the conditions prevailing in these situations bare surfaces are continually being formed, and each new bare space marks the beginning of a plant parade. Such cycles go on in nature continuously. The lichen stage is by far the longest, probably lasting hundreds of years, yet even after these plants, with their uncanny ability to cling to smooth surfaces, have pioneered the way by decomposing and disintegrating the rock, it is still a matter of hundreds of years until the

363

desert outposts have been completely converted into a forest type that cannot be displaced unless the environment changes.

"Biologically speaking, nature abhors a bare spot." It continually strives to cover up the bare places, but, even as it gradually succeeds in one area, rapid erosion and an arid climate combine in the Plateau Country to form new ones. Bare spots may develop as the result of rock falls, landslides, or talus development; they may be formed by flood plains or sand dunes, or, locally, they may even be the results of biologic factors as illustrated by anthills, prairie-dog mounds, or man-made roads. Sometimes, also, forces such as fire from lightning and destruction by overgrazing partly nullify the progress of a cycle and cause at least the later stages in the succession to be repeated.

Even though the very time-consuming stage of lichens and the lengthy stage of mosses—periods during which the first soil is formed—may not, in many instances, need to be repeated, still the history of return to climax is a long one. Studies made of a recently burned-over area on the South Rim of Grand Canyon clearly show that approximately 300 or 350 years are required for nature to reforest such harsh sites with another stand of mature piñon pines and junipers. Many of the former trees of these species began to grow about the time that the Pilgrims were landing in Massachusetts. Destroyed by fire, the species not only must repeat this long span of growth but, in addition, must await favorable starting conditions for perhaps fifty or seventy-five years. This is a time when other plants in the normal succession pave the way by developing necessary shade, favorable soil, and other suitable factors. During this interval many plants appear that grew only in suppressed condition on the forest floor before the burn; new species migrate,

364

others are eliminated by vigorous competition; many plants must come and go. Little wonder it is that the National Forests are continually campaigning for greater care in avoiding forest fires!

The succession of plants as presented thus far is a purely biotic succession and is confined to a particular environment. In the Canyon Country, however, a second type of succession, consisting of changes in topography and resulting in a succession of environments, is a very striking feature of the biological world. Especially at the upper ends of canyons where erosion is working headward, and along canyon rims that are gradually retreating, is this parade of plant communities manifest. It is infinitely slow when judged from a human standpoint, yet all stages of the progression are apparent in every desert canyon. That it is a reality seems clear.

As a canyon becomes longer or wider by the process of erosion, the plant communities of a given place pass through a series of stages from the coniferous forest of the plateau above, through successive types represented on the canyon sides, and finally to the desert stage trailing in the wake. Communities of plants move bodily forward with the retreating canyon, in a remarkable succession of biotic changes correlated with the physical adjustments. The drama of this ever shifting scene is as impressive as it is inevitable. In the Canyon Country it leads one to think of that other great drama of changing life and landscape represented by the succession of fossils and of contrasting strata of past ages found so magnificently preserved in the walls of Grand Canyon.

ANIMAL CENSUS

Two of the most extensive areas of land in the United States which have largely escaped the encroachments and developments of man and have remained wild are within the Canyon Country of the Southwest. One is the western portion of Grand Canyon; the other is the Kaiparowits region of southeastern Utah. In addition, many lesser sections of the Plateau—because of desert climate, unfavorable topography, or both—have retained their primitive character, as yet little affected by the advances of civilization. It follows that animal life native to the region is also relatively unchanged by the coming of man and, as a matter of fact, is still by no means thoroughly known. Various animals previously unrecorded in the region are constantly being reported, and species or subspecies altogether new to science are still being discovered periodically. Among the latter may be cited the Grand Canyon rattlesnake and the Arizona screech owl—both collected for the first time from Grand Canyon and described within recent years.

Mammals of the Canyon Country, with the exception of some of the larger species, are for the most part local in distribution and distinctive in character. Islands of forest surrounded by desert, tongues of desert extending into wooded plateaus, and streams or springs fringed by lush growth but isolated in the midst of barren wastes are some of many features that tend to increase the number of distinct habitats and to isolate many of the animals in these habitats. Such names as San Francisco Mountain wood rat, Kaibab squirrel, and Painted Desert pocket gopher suggest at once the local character of many species. Al-

366

though available records indicate at least ninety species and sub-species in Grand Canyon National Park and about forty-eight each in Zion Canyon and the northern Navajo Reservation, these numbers probably will be greatly increased with additional field study. Furthermore, much remains to be learned about the ranges of individual species and the problems of variation.

The carnivora or flesh-eating mammals are represented in the Canyon Country by most of the types commonly found throughout western America. Many of the larger ones are wide-ranging species, apparently identical with corresponding forms in neighboring regions. The Plateau area is believed to be the southern limit of certain types such as the Kaibab Mountain Lion, the Plains Wolf, and the Utah Grizzly Bear, and, at the same time, it is the northern limit of related Mexican varieties —the Gray Mountain Lion, the Mexican Wolf, and the Arizona Grizzly. Grand Canyon forms the line of separation. Some of these species are today nearly or entirely extinct in the region, but the mountain lions, often known as cougars or panthers, are still fairly numerous locally and may occasionally be seen by the traveler. Another great cat—the jaguar—which looks like an African leopard but is more powerful and heavier, formerly ranged north from Mexico as far as Grand Canyon, although it probably is extinct in the region today.

Conspicuous among the smaller carnivora of the Plateau Region are at least three varieties of coyotes, ranging in size from the small Painted Desert coyote to the large mountain coyote of the Kaibab. Most of the recent reports of "wolves" supposedly seen in that area doubtless refer to the latter animal. The fox tribe is represented chiefly by the Arizona gray fox, a species completely at home in the desert canyons, and by

367

a small red fox reported from Navajo Mountain near Glen Canyon on the Arizona-Utah line. The Plateau bobcat or wildcat is fairly common throughout the region, chiefly in wooded areas and, although a nocturnal hunter, is not infrequently seen near roads or trails. Its cousin, the Canada lynx, of north woods fame, has been found near Zion Canyon, which probably marks the southern limit of its range.

Perhaps the most interesting small carnivore, and certainly one of the most typical in the desert canyons, is the ring-tailed cat or bassariscus. It is not a cat, by any stretch of the imagination, but closer in relationship to the raccoon. With its sharp, foxlike face, large pointed ears, slender body, and very long, banded tail, its presence around a camp site is one of the common and pleasant experiences that comes to many a camper in the Plateau Province. In the light of the moon or glow of a fire, I have often seen its intelligent little face, full of curiosity, as it prowled about my camp larder. Many a prospector has kept a tame ringtail at his desert cabin to eliminate mice and to keep him company. Two ringtails lived for many months in the large dining room of El Tovar Hotel at Grand Canyon, staying among the log rafters overhead, from which vantage point the animals would frequently peer down at some amazed hotel guest and then disappear as suddenly as they appeared.

Other small carnivora of the Canyon Country include a species of desert raccoon, two types of skunk, the weasel, the badger, and, along the Colorado River, the otter. The little spotted skunk, which in many places carries the undeserved name of hydrophobia skunk or phoby cat, is rather common in the bottoms of most desert canyons, where it lives in caves or cracks in the cliffs and subsists largely on rodents, insects, and

368

cactus fruit. It becomes very tame. I know of one case where a ranger, while sleeping in a remote portion of Grand Canyon, had his hair tugged numerous times during the course of a night—the result of the curiosity of some of these little animals. Every time the man was awakened, the spotted skunks scurried harmlessly away, but, of course, he didn't dare throw anything at them.

The ungulates or hoofed mammals are represented in the Canyon Country by the mule deer, the pronghorn antelope, the mountain sheep, and a few elk. Mule deer, unlike their white-tailed cousins, are not very fast runners on the level but are well adapted to the rugged canyon terrain, moving with a series of stiff-legged bounds in which all four feet leave and strike the ground together. They are found throughout the region, almost everywhere above the lower tree line, and even drift down into the bottoms of desert canyons. Antelope, on the other hand, are primarily animals of the open country, not adapted to life in the canyons, and they are found principally in the flat stretches of the Plateau, especially south of Grand Canyon. Although a few years ago antelope were very scarce and facing extinction in this region, they are today numerous in several favorable localities. A small herd was introduced down in Grand Canyon in the 1920's; however, it failed to do well in that restricted environment and entirely disappeared a few years after artificial feeding was discontinued.

To one accustomed to associating mountain sheep with high ranges of the North, these animals seem strangely out of place in the hot, dry canyons of the Southwest. Actually the desert bighorn is just as much at home in, and adapted to, the environment of Grand Canyon's walls as is the Rocky Mountain sheep

369

to the peaks of Glacier National Park. Individuals or small groups are occasionally seen from the trails or the rim above as they travel along difficult and dangerous slopes where few enemies will follow. Mountain sheep in the Zion Canyon area and also those along upper canyons of the Colorado River have been referred to the larger, darker form known as the Rocky Mountain sheep.

A large majority of the species of mammals in the Canyon Country belong to the order of rodents. The largest of these are the porcupines, common in the higher, forested areas, and the beaver that use the permanent stream courses as highways of travel in an endless search for something they cannot find—a home that is secure. Normally a colonizer and lover of community life, the beaver in this inhospitable land are forced to a solitary life. They cut trees and construct dams, they build dens in the mudbanks, but invariably the violent seasonal storms and cloudbursts destroy their handiwork in the narrow canyons, and they become wanderers and nomads. Still they persist.

Of the smaller rodents, many are interesting because of their peculiar adaptations to the desert country. There is the yellow-brown kangaroo rat with long, powerful hind legs for jumping in sand and with fur-lined outer cheek pockets for carrying food and nest material. There are the tiny, silky-haired pocket mice that also have long tails and hind legs and are remarkable jumpers. Common also are prairie dogs—squirrel-like animals that live in colonies or "towns" consisting of deep burrows with low earth mounds at their entrances and located frequently far from any permanent water. In dry periods these animals apparently are able to go for many weeks without drinking and obtain all necessary moisture from the plants that they eat.

Other common rodents of the Canyon Country include several types of tree squirrels and ground squirrels, numerous varieties of pocket gophers and meadow mice or voles, and many kinds of white-footed mice and wood rats. Members of the last-named group are among the most interesting because of their peculiar habit of collecting all types of odds and ends which they drag to their homes. Because of this insatiable desire to collect, they often are referred to as "pack rats" or "trade rats." In the stick and trash house of one individual, located near the archaeological museum at Grand Canyon, the following group of articles was found by Mr. Russell Grater:

1 piece of gauze	1 piece of isinglass
2 burnt matches	1 cigar wrapper
1 piece of tire tape	1 piece of cellophane
1 piece of tin foil	1 piece of cloth
1 button	1 small paper box

3 blue-headed pins (from museum)
3 grains of corn (Hopi Indian variety)
3 different colors of thread
A quantity of electric-light wire
2 types of beans (from museum exhibit)
1 part of comic strip from newspaper
1 length of lantern-slide binding tape
A few piñon nuts
A quantity of juniper berries

In order to complete the survey of mammals native to the Canyon Country, three other orders must be mentioned. One is the rabbit tribe, represented by several varieties of cottontails and jack rabbits. Another is the insectivores, and includes the smallest of the North American mammals—the shrew. One type of shrew lives in the moister portion of high mountains in the

371

region, but the rare little short-tailed desert shrew occurs in the dry bottoms of a few canyons. With long sharp muzzle, tiny eyes, and slender body, it is an intensely interesting animal with a voracious appetite and great courage, never hesitating to attack animals several times its own weight. The third order of mammals to be mentioned is that of the bats, which is well represented with more than a dozen species found in Grand Canyon and other varieties common in the surrounding country. The many dry caves in the region are particularly favorable to the concentration of bats, and isolated water bodies in this dry country usually attract swarms of various types about dusk during the summer season.

Birds of the Canyon Country are better known than the representatives of any other large group of animals. Nevertheless, it is surprising to visitors from other parts of the United States how many of the bird species are different from corresponding types of their acquaintance. There are, for instance, robins and bluebirds, chickadees and nuthatches, phoebes and flickers, all similar to those found east of the Mississippi and yet definitely different. To a lesser extent this holds true of many corresponding types native to the West Coast. It gives a person from the East a queer feeling when he finds a white-breasted nuthatch or a meadowlark that looks perfectly normal but makes a sound when it calls or sings very different from the one expected. To be sure not all of the varieties have such apparent differences, and many can only be distinguished in hand specimens and by a specialist, but the differences are there. The red-breasted nuthatch, the olive-sided flycatcher and the bank swallow are some of the very few species of small birds that are indistinguishable from far eastern representatives.

372

The number of species of birds found in the Plateau Province is surprisingly large, especially when it is realized that shore birds and water birds are definitely limited in number and variety by the dry character of the country. On the other hand, the large number of life zones or climatic belts resulting from the extremes in elevation definitely favor a wide variety of birds and doubtless are chiefly responsible for the fact that over 190 species and subspecies have been recorded from Grand Canyon National Park. Check lists developed for Zion, Bryce, and Cedar Breaks show about 170 species, and one compiled for the canyons of the northern Navajo Country lists 102.

One especially attractive feature of the bird life in the Canyon Country is the tameness of most species. This is doubtless due in part to the aridity of the country, for many birds are forced to depend on man for their local water supply, or, at least, to share it with him. Another factor is that many of the canyons are in National Parks or Monuments where domestic cats and dogs are excluded and where wild life is given rigid protection. At Grand Canyon the Park Service has gone a step further and developed many rustic bird baths and feeding stations, the result being that several species of birds—notably the pygmy nuthatches, titmice, and chickadees—are so tame that they will readily eat out of a stranger's hand. Many a visitor to the South Rim of Grand Canyon has had a thrill out of this experience.

The reptilian life of the Canyon Country is so striking in character that it attracts widespread interest among both herpetologists and laymen. There is not only an abundance of individuals but also a large variety of species, including both lizards and snakes. At Grand Canyon, where the range in climatic belts

373

is especially great, a total of fourteen types of lizards and four-teen of snakes is known. The number of each found at Zion Canyon is almost as great, and from the desert region in the northern part of the Navajo Reservation thirteen types of lizards and seven of snakes have been recorded. Only in the higher parts of the region, as at Bryce Canyon, are the numbers greatly limited.

Largest of the serpents is the gopher snake, sometimes called bull snake or blow snake, which is especially common in the piñon pine-juniper belt throughout the area. One specimen I saw on the Kaibab Plateau on the north side of Grand Canyon measured six feet one inch. Despite its size this snake is entirely harmless and, indeed, is very beneficial to man because of the great number of rodents that it eats. Some ranchers in the region even keep gopher snakes in their barns for reducing the mouse population.

Rattlesnakes are not very common over most of the region but are represented by at least six distinct species or subspecies. Perhaps the most remarkable of these is the unique pink rattle-snake of Grand Canyon. It appears to be restricted to this can-yon and differs considerably from its cousin, the prairie rattler, to the south, and from the dark Great Basin variety to the north. Its reddish color causes it to blend in remarkably well with the red rocks of its habitat. The interesting problem of the geo-graphical distribution of the rattlesnakes in this region has been the subject of a very detailed study by Mr. L. M. Klauber of the San Diego Museum of Natural History.

One of the most curious and common of the lizards in the Plateau Region is the horned lizard or horned toad, as it is com-monly called. A short-horned variety is extremely abundant in

374

dry flat areas beneath forests of piñon or yellow pine, especially on canyon rims. During the month of August, when the young horned toads arrive, they may be found in great numbers almost everywhere, so prolific is this reptile. One plump female that was sent by mail to a museum in California arrived at its destination accompanied by eleven young. A joke then went the rounds that "this must have been special delivery."

Amphibians and fish, in general, find conditions as unfavorable in the Canyon Country as reptiles find them favorable. Still, there are some species of toads, frogs, salamanders, and fish peculiarly adapted to life in this region, and they appear to thrive. All permanent water bodies, as well as many intermittent ones, have an amphibian fauna. The questions of how and when they got to these isolated habitats, and how such isolation has affected the species, are still awaiting answer. Fish are numerous in the Colorado River despite its very muddy character; such types as catfish and members of the sucker group are especially common. One of the most interesting fish in the region because of its distribution, however, is a minnow known as Tiaroga cobitis. This species is abundant in a small stream of clear water near Indian Gardens at the bottom of Grand Canyon. It does not go into the muddy Colorado, and the only other place where it has been found to date is in a similar isolated desert stream several hundreds of miles away in southern Arizona.

Channel catfish and common carp were introduced into the Colorado River drainage, but the largest and the oddest types of fish found there are native. One of these is a huge minnow with big mouth, called by local people the "white salmon." It weighs up to eighty pounds and is listed by the United States National Museum as the largest of American minnows. Another omniv-

375

orous minnow, and one of peculiar form, is the so-called bony-tail, which is abundant. The strangest looking of all the fish in these muddy waters, however, is the humped-back sucker, which commonly weighs six or seven pounds and has an enormous forward-projecting hump in the front part of its back. Other species of the Colorado include the small Yarrow's dace, adapted to swift water, and the bigmouth and blue-head suckers, both sluggish bottom-feeders found around pools and quiet stretches.

INDEX

INDEX

INDEX

Fossils, 66-82, 280-285, 299, 302; marine, 80-82, 282; plant, 76-77; reptile tracks mystery, 77-80
Fox: gray, 335, 350, 367; red, 368
Franciscans, 98, 100, 103, 250
Fredonia, 33, 34
Fremont Peak, 54
Fumaroles, 60
Fur trade, 132-134

Gaiena, 295
Galloway, Nathan, boatman, 180-181
Garcés, Francisco Tomas Hermene-Gildo, 100-103, 114, 125, 137
Geology, 22, 43-65, 280-285. *See also* Ag of reptiles, Archaean age, Basalt, Benches, Erosion, Faults, Fossils, Glaciation, Ice age, Jurassic age, Laccolith, Landslides, Lava, Limestone, Minerals, Petrology, Rockfalls, Sand waves, Shale, Vulcanism
Gila River, 100, 132
Gilbert, G. K., 56, 307
Gilboa, N. Y., petrified forests, 72
Gilmore, Dr. Charles, 78
Glaciation, 342
Glen Canyon, 106, 145, 161, 244-245, 320, 321
Gnatcatcher, western, 335
Gold rush, 144, 233
Goldenrod, 331
Gooseberry, as food, 359
Gooseneck Canyon, 235-236
Gopher, 337
Goshawk, 338
Goulding, Harry, trader, 229
Government: Cave, 22; Rapids, 238
Gowen, David, pioneer, 52-53
Grand Canyon, village, 23, 25, 302
Grand Canyon of the Colorado, *see* Colorado River, Grand Canyon of
Grand Canyon Stage Line, 147
Grand: Falls, 23; River, 104, 133, 138; change of name, 156-157
Grand Junction, Colo., 143, 159
Grandview: Point, 25, 146, 147; Trail, 289, 299, 301
Granite Falls, 199
Grant, Alexander Z., boatman, 188

Grapevine Rapids, 197
Grater, Russell, 316, 371
Great Arch Trail, 309
Great Basin microphyll desert, 330
Great Salt Lake: Desert, 104; Valley, 104, 139
Great Thumb, 304
Great White City, 92
Great White Throne, 313
Green River, 30, 104, 133, 138, 139
Green River, Wyo., 154, 159
Greenland Lake, 48
Greenriver, Utah, 30, 143, 159, 182
Gregory, Herbert E., 52, 72, 327
Grosbeak: evening, 338; Rocky Mountain, 337
Guadalupe Hidalgo, Treaty of, 112
Gunnison River, 104
Gypsum Cave, 70

Hacks Canyon, 307
Hamblin, Jacob, pioneer, 140-141, 173
Hance, John, guide, 146, 289, 300
Hance: Rapids, 196, 300; Trail, 300
Hanksville, 144
Hartford, Conn., weather, 23
Harvey, Fred, 147
Havasu: Canyon, 38, 114, 204, 293, 294, 295, 304; Creek, 38, 296; Reservation, 114; Waterfall, 295
Havasupai: Creek, 125; Indians, 38-39, 102, 113-114, 125, 137, 146, 290, 293, 300, 302; origin of name, 294; Point, 146
Hawikuh, 92; battle, 95
Hayden survey, 177
Heald, Weldon F., 6, 11-40, 85-107, 131-252
Hearst, William Randolph, 147
Helper, 143; origin of name, 144
Henderson, Randall, editor, 212-213
Henry, Joseph, 162
Hermit, Basin, 301, 302; Canyon, 301, 302; Falls, 199; Rest, 25; Trail, 77, 343
Heron: blue, 237; Treganza, 362
Hidden Canyon Trail, 313
Hidden Passage, 235, 245-246
Hiking, 289-321. *See also* Camping
History, *see* Southwest
Hite, Cass, prospector, 144-145
Hite, Utah, 159